D1623875

ASMS Publications
Classic Works in Mass
Spectrometry
Volume 1

MASS SPECTROMETRY
Organic Chemical Applications

Klaus Biemann

Published Originally in 1962

McGRAW-HILL SERIES IN ADVANCED CHEMISTRY

MASS SPECTROMETRY

Organic Chemical Applications

KLAUS BIEMANN
Professor of Chemistry
Massachusetts Institute of Technology

McGRAW-HILL BOOK COMPANY, INC.
New York, San Francisco, Toronto, London

Preface

Mass spectrometry is now a well-developed technique with which excellent spectra of rather complex organic molecules can be obtained without much difficulty. However, in part because much of the earlier work in this field was directed toward problems in physical or analytical chemistry and published in the journals of those two branches of chemistry, in general the organic chemist is not sufficiently aware of the potentialities of mass spectrometry.

The interest of the audience in a series of lectures on organic mass spectrometry which I presented both at Stanford University and at the National Institutes of Health suggested that a book written by an organic chemist for organic chemists might be helpful in acquainting them with the usefulness of mass spectrometry in the solution of both simple and quite complex problems.

The book has been written with the intention of enabling the reader to judge the feasibility of this technique in a particular investigation and, if it is used, to interpret the rather complex spectra frequently obtained. It is also hoped that it may inspire some laboratories to enter this field actively and that it may provide some initial guidance. It will be even more rewarding if some of the chapters, particularly the later ones, help already existing but more analytically oriented mass-spectrometry groups to better understand and solve the problems of their colleagues in organic chemistry.

With these basic aims in mind I have attempted to survey the entire subject, presenting only the basic principles of the instrumentation while emphasizing some of the techniques of particular importance for work with relatively large organic molecules. A considerable part of the text is devoted to a general discussion of the fragmentation of such molecules and the interpretation of the resulting spectra. The behavior of polyfunctional compounds is stressed, as it is these which are most frequently encountered. Graphic presentation of spectra has been used liberally to acquaint the reader with their appearance. Familiarity with the characteristics of the spectra is imperative for a speedy and correct interpretation, as in other spectroscopic techniques.

In the chapters dealing with specific areas in which the technique has been applied numerous examples are presented that illustrate its usefulness and, in some instances, its shortcomings. It may seem that the selection of examples heavily favors our own work; this is due both to the desire to discuss results as thoroughly as possible, which frequently has necessitated giving details not available in primary publications, and to the fact that there are at present very few laboratories actively engaged in the determination of complex structures by mass spectrometry. I hope that this book may, in the near future, help to remedy the latter situation.

Most of the work related to determining the structure of more complex molecules, such as those of natural products, has been done in the past few years, and this field is now developing very rapidly. I have therefore attempted to incorporate the very latest results, many of them still unpublished, and thanks to the efforts of the publisher, it is expected that the material presented will not have lagged behind advances reported in the literature during the preparation of this book.

I would like to thank Professors G. H. Büchi, F. D. Greene, and H. O. House and Mr. A. L. Burlingame who have gone to the trouble of reading various parts of the manuscript and commented on them. I am particularly indebted to Dr. Walter Vetter for reading the entire manuscript and for his valuable criticism. Gratefully acknowledged is permission to use illustrations published elsewhere (as indicated in the captions) by the copyright owners of "Advances in Mass Spectrometry," "Encyclopedia of Spectroscopy," *Geochimica et Cosmochimica Acta, Journal of the American Chemical Society, Journal of Lipid Research, Proceedings of the European Brewery Convention* (1960), *Transactions of the Faraday Society,* and *Zeitschrift für analytische Chemie.*

Finally, I should like to express my gratitude to all my associates whose work is frequently discussed in this book, especially Drs. Josef Seibl and Walter Vetter, for their help in the determination of many essential spectra not directly related to their researches. Our work could not have been done without the generous support received from a number of individuals and organizations, especially the National Institutes of Health, the

National Science Foundation, and the Petroleum Research Fund of the American Chemical Society, whose assistance made it possible to acquire the necessary equipment and to conduct our investigations. I also should like to thank Miss K. Kelly for her help in the preparation of the manuscript.

K. BIEMANN

Contents

Introduction

Since the late thirties the organic chemist has made increasing use of physical methods in supplementing chemical information or in the characterization of compounds.

The widespread application of ultraviolet, infrared, and, more recently, nuclear magnetic resonance spectroscopy has led to a considerable decrease in time required to solve certain problems or has made it possible to attack very complex problems successfully.

Mass spectrometry, in comparison, has as yet been largely neglected as a tool to be used in experiments in organic chemistry, in part perhaps because of the widespread notion that the instrumentation involved is very complex, tricky to handle, and expensive. While this was correct years ago, it is now possible to purchase very reliable instruments which can be run by an organic chemist without training in electronics. The price is still high, but the wide distribution of nuclear magnetic resonance spectrometers has shown that high price is not so serious an obstacle. In complexity, the mass spectrometer and the NMR spectrometer are about equal.

Another reason for the little attention which mass spectrometry has received from the majority of organic chemists is that its high accuracy and sensitivity have made it better known as a technique for quantitative analysis or detection of trace constituents, in addition to its well-established use in the determination of stable isotopes. The first two applications have now, in part, been taken over by gas chromatography; thus the more valuable mass spectrometers have been relieved of such routine tasks.

A comparison of information obtained from a mass spectrum with the

1

data obtained by the other spectroscopic methods mentioned above shows that mass spectrometry complements these techniques rather than supplants any of them. As will be shown in the following chapters, the mass spectrum does not indicate directly which functional groups are present or which ones are absent—information which can more easily be obtained from the UV and IR spectrum—but rather which and how many atoms are connected with one another in certain areas of the molecule. The two molecules norisoephedrine (A) and norephedrine (B)

$$
\begin{array}{ccc}
\overset{\text{Mass 106}}{} & \overset{\text{Mass 45}}{} & \\
\bigcirc\!\!-\!\!\underset{\underset{\text{NH}_2}{|}}{\text{CH}}\!\!-\!\!\underset{\underset{\text{OH}}{|}}{\text{CH}}\!\!-\!\!\text{CH}_3 & \\
& \text{Mass 136} &
\end{array}
\qquad
\begin{array}{ccc}
\overset{\text{Mass 107}}{} & \overset{\text{Mass 44}}{} & \\
\bigcirc\!\!-\!\!\underset{\underset{\text{OH}}{|}}{\text{CH}}\!\!-\!\!\underset{\underset{\text{NH}_2}{|}}{\text{CH}}\!\!-\!\!\text{CH}_3 & \\
& \text{Mass 136} &
\end{array}
$$

$$
\qquad\qquad A \qquad\qquad\qquad\qquad\qquad\qquad B
$$

give, for example, different mass spectra, because in A the phenyl group is attached to a carbon atom bearing an amino group, while in B there is a hydroxyl group in that position. The resulting difference of 1 mass unit in the mass of these two fragments can easily be resolved. The same holds for the fragments of mass 44 and 45, respectively, while the fragment of mass 136 indicates that both the oxygen and the nitrogen atom are connected to a C_8 fragment. The mol. wt 151 is of course also borne out by the spectrum.

This simple example may serve to illustrate the fact that the mass spectrometer characterizes the molecular species of the sample, rather than bulk properties as in the case of absorption spectroscopy.

An important aspect of mass spectrometry is the small amount of sample required to obtain a usable mass spectrum, and it is probably correct to state that this technique, whenever applicable, gives the largest amount of specific information per microgram, in comparison with the other instrumental methods at the disposal of the organic chemist.

The major limitation of mass spectrometry is without doubt the requirement for vaporization of the sample, which rules out certain areas of organic chemistry (such as highly polar compounds and polymers), although much can be done by chemical conversion of the sample into a more volatile compound, as illustrated by many examples in this book. The further development of auxiliary techniques, such as vaporization of the compound within the ion source, is another promising approach.

In the chapters that follow, particularly in Chap. 3, an attempt will be made to summarize the relationship between the structure of a molecule and its mass spectrum. Those readers not yet experienced in this field are warned of one existing danger in the interpretation of mass spectra: the spectra are composed of a large number of peaks, one at almost every mass number, and the seemingly straightforward interpretation of the nature of a peak by simply adding atomic weights (1, 12, 14, 16, etc.) presents the temptation to select just those peaks which fit a preconceived opinion of the nature of the compound, while all other peaks are neglected.

As is the case with similar techniques, the experience gained by thoughtful consideration of many spectra of widely differing compounds is the best basis for the correct interpretation of the spectrum of a substance of unknown structure.

It should also be pointed out that, for reasons discussed later, the actual determination of the spectrum will have to be varied from case to case, depending on the nature of the compound and of the information desired. It is for this reason that the most useful data are obtained if the originator of the problem and the person determining the spectrum are in close contact. The most ideal situation results if both the chemistry and the mass spectrometry required for the solution of a given problem are carried out by the same individual, as they are in the author's laboratory. While this is probably not possible everywhere, close communication between the people involved is highly desirable.

1. Instrumentation

1-1. HISTORICAL DEVELOPMENT

The basic principle of mass spectrometry, the separation and registration of atomic masses, was demonstrated many years ago. Wien,[1] in 1898, deflected positive rays in electric and magnetic fields, and Thomson (1912)[2] was able to demonstrate the existence of two neon isotopes. The first instruments of more sophisticated design were built by Dempster (1918)[3] and Aston (1919).[4] Aston's mass spectrograph was particularly useful for accurate mass measurements because all the ions were focused in one plane, occupied by a photographic plate. Dempster's instrument was less suitable for this purpose but permitted a more accurate measurement of abundances; both designs, refined over the years, have been used both to measure the masses accurately and to measure the relative abundance of a great number of isotopes of the elements. Of considerable importance were the advances made during the second quarter of the century in the art of electronics that made possible the construction of reliable, accurate, and easy-to-handle mass spectrometers. The remarkable reproducibility of the mass spectra of gases and of the more volatile hydrocarbons led to the development two decades ago of mass spectrometry as a tool for quantitative analysis,[5] particularly in the petroleum industry since it permitted the fast and accurate analysis of very complex mixtures of hydrocarbons. The method gained importance at that particular time

[1] W. Wien, *Ann. Physik*, **65**, 440 (1898).

[2] J. J. Thomson, *Phil. Mag.*, **21**, 225 (1911).

[3] A. J. Dempster, *Phys. Rev.*, **11**, 316 (1918).

[4] F. W. Aston, *Phil. Mag.*, **38**, 707 (1919).

[5] H. W. Washburn, H. F. Wiley, and S. M. Rock, *Ind. Eng. Chem. Anal. Ed.*, **15**, 541 (1943).

4

because of the high demand of the aviation industry for high-quality fuels, a situation aggravated by World War II. This potential market made feasible the commercial production of reliable mass spectrometers useful for work with organic compounds. These instruments have been improved more and more during recent years. One of the more important developments for the organic chemist was the introduction of heatable sample inlet systems [6] permitting the determination of the mass spectra of compounds of low volatility.

Another area in which the mass spectrometer has become an important tool is the routine determination of stable isotopes in inorganic and organic materials. The isotope-ratio mass spectrometer originally designed by Nier [7] was produced commercially, particularly for determining stable isotopes in organic materials. The vast amount of information on chemical and biological reaction mechanisms obtained during the past two decades is due to a considerable extent to work with stable isotopes. The required accurate abundance measurements were possible only with an instrument of the type discussed in Sec. 1-2F.

1-2. CURRENT INSTRUMENTATION

In this chapter the general principles will be discussed by which charged particles can be separated according to their mass. These will be dealt with briefly, because, first, excellent books [8-11] dealing in detail with this subject are available and, second, the instrumentation of mass spectrometry has reached a high level, providing us with highly dependable instruments no longer requiring an intimate knowledge of the construction details for their continuous operation.

A mass spectrometer to be used for the problems encountered in organic chemistry must be capable of recording the complete mass spectrum of the compound with a resolution that makes it possible to determine at least the integral mass number for each peak of the spectrum. Among the considerable number of basic physical principles that can be used to pro-

[6] M. J. O'Neal and T. P. Wier, *Anal. Chem.*, **23**, 830 (1951).

[7] A. O. Nier, E. P. Ney, and M. G. Inghram, *Rev. Sci. Instr.*, **18**, 294 (1947).

[8] G. P. Barnard, "Modern Mass Spectrometry," The Institute of Physics, London, 1953.

[9] H. Ewald and H. Hintenberger, "Methoden und Anwendungen der Massenspectroskopie," Verlag Chemie, GMBH, Weinheim, 1953.

[10] H. E. Duckworth, "Mass Spectroscopy," Cambridge University Press, New York, 1958.

[11] J. H. Beynon, "Mass Spectrometry and Its Applications to Organic Chemistry," Elsevier Publishing Company, Amsterdam, 1960.

duce a mass spectrum, only a few have been developed to a point where the resulting instrument fulfills the basic requirements stated above. The following more detailed discussion of the principles and designs of these instruments is based on the commercially available instruments used as examples and has been kept within the specific scope of this book, which is directed to the organic chemist, who in general would rather purchase such an instrument than construct one on his own.

A. Single-focusing Magnetic Deflection

Semicircular Path. The principle used by Dempster [3] in his first mass spectrometer, the 180° deflection in a magnetic field of charged particles initially accelerated in an electric field, is still employed in one of the most widely used instruments. Its basic design is schematically shown in

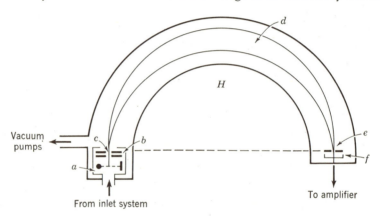

Fig. 1-1. Principle of a 180° deflection mass spectrometer. (For details see text.)

Fig. 1-1. The ions produced in ion source a (details in Fig. 1-3) are accelerated by a potential of a few thousand volts between two plates b and deflected by the magnetic field H after passing through source slit c. The focusing properties of the magnetic field are such that the ion beam d is refocused after a deflection of 180° and slit e is placed at that point. The ions passing through the slit impinge on collector f. The electrical signal is then amplified in one of various ways, generally with an electrometer-tube d-c amplifier or, less frequently, a vibrating-reed amplifier or electron multiplier.

To produce a "mass spectrum," a recording of the relative abundance of charged particles versus their mass, the ion beams of different mass have to pass one after another through the collector slit. The radius of the semicircular path described by a particle of charge e depends on the accelerating potential V and the strength of the magnetic field H. The potential energy eV of the particle will be equal to its kinetic energy after full acceleration:

$$eV = \tfrac{1}{2}Mv^2$$

In the magnetic field, the particle will experience a centripetal force, Hev, which is counterbalanced by a centrifugal force Mv^2/r:

$$Hev = \frac{Mv^2}{r}$$

$$r = \frac{Mv}{eH}$$

Elimination of v from the above results in

$$\frac{M}{e} = \frac{H^2r^2}{2V} \tag{1-1}$$

A number of important practical conclusions can be drawn from Eq. (1-1). First, at given values of H and V not only particles of mass M arrive at the collector placed $2r$ from the source slit but also those of mass $M'/2$, $M''/3$, and so forth (where M' has twice the mass of M and M'' has three times the mass of M). Under the conditions generally employed for the recording of mass spectra of organic compounds, most of the particles formed are singly charged; the doubly charged ions discussed in Sec. 3-4 are encountered much less frequently. Ions of higher charge are not produced to any significant amount under these conditions. For this reason we have to keep in mind that the particular signal recorded always refers to the mass-to-charge ratio of the species and not to its absolute mass, a fact of practical importance for the interpretation of a spectrum. Second, Eq. (1-1) shows that the radius r of a particle of given mass-to-charge ratio can be changed by variation of either V or H. For purely technical reasons, it is obviously not feasible to record a mass spectrum by moving the collector and thus changing r. Rather, it is fixed at a given distance ($2r$) from the exit slit, and either magnetic scanning (change of H) or electric scanning (change of V) is used. In this way one m/e after another attains the value of r fixed for the instrument. In the case of electric scanning, H is kept constant, and continuous decrease of V in a reproducible manner leads to the recording of the ions, starting with the lightest one and ending with the heaviest. The same is achieved if V is kept constant and the magnetic field is increased slowly (magnetic scanning).

Both these principles are in use and have advantages as well as disadvantages. With the magnetic scan, a larger mass range can be covered in a single sweep (at fixed accelerating potential the recorded mass is proportional to the square root of the field strength), and resolution and intensity are less adversely affected at high mass. For reasons discussed on page 14, both fall off at lower accelerating potential because of the increased relative contribution of initial thermal and kinetic energy of the particle, which is negligible as long as high accelerating potentials are employed. On the other hand, electric scanning is easier to achieve electronically, and the influence of the magnetic field surrounding the ion source is kept constant. The mass range which can be scanned in this manner is limited to a factor of 10 if, for example, one scans from 4,000 to 400 volts. To start at higher potentials poses more severe insulation problems, and to scan to lower values of V is not advisable because of the increasing loss in resolution which is particularly important for the higher

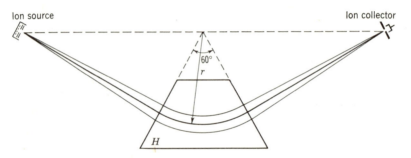

Fig. 1-2. Principle of a sector (60°) instrument.

masses that are recorded at the lower end of the potential scan. The use of two different settings of the strength of the magnetic field (H) is imperative when scanning spectra of wide mass range electrically.

In order to function properly, the ion source and the path through which the ions travel to the collector have to be kept under very low pressure of the order of 10^{-7} mm Hg. This is generally achieved by a combination of a mechanical forepump with a multistage mercury diffusion pump or, more recently, with magnetic ("getter") pumps, connected to the analyzer tube in the source region (Fig. 1-1).

Sector Instruments. The focusing properties of a magnetic field are not restricted to an angle of deflection of 180°; wedge-shaped magnetic fields are also capable of focusing deflected ion beams. Commonly used is 60 or 90° deflection. The use of 60° deflection is illustrated in Fig. 1-2, which shows one of the most important differences (from a practical point of view) between this and a semicircular-deflection instrument: both ion source and collector are outside the magnetic field and relatively far removed from the magnet gap. This greater accessibility is important for special experiments in which the species investigated has to be produced in or near the ion source, or if an electron multiplier is to be used as a collector, or for isotope-ratio measurements employing a double collector (see Sec. 1-2F). The size of the magnet is reduced for sector instruments, but the ion path increases, giving rise to a loss of intensity by the scattering of gas if the pressure in the ion path is not kept sufficiently low. The basic techniques of production and acceleration of the ions and their recording are the same for both semicircular-deflection and sector instruments.

B. The Production of Ions

The ionization of atoms and molecules can be achieved in a number of ways. Electron bombardment is most commonly employed for organic

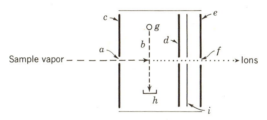

Fig. 1-3. Ion source. (For details see text.)

molecules. The vaporized compound is admitted into the ion source (Fig. 1-3) through hole or slit a in the back of the chamber and passes through collimated electron beam b. On impact positive ions (to a small extent also negative ones) are produced. A small positive potential ("repeller potential") between back wall c of the ion source and first accelerator plate d pushes the positive ions toward the accelerating region and at the same time attracts the negative ions which are then discharged at repeller plate c. The positive ions are accelerated by the potential difference applied to plates d and e, pass through the exit slit f, and continue toward the collector.

The energy of the impinging electrons (the potential difference between filament g and the area of impact) can be adjusted and regulated by appropriate choice of the potential difference between filament and anode h. The effect of the electron energy on the mass spectrum will be discussed in Sec. 2-8. The intensity of the electron beam has to be kept constant over the whole scan of the spectrum if reproducible spectra are to be obtained. The number of ions formed, and therefore the intensity of the peaks recorded, is directly proportional to the electron current to which the vapor is exposed, assuming constant pressure (= concentration) of the sample. Stabilization of the ionizing current is thus an important feature of the mass spectrometer. Adjustment of the magnitude of the ionizing current is one way by which the intensity of the spectrum can be varied.

C. Recording of the Mass Spectrum

The signal produced by the ion arriving at the collector or electron multiplier has to be recorded after proper amplification. A recording oscillograph, a pen-and-ink recorder, or a digitizer is commonly employed. Occasionally, the spectrum—or part of it—is displayed on an oscilloscope screen.

The recording of a mass spectrum poses two problems not encountered in optical spectroscopy: First, whereas the intensity ratios of the signals produced are very large, they must all be recorded with equal accuracy because of the importance of certain peaks of low intensity. In spite of their low intensity such peaks are produced with a high degree of reproducibility and may thus be recorded along with the peaks of high intensity. A recording device of varying sensitivity is imperative. Secondly, a mass spectrum consists of a large number of narrow peaks without overlap (if the instrument has the required resolving power). The recording system must have a fast response time if the mass spectrum of a compound of mol. wt 200 to 400, which will consist of about 150 to 350 peaks, is to be scanned in a reasonably short time (5 to 20 min).

A recording oscillograph is at present the best solution to this problem. The output of the amplifier is fed into a mirror galvanometer containing five coils and mirrors placed in the same magnetic field. Proper adjustment of the number of turns in the coils leads to various degrees of deflection of the mirrors by a given signal. The light beams reflected play on photographic paper, which is then developed. More recently, ultraviolet light has been employed for such recordings, making the developing process unnecessary. With five coils of sensitivity ratios $1 : \frac{1}{3} : \frac{1}{10} : \frac{1}{30} : \frac{1}{100}$ a record is produced (Fig. 1-4) which contains five traces permitting the recording of intensity ratios up to 1 : 50,000. A strong signal deflects the more sensitive galvanometers beyond the top of the paper, while the least sensitive ones will still be on the record and can then be multiplied by the appropriate factor. A very small peak will not be noticeable on that trace but will be of measurable intensity on the most sensitive trace. The recording speed of such a system easily fulfills the requirements stated above.

If a pen-and-ink recorder is to be used, the scanning speed has to be lower, and provisions have to be made for the proper attenuation peak by peak. Manual attenuation is feasible only if the spectrum is known or first scanned at a fixed setting and repeated with careful switching of

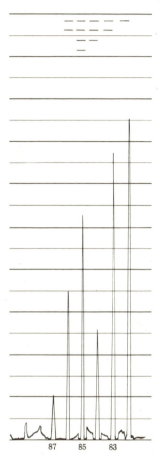

Fig. 1-4. Part of the mass spectrum hexadecane, obtained with a recording oscillograph. The factors by which peak heights are to be multiplied are, starting with the lowest trace, 100, 30, 10, 3, 1.

Fig. 1-5. The same part of the mass spectrum of hexadecane as that shown in Fig. 1-4 but obtained with an automatically attenuating pen-and-ink recorder. The horizontal lines above the peaks indicate the attenuation factor.

the sensitivity of the recorder, as demanded by the spectrum. Obviously, this method is not practicable for the frequent recording of complex mass spectra.

Automatic attenuation is therefore desirable and can be achieved with the aid of an auxiliary collector placed before the actual working collector. This additional device responds to the intensity of the ion beam before it reaches the collector slit and adjusts the sensitivity of the recorder accordingly, simultaneously printing the attenuation factor or an appropriate symbol on the record (Fig. 1-5).

Although this system can be used for purposes of quantitative analysis, in which the correct intensity of a limited number of peaks is the only information sought, it is not practical if the mass spectrum is to be interpreted in terms of the structure of a complex molecule. Furthermore, the automatic attenuator ceases to function properly when the spacing between adjacent masses becomes narrower than the distance between the two collectors. The decreased scanning speed increases the time required for the recording of the spectrum. For reasons discussed in Sec. 2-6C more sample is then necessary. By far the greatest disadvantage of automatic or manual attenuation is that, because of the appearance of the spectrum, it is very difficult to recognize its significant features at first glance. In such a spectrum the highest peak of a group is not necessarily the most intense one but may instead be a low-intensity peak recorded at much higher sensitivity (e.g., m/e 82 in Fig. 1-5), a fact realized only after consideration of the respective attenuation factors. Such a record has, therefore, first to be converted—mentally or on paper—into another one, showing the actual situation. The oscillograph record, on the other hand, always displays on the lowest trace a miniature spectrum containing all peaks in correct proportions. Once one has become accustomed to the appearance of such spectra, one will find no difficulty in grasping the essential points at a glance, just as one is able to spot the significant features of an IR or NMR spectrum.

The third recording system employed in conjunction with a mass spectrometer is a so-called "digitizer," which produces the mass spectrum in the form of numbers; that is, it prints the mass number of a peak along with its intensity. In this case the intensities recorded are not absolute intensities either, but rather relative ones accompanied by a symbol indicating the attenuation factor. For this reason such a recording system shares some of the disadvantages outlined for the automatically attenuated pen-and-ink recorder. It is rather difficult to recognize the general appearance of the mass spectrum from a tape containing the information in the form of numbers, and also here the information obtained has first to be converted to some sort of picture before the spectrum is suitable for interpretation. A very useful feature of such a recording system—particularly if one is dealing with the mass spectrum of a compound of high molecular weight—is the automatic recording of the mass number along with the intensity of the peak. Careful and frequent adjustment of the digitizer is necessary, and changing the magnetic field, a process which would require recalibration, should be avoided. This digitizer is presently commercially available only in conjunction with electrically scanning mass spectrometers. Magnetically scanning instruments would require continuous monitoring of the strength of the magnetic field in order to convert the values into mass numbers, a more difficult process than the monitoring of a change in potential; the use of a digitizer does not exclude, however, the simultaneous recording of the mass spectrum by other means, such as the oscillograph, and a combination of these two systems may offer certain advantages.

D. *Resolving Power*

The resolution obtainable with single-focusing magnetic-deflection mass spectrometers increases with both the radius of the path of deflection and the acceleration potential. The factors which have to be considered in the production of mass spectrometers somewhat limit both these parameters, resulting in resolutions (defined in the paragraphs that follow) somewhere between 300 and 600. The width of source slit and collector slit determines the extent of overlap of the recorded peaks; slits 0.1 to 0.5 mm wide can be tolerated without appreciable loss in sensitivity leading to the resolutions mentioned above.

The term "resolution" is used in different ways. For analytical purposes it is important that the maximum of the peak be a measure of the intensity of the ion beam of this particular mass with no appreciable contribution from the adjacent peak. For two adjacent peaks of equal height this contribution, expressed in per cent of the intensity of the interfering peak, is called "cross talk," or "interference." For qualitative interpretation, it is more important that the peaks be clearly distinguishable. The height of the "valley" between two peaks of equal intensity is therefore an indication of the separation of the peaks on the record. There is no definite relationship between these two rather arbitrary definitions, because the values depend on the shape of the peaks. Throughout this book resolution will be considered as $M/\Delta M$ with the specification that two ion beams, M and $M + \Delta M$, of equal intensity be recorded as two peaks between which the recorder trace returns to less than 2 per cent of the intensity of peak M. This admittedly very arbitrary definition is chosen in consideration of the information which we wish to obtain from the recorded spectrum:

1. A clear indication of the mass number of the fragment, accurate to the individual mass number. As will be seen from the discussions in later sections, it is of utmost importance to be able to determine whether the m/e of a particular fragment is 300 or 299 or 301. This is best assured if one is able to count from the low mass region up to the molecular weight, beginning with peaks of easily identifiable mass (e.g., 28 and 32 due to air). In compounds containing a considerable number of carbon and hydrogen atoms, one finds a peak at almost every mass number which provides an internal mass scale, if each is adequately resolved from the next.

2. For certain conclusions to be drawn the ratios of adjacent peaks have to be measured quite accurately, most frequently to determine the intensity of the peak due to species containing a heavy isotope, a determination which often involves the measurement of a peak next to a much more intense one. A valley of 2 per cent of the higher peak will, in general, allow the measurement of the smaller peak with the accuracy required for the purposes discussed in Sec. 3-1*B*.

E. Double-focusing Mass Spectrometers

Equation (1-1) indicates that at constant magnetic field H a spread in the magnitude of V will result in a spread in r for given values of m/e. This spread is produced by the contributions of initial kinetic or thermal energy to the kinetic energy gained by the particle during acceleration in the electric field V. The ion beam will, therefore, be refocused over a wider area, which limits the resolution of the systems employing only direction focusing, as described in Sec. 1-2*A*. Considerable increase in resolving power is achieved by elimination of this energy spread in the ion beam before entering the magnetic field. Ions passing through a radial electrostatic field suffer velocity focusing, and the ions of a certain kinetic energy may be selected by a slit placed between the electrostatic analyzer and the magnetic field. Such instruments, using electrostatic and magnetic fields and achieving thus both velocity and direction focusing, are described as "double-focusing" mass spectrometers. The resolution obtainable with such instruments is of the order of several thousand or higher. The significance of this feature lies not so much in the possibility of resolving particles the masses of which are a few thousand mass units but which differ by one unit; rather, it lies in the ability to distinguish between much lower masses differing by a small fraction of a mass unit. The usefulness of such a resolving power for problems in organic chemistry will be discussed in Sec. 4-6.

The design of Mattauch and Herzog [12] (Fig. 1-6) is one of the earliest and probably the most widely used; it has now also been incorporated in instruments available commercially.[13] Its chief characteristic is the ability to focus all masses in one plane in which a photographic plate can be placed. A spectrum of lines is obtained, and their spacing on the photo-plate is related to m/e, their blackness to intensity. Measurement of both values with a microdensitometer is necessary. Conventional recording, peak by peak, is also possible and can be achieved by placing a suitable collector (preferably an electron multiplier because of the lower intensity of highly resolved ion beams) at a fixed position of the focal plane and scanning magnetically.

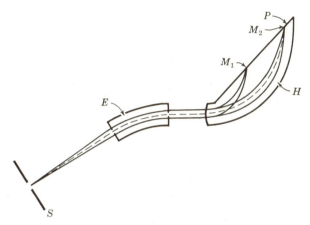

Fig. 1-6. Double-focusing design of Mattauch and Herzog (S, source slit; E, electro-static field; H, magnetic field; P, focal plane; M_1, image of a light particle; M_2, image of a heavy particle). (*Adapted from Ref. 13.*)

The recording of a complete spectrum of an organic compound of medium molecular weight using an instrument capable of high resolving power is a rather time-consuming process. Fortunately, one will frequently be interested in the highest possible resolution over only a limited mass range or of only a few peaks. The photographic plate may, however, find a useful place in situations where a complete spectrum has to be recorded within a short period of time. A few seconds or minutes suffice for one exposure, and a mass range with a ratio of 1:30 (lightest to heaviest mass) can be covered with one setting of the magnetic field.

[12] J. Mattauch and R. Herzog, Z. *Physik*, **89**, 786 (1934).
[13] C. F. Robinson, G. D. Perkins, and N. W. Bell, in H. Von Koch and G. Ljung-berg (eds.), "Instruments and Measurements," p. 261, Academic Press, Inc., New York, 1961.

Another instrument based on the double-focusing principle has been designed by Nier and Johnson.[14] It consists of a 90° electrostatic analyzer followed by a 90° magnetic sector (Fig. 1-7). Scanning of the magnetic field is used to direct one mass after another into the collector placed at

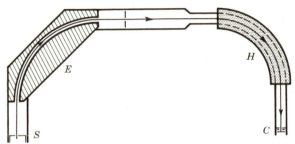

Fig. 1-7. Double-focusing design of Nier (S, source slit; E, electrostatic field; H, magnetic field; C, collector). (*Adapted from Ref. 15.*)

the image point of the magnetic analyzer. This principle is also the basis of a commercially available instrument.[15] Its prototype has been used by Beynon[16] in his pioneering work on high-resolution mass spectrometry of organic molecules.

F. The Isotope-ratio Mass Spectrometer

For the purpose of measuring the ratio of isotopes with high accuracy, a magnetic-deflection instrument of the sector type first proposed by Nier[7] is most frequently used. It differs from the conventional type, which produces the entire spectrum, mainly in the manner by which the ions are collected and the signal is amplified and recorded. To eliminate most of the factors which may influence the intensity of the ion beam arriving at the collector, it is necessary to register the ratio of the light and the heavy particles simultaneously, eliminating the effect of slight fluctuations in the intensity of the ionizing electron beam. Both types of ions also have to be accelerated by the same potential to keep constant the ratio of initial energy of the ion to the accelerating energy, thus minimizing "mass discrimination." The two ion beams will, therefore, follow different paths, and if a collector is placed at each of the two focal points, the ions may be collected and recorded simultaneously. In such a "double-collector"

[14] E. G. Johnson and A. O. Nier, *Phys. Rev.*, **91**, 10 (1953).

[15] R. M. Elliott, R. D. Craig, and G. A. Errock, in H. Von Koch and G. Ljungberg (eds.), "Instruments and Measurements," p. 271, Academic Press, Inc., New York, 1961.

[16] J. H. Beynon, in J. D. Waldron (ed.), "Advances in Mass Spectrometry," pp. 328–354, Pergamon Press, London, 1959.

instrument the exact ratio measurement is accomplished by a pair of matched amplifiers, one for each ion beam, and the ratio of their outputs is measured by a null bridge. Slight changes in isotope ratio may be detected in this manner with considerable accuracy and precision.

Such an arrangement is, on the other hand, totally impractical for the recording of the entire mass spectrum, the process which we are exclusively concerned with throughout this book. The working principle of the double-collector instrument has been discussed in some detail in order to make this point clear. Conversely, it must be realized that a scanning single-collector instrument of the type more useful to the organic chemist can never give isotope ratios comparable in accuracy to the ones obtained with a double collector and a pair of matched amplifiers. However, both systems can be incorporated into one mass spectrometer, and at least one such combination is commercially available. Most isotope ratios of elements occurring in organic compounds are measured in the form of low-molecular-weight gases (N_2, Co_2), where the ion beams to be measured are sufficiently separated in space to permit their separate collection, employing a deflection system of moderate resolving power. For the measurement of the isotope ratios of much larger molecules, which is sometimes desirable (Sec. 3-1B and Chap. 5), the resolution of the instrument sets a limit to the mass up to which the double-collector principle can be applied.

G. Other Types of Mass Spectrometers

Cycloidal-focusing Mass Spectrometer. A beam of ions injected into crossed electric and magnetic fields will describe a cycloidal path [17] as shown in Fig. 1-8. The major advantage of this design is the relatively small radius of curvature of the ion path, which permits the use of a small magnet while a considerable mass range and resolution are retained. An instrument of this type which has recently become available uses a rather small, permanent magnet and a short ion path with a distance of only 4 cm between ion source and collector. The instrument has a mass range of 2 to 280 and a resolution of about 200.

Nonmagnetic Time-of-flight Mass Spectrometer. This instrument is based on a principle completely different from those discussed earlier, as illustrated in Fig. 1-9. The ions are produced in the conventional manner by electron bombardment. The electrons emitted from a hot filament have, however, to pass through a control grid, possible only if a positive potential is applied. This is done in very short pulses (0.25 μsec) of 10,000 cps,

[17] W. Bleakney and J. A. Hipple, *Phys. Rev.*, **53**, 521 (1938).

and the ions produced during this short period of ionization are then accelerated by an electric field pulsed at the same frequency but lagging behind the ionization pulse. All ions obtain the same kinetic energy and attain a velocity which will depend on their mass-to-charge ratio. Because of this difference in velocity, ions of different m/e separate while travel-

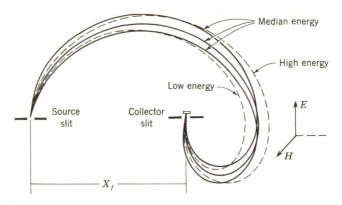

Fig. 1-8. The various ion paths in a cycloidal mass spectrometer.

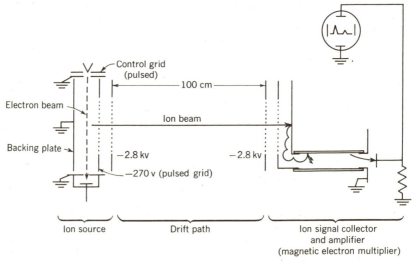

Fig. 1-9. Schematic of a time-of-flight mass spectrometer. (*Adapted from Ref.* 18.)

ing down a field-free, evacuated drift tube of about 1 m in length, at the end of which is placed an electron multiplier, the output of which is used to record the signal either on an oscilloscope screen or conventional recorder. Since all the ions created in a single pulse are collected and can be recorded on the oscilloscope, this principle permits by far the fastest production of a mass spectrum, a characteristic particularly valuable for the study of phenomena of short duration.

The theoretical mass range of the instrument extends from mass 1 to 5,000, because only masses higher than that would travel so slowly as to be overtaken by mass 1 of the next cycle. The resolution of the instrument is, however, much lower, and it would be difficult to determine even the approximate mass of a particle with m/e of a few thousand. The resolving power of the present commercial version of the time-of-flight mass spectrometer is of the order of about 140 as defined in Sec. 1-2D. Mass identification may be achieved through accurate electronic measurement of the ion's flight time, which is directly proportional to the square root of $2M/e$.[18]

While the time-of-flight mass spectrometer cannot match the magnetic instruments in resolving power, long-term reproducibility, and ease of mass identification, it has nevertheless some important advantages. These are mostly due to the ruggedness, open construction and accessibility of the ion source, the instant display of the spectrum, the simultaneous collection of ions of all masses, and the extended mass range. As a relatively small and mobile instrument, it serves as an excellent detector of ionic (or ionizable) species and is thus very useful in connection with a variety of experiments. The investigation of very short-lived species, as they are formed in flames, explosions, and by shock waves, is an excellent example.[19]

For the organic chemist the time-of-flight mass spectrometer is useful in those cases where low volatility of the sample, or its sensitivity to heat or contact with surfaces, requires placing it directly in the ion source, which is much less delicate and sensitive to contamination in this type of spectrometer than are those of magnetic spectrometers. In addition, the speed by which the spectrum can be recorded is an advantage for samples of short life or transit times (see Sec. 2-5C). Some examples of its use in organic chemistry will be discussed in Sec. 7-3 and Chap. 10.

[18] For a more detailed description of the time-of-flight mass spectrometer see D. B. Harrington, in C. L. Clark (ed.), "Encyclopedia of Spectroscopy," pp. 628–647, Reinhold Publishing Corporation, New York, 1960.

[19] For example, see J. N. Bradley and G. B. Kistiakowsky, *J. Chem. Phys.*, **35**, 256 (1961).

2. Sample Handling and Operating Techniques

In Chap. 1 we omitted the discussion of the steps necessary to convert a sample of an organic compound into positively charged particles in a reproducible manner. From a practical point of view these steps have great importance, as the usefulness of the recorded mass spectrum will depend to a considerable extent on the method by which the sample was brought into the ion source and under what conditions it was bombarded by the electron beam. This chapter will be devoted entirely to this aspect of mass spectrometry.

2-1. THE INLET SYSTEM

Previously, it was assumed that the sample is present in the ion source in the vapor state. Since the compound of interest will frequently be a liquid or a solid, provisions have to be made for introducing the sample into the ion source. Furthermore, the concentration of the sample (its pressure) in the source has to be kept reasonably constant over the period of time needed for scanning the spectrum, if reproducible spectra are to be obtained. Allowing the sample, kept in a reservoir (1 to 5 liters volume) under a pressure one to two orders of magnitude higher than the one required in the ion source, to leak through a very small hole into the ionization region produces a constant stream of the sample through the ion source.

The part of the instrument containing the reservoir, the ports for sample introduction, and the valves and the vacuum pumps required to

20

remove the sample from the reservoir after the run—all these are referred to as the "inlet system," shown schematically in Fig. 2-1. It may be constructed of stainless steel or glass, or a combination of both. While metal is more convenient for constructing an inlet system, particularly because metal valves are easier to manipulate than glass valves at elevated temperatures and low pressures, in inlet systems made entirely from glass the thermal decomposition of organic materials at high temperatures (above 200°) is reduced considerably. At such temperatures glass systems are therefore preferable.

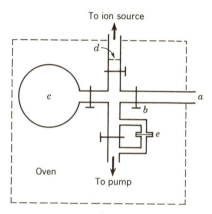

Fig. 2-1. Schematic diagram of inlet system. (*a*) Port for sample introduction system; (*b*) valves; (*c*) reservoir; (*d*) leak; (*e*) manometer.

The volume of the reservoir ranges from 2 to 5 liters in the commercial instruments, which usually are designed for quantitative analysis; the large volume minimizes depletion of the sample during the run. The valves make it possible to prevent the sample from entering the ion source except when the spectrum is to be scanned, to connect reservoir and sample-introduction port while a substance is being admitted into the evacuated reservoir, and to disconnect the vacuum system (mechanical forepump plus oil diffusion pump) from the reservoir during the measurement. A sensitive pressure-measuring device frequently is also a part of the inlet system. Such a device makes it possible to determine accurately the amount of sample in the reservoir in terms of its pressure. This measurement is important for quantitative analyses, for which it is necessary to determine the intensity of one or more peaks of each component in terms of a common unit (microns of pressure), but it is rather irrelevant if the spectrum is to be used for qualitative purposes, for which the *rela-*

tive intensities of the peaks are of interest. To have such a pressure gauge is convenient, because it tells the whereabouts of the sample and its magnitude and can be used to indicate leaks in the inlet system.

2-2. VAPOR-PRESSURE REQUIREMENTS

The pressure of the sample in the ion source should be of the order of 10^{-5} mm Hg to yield a mass spectrum of average intensity. To achieve this with the vapor entering through a very small hole, which again is essential in order to avoid depleting the sample appreciably over a period of 10 to 30 min, the pressure in the reservoir across this leak has to be of the order of about 10^{-2} mm Hg. It follows that the vapor pressure of the sample must be at least 10^{-2} mm Hg at the inlet-system temperature. Obviously, the range of applicability of a mass spectrometer is considerably increased if the inlet system is placed in an oven. Temperatures up to 400° have been used, particularly in the petroleum industry. It must be pointed out, however, that a high temperature is not the best solution to the volatility problem if one deals with organic compounds other than hydrocarbons. Molecules containing functional groups are in general more temperature-sensitive, and thermal decomposition of the sample must be avoided if a mass spectrum representative of the original sample is to be obtained. A temperature between 150 to 250°, preferably below 200°, is recommended for working with a wide variety of organic compounds. At such temperatures a vapor pressure of 10^{-2} mm Hg or higher is produced even by many rather complex molecules.

A minimum vapor pressure is not only an important prerequisite for the production of the mass spectrum but is also essential for removing the sample after the run. The lower the vapor pressure, the more difficult it is to pump the sample off completely. This is a problem which again is more important for quantitative analysis than for qualitative interpretation of spectra and is one reason why it is frequently possible to get excellent qualitative results with substances not suitable for quantitative analysis by mass spectrometry. For quantitative analysis the required vapor pressure has to be higher to assure that the sample is completely vaporized. If this were not the case, the components with the lower vapor pressure would give low results or would not be found at all.

Substances of vapor pressure below 10^{-2} mm Hg may be made directly or indirectly amenable to mass spectrometry, at least for qualitative analysis of spectra, in a number of ways:

1. The use of a somewhat larger leak between reservoir and ion source

gives the same pressure in the latter in spite of the lower pressure in the reservoir. The enhanced rate of leak leads to faster depletion of the sample, which is, however, not a serious effect, since the slight decrease in reproducibility of the spectra is of no consequence in their qualitative interpretation. The vapor pressure required may be one order of magnitude lower in this case.

2. An extension of this principle is the complete elimination of the leak, made possible by placing the sample directly in the ion source, where a vapor pressure of less than 10^{-5} mm Hg suffices, as indicated above. This technique will be discussed in more detail in Sec. 2-5E.

3. Another approach is the conversion of the sample by a simple chemical reaction into a more volatile derivative still retaining all the structural features of the parent compound. Where applicable, this approach is the most valuable one, in the author's opinion, and a number of the specific areas of application of mass spectrometry discussed in later chapters will illustrate the effectiveness of this approach.

4. In some particular cases which do not lend themselves to any one of the methods outlined above, deliberate pyrolysis of the sample can lead to volatile products. It may then be possible to deduce the identity or structure of the substance, at least in part, through identification of the pyrolysis products. This approach has been suggested for investigation of the nature of polymers (see Sec. 4-5B).

2-3. AMOUNT OF SAMPLE REQUIRED

As can be easily calculated about 1 μmole of a pure compound is required to exert a pressure of 10^{-2} mm Hg in a volume of 3 liters at 150°. One or two micromoles (a few tenths of a milligram) is thus an average sample which can be handled without special arrangements. Frequently one will wish to obtain the mass spectrum of a considerably smaller sample. This may be done in a number of ways, because the amount of material actually needed to produce the ions which give rise to the spectrum is rather small. Only a few per cent of the sample introduced into the reservoir ever enters the ion source, and of that, only about 0.1 per cent becomes ionized. In effect it is merely necessary to increase the efficiency of utilization of the sample to obtain a mass spectrum of the same intensity, using a very much smaller sample than usual. The following methods are suggested to achieve this objective:

1. Reduction of the reservoir volume to 300 ml, for example, will permit the use of ten times less sample than is necessary to obtain the same

pressure in a 3-liter volume. Again one sacrifices some constancy in sample pressure.

2. The use of a larger leak suggested earlier for samples of low volatility has the same effect as method 1.

3. Increased intensity of the ionizing electron beam gives a proportional increase in peak height and thus permits the use of proportionally lower pressures in the ion source and therefore also in the reservoir.

4. Increase in the amplification of the signal produced at the collector by means of a vibrating-reed amplifier or electron multiplier.

5. Introduction of the sample into the ion source with the exhaust pumps closed off permits a very efficient utilization of the sample. This is the most effective but also the most elaborate technique which permits work with extremely small amounts of material.

A combination of some of or all these possibilities allows one to obtain a mass spectrum with microgram amounts or less. The disturbing effect of faster sample depletion when method 1 or 2 is used can be offset by a faster scan rate. When methods 3 and 4 are employed, contributions of the background due to previous samples or backstreaming pump oil are increased along with the spectrum of the sample itself.

A more serious limitation in working with extremely small samples is presented, not by the mass spectrometer, which is one of the most sensitive instruments (aside from those of radioactivity measurements) at the disposal of the organic chemist, but by the difficulties associated with the isolation and manipulation of microgram amounts of liquids or solids. The accumulated impurities like grease, oil, residual solvents, and plasticizers eluted from tubings and gaskets, etc., may amount to the major component in such samples unless extreme care is taken.

Compounds available only in the form of a dilute solution present here more of a problem than they do in optical spectroscopy, where a longer path is a convenient solution. In mass spectrometry there is also an upper limit set to the total amount of sample which can be used in a measurement, because if too much of it is introduced, the pressure in the ion source rises to a level at which the instrument ceases to function properly. The filament temperature increases, both because of the reduced heat loss and because it is necessary to emit more electrons to maintain the selected intensity of the beam. In addition, at higher pressures in the analyzer tube a considerable amount of the ions get lost because of collisions on their flight toward the collector.

Furthermore, the very strong contributions of the solvent to the mass spectrum make it rather useless in the region below the molecular weight of the solvent. Therefore, it is necessary to concentrate such solutions or, better, to remove the solvent completely prior to introduction of the sample into the mass spectrometer. A special technique permitting this to be done without loss of material or fractionation of a mixture is outlined in Sec. 2-5A.

Although mass spectrometry is generally considered to be a "destructive" method in contrast to UV, IR, and NMR spectroscopy, which permit regeneration of the sample, this is not entirely true, because, as pointed out earlier, only a negligible amount of the material is actually consumed. If so desired, the sample still present in the reservoir after completion of the run may be recovered by recondensing it in a container kept at a suitably low temperature. Most frequently one will, however, prefer to use a smaller sample.

2-4. INTRODUCTION OF THE SAMPLE INTO THE SPECTROMETER

The sample may be a gas, a liquid, or a solid, and the introduction techniques vary accordingly. *Gases* are usually kept in a gas bottle (Fig. 2-2) a spherical flask equipped with a vacuum stopcock and a tapered joint suitable for connection to the mass spectrometer. After the connection between joint and inlet system has been made and evacuated, a small amount of the gas sample is admitted by the careful opening of the stopcock. If the sample is very small, however, the pressure in the sample

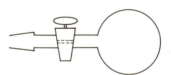

Fig. 2-2. Gas-sample bottle.

bottle will be very low, with greater danger of an air leak, which would lead to considerable dilution of the sample. It is therefore preferable to seal a very small sample in a small ampoule, one end of which is drawn to a fine capillary. The sample can be admitted into the mass spectrometer, by means of a special adapter (Fig. 2-3). The ampoule is placed in the adapter, which is then attached to the inlet system of the mass spectrometer and evacuated. Simply turning the stopcock breaks the capillary, and the gas contained in the ampoule expands into the reservoir of the mass spectrometer. This technique is particularly useful for the study of gaseous products of pyrolysis of an otherwise nonvolatile

compound, or of the products formed in other thermal-degradation reactions, performed directly in the ampoule. A variation permitting the
investigation of less volatile products from a thermal decomposition is
discussed in Sec. 8-1.

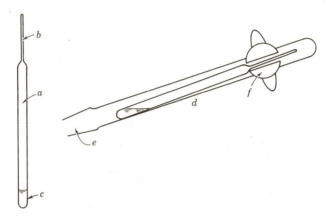

Fig. 2-3. (*a*) Ampoule for manipulating small gas samples; (*b*) capillary tip; (*c*)
nonvolatile residue, if the gaseous sample was produced by a reaction performed in
the ampoule; (*d*) adapter; (*e*) tapered joint (12/30); (*f*) stopcock for breaking
capillary.

There are a number of ways of introducing *liquids* into the inlet system. The technique used in the petroleum industry in quantitative analysis
is as follows: Attached to the inlet system is a glass tube containing a
sintered glass disk covered with molten gallium (Fig. 2-4). The liquid

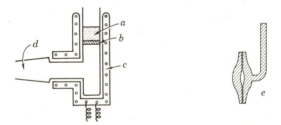

Fig. 2-4. Sintered-disk assembly. (*a*) Gallium; (*b*) disk of sintered glass; (*c*) heater;
(*d*) tapered joint (12/30); (*e*) micropipette (not to scale).

sample is drawn into a micropipette of 0.1 to 1 μl capacity, which is
then inserted into the molten gallium. When the tip of the pipette touches
the sintered glass disk, the liquid is drawn into the evacuated reservoir
and evaporated immediately. There are several practical problems asso-

ciated with this technique: i.e., creeping of gallium, clogging of the
sintered disk, difficulty of filling the capillary with samples of high viscosity. The advantage, on the other hand, is that this type of introduction
system can be operated at any elevated temperature desirable. A cleaner
and more convenient technique is the following one: The sample is drawn
by capillary forces into a small section of a hypodermic needle (22 to 27
gauge, 1.5 to 3 cm long) sharpened at both ends. To facilitate the filling
of the needle, a thin wire is inserted and pulled out while the tip of the
needle is kept under the surface of the liquid. One end is sealed off merely
by pushing it into a piece of silicone rubber. The needle is then pierced
through a silicone-rubber diaphragm attached to the inlet system with the
aid of a heated adapter (Fig. 2-5). After use the needle can be easily
cleaned by using a water aspirator to rinse it with a suitable solvent. The
silicone-rubber material used at present decomposes appreciably at tem-

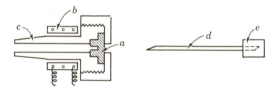

Fig. 2-5. Injection system. (a) Silicone-rubber stopper; (b) heater; (c) tapered
joint (12/30); (d) hypodermic needle (not to scale); (e) small piece of silicone
rubber.

peratures above 200°, which is therefore the upper limit of the temperature range in which this technique may be used. At higher temperatures
peaks arising from the decomposition products of silicone rubber are
found in the spectrum. High-boiling liquids and those of considerable
viscosity are drawn into a piece of melting-point capillary or placed in a
loop of platinum wire and introduced as solid samples are.

For the introduction of *solid samples* a number of techniques have
been devised, some of which are rather cumbersome and complex. Low-
melting solids can be melted and introduced as liquids are by the use of
the micropipette mentioned above, but the high viscosity of such melts
makes the introduction difficult. If the solubility permits, this can be overcome by using a concentrated solution in a solvent of low molecular
weight, for example, methanol. Recently a device has been described [1] in
which the stopcocks of a heated glass inlet system are kept at room temperature but are eventually isolated from the sample in the reservoir by a

[1] H. E. Lumpkin and G. R. Taylor, *Anal. Chem.*, **33**, 476 (1961).

pool of gallium, thus preventing condensation of the sample on the cold parts.

A very simple and convenient method for introduction of solid samples, extensively used in the author's laboratory, is the following: The sample is placed at the end of a glass tube (Fig. 2-6), the joint of which fits into the port of the inlet system. Part of the valve manifold is vented and, after the tube has been attached, re-evacuated with an auxiliary pump. After final evacuation by means of the pumps of the inlet system, the valve to the reservoir is opened and the sample sublimed into the instrument by heating the tube with an external electric heater. Although this technique is not very reliable for quantitative analysis, it is exceedingly simple and reliable if only qualitative information is sought. The difficulties with quantitative analysis lie mainly in the possible danger of fractionating the more volatile components of the mixture into the inlet system, leaving the less volatile components behind.

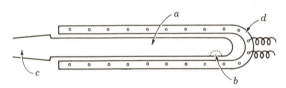

Fig. 2-6. Introduction of solid samples. (*a*) Sample tube; (*b*) sample (not to scale); (*c*) tapered joint (12/30); (*d*) heating mantle.

Some of these techniques are not easily adapted to all-glass inlet systems. With these it may be necessary to seal the sample into a side arm of the reservoir.[2] In this case a glass valve is used to vent the side arm without venting the entire reservoir while changing sample.

2-5. SPECIAL TECHNIQUES

A. Dilute Solutions

Frequently the compound to be investigated is obtained in the form of a dilute solution in the course of a chemical reaction or isolation procedure. This presents no particular problem if the available amount is sufficient for micropreparative distillation of the solvent. The residue can, in such a case, be used as the sample, with or without prior distillation or other purification. If, however, the solute amounts to only a fraction

[2] R. Ryhage, *Arkiv Kemi*, **16**, 19 (1960).

of a milligram, all of which should be introduced into the mass spectrometer without loss, the device shown in Fig. 2-7 has been found to be very useful.[3] The solution is placed in bulb *a*, which is then immersed in a bath at a temperature which permits the evaporation of the solvent. Vigreaux-type intrusions *b* in the vertical part of the tube serve as a small fractionating column. After removal of the major part of the solvent, the tube is connected, via the tapered joint *c*, to the heated inlet system of the mass spectrometer. Following immersion of the vertical part of the

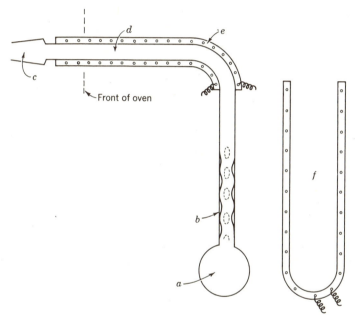

Fig. 2-7. Distillation tube. (For details see text.)

tube in a cooling bath at a temperature which permits removal of the solvent in vacuum without loss of sample (-50 to $-60°$ for ether or dichloromethane), the remaining solvent is removed first with the aid of an auxiliary mechanical pump and then by the diffusion pump of the inlet system. The pressure gauge indicates the progress of the operation and returns to its normal value when all the solvent has been removed. In the meantime, horizontal part *d* of the tube is heated by a coil of resistance wire *e*, and after the valve to the pump has been closed, the sample is distilled or sublimed quickly into the inlet system by replacing

[3] K. Biemann, J. Seibl, and F. Gapp, *J. Am. Chem. Soc.*, **83**, 3795 (1961).

the cooling bath with auxiliary heater *f*. This technique has proved very useful in situations where prior isolation of the solute is difficult, either because of the minute quantity or its instability in concentrated form. An example of the latter is the work with amino acid esters discussed in Sec. 7-1.

B. *Deliberate Fractionation of the Sample*

The distillation adapter described above may also be used to fractionate a sample slowly into the instrument, either to test its homogeneity or to obtain better spectra of the components present in a mixture. Slowly raising the temperature of both auxiliary heater *f* and heating mantle *e* will permit the lower-boiling-point components to enter the inlet system first. A spectrum scanned at that point will represent mainly this fraction (see Fig. 4-2). More exactly, it will be the spectrum of the mixture in which the ratio of the components is proportional to their vapor pressure at the temperature of the coldest spot of the entire system, namely, the sample tube. After the spectrum is scanned, the sample is pumped from the reservoir, the temperature of the tube is increased, and the process repeated until all the sample has been consumed. A more complex fractionating device has been described for enriching impurities present in a sample.[4]

C. *Continuous Scanning of the Effluent of a Gas Chromatograph*

A combination of gas chromatographic techniques with mass spectrometry is exceedingly useful, particularly because any compound which passes through a gas chromatographic column without decomposition is certainly sufficiently volatile for mass spectrometry, and the small amount of sample commonly obtained in a single gas chromatographic run also suffices for a mass spectrum. A technique which permits scanning the entire mass spectrum of a component while it emerges from the gas chromatograph would be an ideal solution to many problems. This has, in fact, been accomplished by passing the effluent across the leak of the mass spectrometer,[5,6] thus permitting a small amount of carrier gas containing the sample to enter the ion source, while the major part of the effluent is used to produce a signal on the conventional recorder of the

[4] C. Bokhofen and H. J. Theeuwen, in J. D. Waldron (ed.), "Advances in Mass Spectrometry," p. 222, Pergamon Press, London, 1959.

[5] R. S. Gohlke, *Anal. Chem.*, **31**, 535 (1959).

[6] L. P. Lindeman and J. L. Annis, *Anal. Chem.*, **32**, 1742 (1960).

gas chromatograph. The main problem is the necessity for a rather fast scan because the entire spectrum has to be recorded while the fraction emerges. In fact, it would be important to require only a fraction of that time, to eliminate the influence exerted upon the mass spectrum by the change of sample concentration from the foot to the tail of the peak. Furthermore, separate mass spectra obtained from consecutive parts of the gas chromatographic peak yield valuable information about its homogeneity or permit the identification of components emerging incompletely separated.

The time-of-flight mass spectrometer (Sec. 1-2G) seems to be the most suitable instrument for this technique,[5] particularly because of its high speed if the spectrum is displayed on an oscilloscope screen. Reasonably fast scan speeds (a few seconds) can also be achieved with magnetic-deflection mass spectrometers.[6] Two serious problems seem to limit the usefulness of this approach for work involving complex molecules. First, it is difficult to establish the mass numbers of peaks in the higher mass range if the spectrum is scanned with high speed, because either the very small peaks of the spectrum are not adequately resolved or the recorder is unable to follow. Those small peaks are very important for establishing the mass scale, as will be pointed out in Sec. 2-6D. Considerable difficulties are also encountered if high masses are to be identified in a spectrum displayed on an oscilloscope screen in the short time during which the spectrum is visible. Second, if the compounds emerging from the gas chromatograph are of low volatility, they may not be pumped out of the ion source before the next fraction enters, and this effect in part will decrease the resolving power of the gas chromatograph.

It is mainly for these two reasons that with the instrumentation presently available this very useful direct combination of a gas chromatograph with a mass spectrometer is not applicable to the majority of problems encountered by the organic chemist, who is in general not interested in the mere identification of known compounds of low molecular weight emerging from a gas chromatograph. If one deals with complex organic molecules, the unknown structure of which is to be deduced from the mass spectrum, not much is gained by the fast production of spectra not suitable for detailed interpretation because of their inferior quality.

D. Collection of Gas Chromatographic Fractions

It is indeed frequently preferable to collect the fractions as they emerge from the gas chromatograph and then to introduce them one by one into the mass spectrometer, a process which leaves ample time for a careful determination of the mass spectrum under a variety of conditions, if necessary. In this way it is, of course, possible to determine the spectra of the more important fractions first and the less important ones later. Furthermore, it does not tie up the mass spectrometer with a given chromatographic apparatus and permits a more flexible use of both those instruments. If a simple and effective procedure for the collection of the fraction and its introduction into the mass spectrometer is used, a considerable saving in instrument time results.

The simplest and most convenient device for the collection of a gas chromatographic fraction of medium or low volatility is a melting-point capillary which is inserted into the heated exit tube of the gas chromatograph when the recorder indicates an emerging peak. The sample immediately condenses in the cold part of the capillary. For collecting compounds that boil below about 150° at atmospheric pressure the capillary can be cooled either by attaching a piece of dry ice to it or using a U-shaped capillary, part of which is inserted in a cooling bath. The collection efficiency of this simple system is between 50 and 100 per cent, ample for qualitative purposes. The introduction of the collected sample into the mass spectrometer is again very convenient. The capillary containing the material is treated as if it were a solid sample; i.e., it is put into the glass tube (Fig. 2-6), which is then attached to the inlet system and evacuated; when the tube is heated, the sample distills or sublimes into the inlet system. If the vapor pressure of the material is too high to permit the evacuation of the tube at room temperature, the tube is cooled with powdered dry ice during the evacuation. As an alternative, the capillary is sealed at both ends and, after evacuation of the introduction system, is broken by means of a magnetically operated iron bar. If the mass spectra of the collected fractions cannot be determined immediately, the capillaries are sealed at both ends for storage.

This simple technique has been used successfully in the author's laboratory with a wide variety of compounds. If the amount of a liquid sample collected in this fashion is about 1 mg or more, it can also be introduced into the mass spectrometer with the hypodermic needle as described in Sec. 2-4. For this purpose one end of the capillary is sealed and the sample centrifuged to form a small puddle at the bottom of the capillary, into which the tip of the needle is inserted. This technique is sometimes to be preferred for materials of considerable volatility, because it eliminates the breaking of a glass capillary in the inlet system, which may lead to malfunctioning of the valves if glass pieces are blown into the valve seats.

E. Introduction of the Sample Directly into the Ion Source

For reasons outlined in Sec. 2-2 it may be necessary to vaporize the sample directly into the electron beam. To achieve this in a reasonably controlled manner the sample may be put in a small cup or on a metal ribbon placed near the electron beam. Heat can be applied to the support

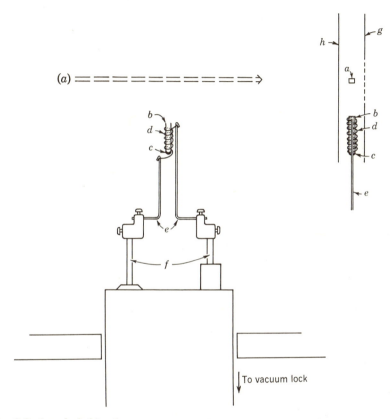

Fig. 2-8. Sample holder for vaporizing a substance into the ion source of a Bendix Time-of-Flight mass spectrometer. (*a*) Electron beam; (*b*) small glass capillary; (*c*) sample; (*d*) heating wire; (*e*) copper wire; (*f*) insulated feed-through of power source; (*g*) pulsed grid; (*h*) backing plate (see Fig. 1-9). All dimensions about 1.3 times actual size.

of the sample, which then sublimes or distills directly into the ion source. An added advantage of this method is that only a very small sample is needed, because it is not necessary to fill the large reservoir merely to achieve a constant stream of the sample. The disadvantages of this approach are the necessity for opening the ion source, which in general requires either venting at least part of the spectrometer or using a more or less elaborate vacuum lock to introduce the sample; the danger of contamination of the ion source and its surroundings by the condensing sample; the difficulty in maintaining a somewhat constant sample pressure because of variations in the rate of evaporation; and finally the danger of pyrolyzing the sample accidentally. A very simple device of this type has been described for use with a magnetic-deflection instrument.[6a]

On the other hand, the accessibility and open construction of the ion source of the Bendix Time-of-Flight mass spectrometer makes that instrument easily adaptable for this purpose, especially as a vacuum lock is available as an accessory. A heatable sample holder (Fig. 2-8), consisting of a helix of resistance wire and a short piece of melting-point capillary which can be moved close to the electron beam, was found to be simple and very effective with respect to sample utilization and ease of sample exchange, as a new capillary is always used. This modification of the commercially available unit is frequently used in the author's laboratory, and some of the results obtained with free amino acids, free peptides, sugars, and nucleosides are discussed in Sec. 7-3 and Chap. 10.

2-6. GENERAL OPERATING CONDITIONS (SINGLE-FOCUSING INSTRUMENT)

Once the sample has been introduced into the inlet system or directly into the ion source (Sec. 2-2), the sample passes through the electron beam, and the mass spectrum can be recorded. Depending on the kind of information sought, it may be necessary to run the spectrum under one or more of the different instrument settings available.

A. Mass Range

Usually a spectrum is scanned from about mass 12 up to the molecular weight of the compound, and somewhat beyond to make sure that any impurities of higher molecular weight are also recorded. The mass range of a spectrometer must, therefore, exceed the molecular weights of the heaviest molecules anticipated in the work of a particular laboratory, since it is not possible to obtain much useful information from a spectrum in which the larger fragments of the compound and its molecular weight are not recorded. The mass range of an instrument of general use to organic chemists should extend into the region of mass 500 to 800. Larger molecules are scarcely ever sufficiently volatile unless they contain a

[6a] R. I. Reed, *J. Chem. Soc.*, 1958, 3432.

number of halogen atoms. Frequently the range below mass 30 may be omitted, because such small fragments are less significant in the spectra of complex molecules. So-called "metastable peaks" (Sec. 3-3), which are of considerable usefulness for the interpretation, may, however, be found in that region which accordingly should not be neglected if a formidable problem of interpretation is anticipated. It is not advisable to start the scan at even higher masses because it may then be too difficult to identify definitely a characteristic mass peak useful for establishing the mass scale.

As has been pointed out in Sec. 1-2A, electric scanning is limited to a relatively short range of a factor of 10 in mass, and if the spectrum is scanned beyond mass 300, one has to sacrifice part of the lower range or to use two settings of the magnetic field. Since the latter can be done in a single switching process, it is to be preferred. Care has to be taken to provide for sufficient overlap of the two parts of the spectrum to make possible the unambiguous identification of a given peak present in both parts. This identification is necessary to be able to continue the mass count correctly (Sec. 2-6D). It is less of a problem with a magnetically scanning instrument, which permits the recording of mass 2 to above 400 in a single sweep.

B. Resolution

The quality of a mass spectrum suitable for detailed interpretation must be such as to permit the correct identification of the mass number of each peak. The resolution of a given spectrometer can be varied by changing the width of source slit and collector slit. In some instruments

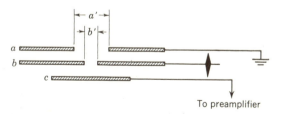

Fig. 2-9. Dual slit for collector. (For details see text.)

this may be done by a micrometer screw, moving one side of the slit with the aid of a vacuum-tight bellows; in others it requires venting of the instrument and replacing the slit, which is of course much less convenient. For the collector a dual-slit system can be employed (Fig. 2-9). Grounding of plate *a* and connecting plate *b* with the collector *c* gives an effective slit width a', because all ions impinging on both plate b and the collector reach the amplifier. If both a and b are grounded, only ions passing through the narrower opening b' produce the signal.

Narrower slits cause loss in sensitivity, of course, and a compromise has to be reached. Decreasing the width of the collector slit decreases the peak height only when the ion beam is wider than the slit itself. The width of the beam at that focal point is related to the geometry of the beam at its origin in the ion source. Some instruments incorporate a focus slit (i in Fig. 1-3) between the two accelerating plates to which a positive potential is applied for the purpose of concentrating the ion beam. The change in beam geometry results in a higher intensity but also decreases the resolution, because more of the ions are likely to pass through the exit slit.

To achieve the highest resolving power possible with a given instrument, the narrowest slit setting has to be selected; the potential of the focus plates should be the same as that of the surroundings, thus diminishing the effect on the ion beam discussed above. Furthermore, for reasons discussed in Sec. 1-2E, the accelerating potential should be as high as possible to reduce the relative contribution of the initial energy of the ion to its total kinetic energy after full acceleration.

As has been pointed out before, the first two of these precautions necessarily decrease the sensitivity of the instrument, and one will use the highest resolution obtainable only when absolutely necessary. Such is the case in the high mass range or in distinguishing between masses due to fragments of the same nominal mass but differing in elemental composition and thus also slightly in mass. Such a distinction can be of great help in the interpretation of the spectrum (see Sec. 4-6) and is, in general, only possible with a double-focusing mass spectrometer, or with single-focusing instruments of rather large radius of deflection. One should not, however, overlook the feasibility of differentiating between peaks due to fragments of different composition by using single-focusing instruments of moderate size, particularly in the lower mass range, where such mass differences are larger in relation to the total mass of the particle and therefore require a lower resolving power. Oddly shaped peaks are sometimes observed with single-focusing instruments. These are due to unresolved doublets, such as $(Ar^{40})^+$ and $(C_3H_4)^+$, or halogen-containing ions (from residual solvents) and others of the same nominal mass (for example, $CHCl_2^{35}$ and C_6H_{11} at m/e 83; $CH_2Cl^{35}Cl^{37}$ and $C_5H_{12}N$ at m/e 86; or CCl_3^{35} and C_9H_9 at m/e 117). In practice, these peaks are used more for corroborating the correctness of the mass count or the detection of these impurities than for deducing the elemental composition.

The desire to increase the effective resolution is a universal one, even with double-focusing instruments, as it is sometimes necessary to resolve very close doublets. A promising approach might involve further graphic resolution of the recorded, incompletely resolved multiplet using a "repetitive analog computer for analysis of sums of distribution functions."[7] It involves matching the experimental curve with another one obtained by combining electronically a given number of single functions and displaying the sum on an oscilloscope screen. Each contributing curve can then be displayed and traced separately on the record. The technique has been used with IR and UV spectra and seems to be applicable also to mass spectra.[7a]

C. Scan Rate

Care has to be taken not to lose in the amplifier or recorder the resolution inherent in the analyzer. Particularly in the region of higher masses the peaks follow each other rather closely and rapidly. The response time of amplifier and recording system must follow truly the signal produced in the detector, and overdamping of either of the two systems must be avoided. Frequently, to prevent loss of resolution, it is safest to reduce the scan rate while the higher masses are recorded.

Scanning from mass 12 to 500 with a magnetic-deflection instrument equipped with a recording oscillograph (Sec. 1-2C) requires about 10 to 20 min, which is fast enough for most purposes. Considerably higher speed may be required for certain special problems:

1. If the mass spectrum of an extremely small sample, of the order of 1 μg or less, is to be recorded, the use of a reservoir volume of only a few milliliters would still make it possible to obtain a reasonable sample pressure, which can, however, be maintained for only a short period. A 1-min scan would give a spectrum of useful intensity.

2. Direct recording of mass spectra of the fractions emerging from a gas chromatograph makes it desirable to scan from mass 25 to about 350 within 1 to 10 sec for reasons discussed in Sec. 2-5C.

3. To follow fast reactions, scan times of the order of milliseconds to microseconds are required. The time-of-flight mass spectrometer (Sec. 1-2G) is most suitable for such experiments.

[7] F. W. Noble, J. E. Hayes, Jr., and M. Eden, *Proc. IRE*, **47**,1952 (1959).
[7a] The author is indebted to W. Hahn for preliminary experiments with this technique.

For the purpose of interpretation rather than mere identification by matching of the spectrum of the unknown material with that of an authentic sample, a spectrum of high quality with respect to mass identification and intensity ratios is of utmost importance. At the present time the available recording systems are not suitable for this purpose at very fast scan rates, but the situation may change. Another consequence of high-speed scanning is a decrease in signal intensity. The instantaneous recording of a spectrum of wide mass range with high resolution, possible with the double-focusing Mattauch-type instrument utilizing a photographic plate (Sec. 1-2E), may prove to be one solution for some of these problems (1 and 2 above). Aside from the short time required for an exposure, the integrating properties of the emulsion eliminate the problem of variations in sample pressure caused by depletion of a very small sample or occurring during the emergence of a gas chromatographic fraction.

D. Identification of Masses

It has been repeatedly mentioned that the nominal mass of each peak has to be determined beyond doubt if the mass spectrum is to be interpreted correctly. This can be done, in principle, in a variety of ways of which only a few are both convenient and safe.

It should be pointed out that, in contrast to other spectrometers, it is not feasible in mass spectrometry to use precalibrated chart paper. One difficulty is the fact that the peaks at about mass 350 are only approximately 3 mm apart per mass unit, and this is at the end of a record 1 to 1.5 m long which moves at moderate speed through the recorder. Furthermore, a reproducible mass scale would require a considerable degree of stabilization of both the magnetic field and acceleration potential, and frequent recalibration. Instead, the following methods are used for the identification of masses:

1. In over 95 per cent of the mass spectra of organic compounds containing no elements other than C, H, N, O, and S, it is possible to start at a low mass which can be definitely identified and continue up to the highest peak in the spectrum. Compounds of this type give at least a very small peak at almost every mass up to the molecular weight, and owing to the extremely low noise level of mass spectrometers these peaks can be recognized clearly. A slight air leak in the instrument is an advantage here, since it gives rise to recognizable peaks at mass 28 and 32, and the mass difference between Ar^+ and fragments of mass 40 of organic compounds suffices to make that peak frequently slightly asymmetrical.

The regions from mass 20 to 23, 33 to 35, and 46 to 47 are often devoid of peaks, but they can easily be bridged by interpolation. Another region difficult to count is sometimes found between the molecular weight and the heaviest fragment(s). In such a case, it is advisable to rescan this region at a sensitivity setting sufficiently high to increase the height of even the smallest peaks of the spectrum, which may be due in part to a small hydrocarbon background. The major part of the spectrum will always contain a peak at almost every mass number and presents no difficulties in this respect provided the compound does not contain a number of halogens or other atoms of higher mass.

2. If such is the case or for the identification of peaks at such high mass that the resolving power of the instrument does not permit a clear resolution of all the small peaks used to follow the mass scale, a calibration compound has to be added to the sample after its spectrum has been determined. The new peaks in the spectrum are due to the added material and provide a reliable mass scale, since their mass is known. Perfluorinated compounds are particularly suitable for this purpose because of their high volatility at considerable molecular weight and the even spacing of relatively few peaks.

3. Automatic mass markers. The strength of the magnetic and electric fields applied determine m/e for a fixed radius [Eq. (1-1)]. Since one of these two values is kept constant during the scan, while the other one varies continuously, it is possible to monitor the latter for the purpose of establishing a mass scale. For instruments employing electric scanning, a device is available that produces a mark on the record at certain values of the acceleration potential corresponding to a given mass. The same is possible for magnetically scanning mass spectrometers, although it is somewhat more difficult to monitor changes in magnetic field strength.

The major difficulty encountered with these devices is the fact that their accuracy is in general not sufficient at that part of the spectrum where it is needed most: in the region of high masses peaks follow one another so closely that only slight changes in accelerating potential or magnetic field are required to bring the adjacent peak into focus at the slit. Elaborate circuitry and servomechanisms combined with careful and frequent calibration are necessary to make such automatic measurements reliable. The mass digitizer mentioned in Sec. 1-2C is the only commercially available (at a price!) device of this kind.

4. Measurement of an individual peak. The same principle can be used in a nonautomatic fashion while the sample is in the instrument and if at least one peak of known mass can be definitely recognized. If possible, it should be close to the peak of unknown mass to be measured.

According to Eq. (1-1), at constant magnetic-field strength and radius, the masses M_1 and M_2 are inversely proportional to the accelerating potential (V_1 and V_2, respectively) required to direct the respective ion beams into the collector. Thus

$$M_1 \times V_1 = M_2 \times V_2$$

The value of M_2 can be calculated if M_1 is known and V_1 and V_2 have been measured with sufficient accuracy.

Obviously this procedure is rather time-consuming if it has to be applied to more than a few peaks. In addition, the stability of the magnetic field and also of the accelerating potential must be checked; these may sometimes fluctuate because of faulty vacuum tubes or conducting films on the insulators in the ion source. Such small fluctuations, not serious in the normal functioning of the mass spectrometer, could lead to considerable error in mass measurement. The state of performance of the instrument in this respect may be easily checked by attempting to keep a peak in register over a period of time with the instrument set for good resolution. If both magnetic and electric fields are stable, the ion beam will remain focused at the collector.

2-7. IONIZING CURRENT

The intensity of the bombarding electron beam is adjusted to a value which results in a spectrum sufficiently intense to display peaks for all the fragments of interest. It must be remembered that at high ionization efficiency the intensities of the background peaks too are increased and a lower ionizing current (10 μamp) and a larger sample are preferable. A compound of low vapor pressure, a sacrifice of sensitivity to obtain the highest resolution possible, or the use of decreased electron energy (Sec. 2-8), which results in a much lower ionization efficiency, may require the highest possible ion yield; ionizing currents of 50 to 100 μamp are necessary under such conditions.

2-8. IONIZING POTENTIAL

The energy of the bombarding electrons is derived from the potential difference encountered while traveling from the filament to the point of impact and can be varied by changing the potential applied to the filament with respect to the anode or the walls of the ion source. Two ranges are of interest: One is the region of about 50 to 80 ev, an area in which the peak height changes little if the ionizing potential fluctuates a few volts. Very reproducible spectra are the result. The second important region lies between about 6 and 15 ev. At these energies fewer fragments are formed or none at all (see Figs. 4-1 and 7-10), and valuable information can be obtained if the spectrum of a compound is scanned at various electron energies, as will be discussed in Sec. 4-2.

2-9. PURITY OF THE SAMPLE

The inherent high sensitivity is apt to create the impression that a high-purity sample is a prerequisite. This is far from being correct, because the separating action of the mass spectrometer may eliminate the interference from the area of interest in the spectrum. The requirements with regard to the purity of the sample depend, therefore, largely on the problem to be investigated and the information sought; no general rule can be set. A few examples will illustrate some of the different situations.

If the interpretation of a spectrum rests almost exclusively on fragments of high mass, even an appreciable amount of a contaminant of low molecular weight, such as remaining solvent, is not disturbing. An example may be found in the elucidation of the size and structure of an aliphatic or alicyclic system attached to an aromatic ring. If the nature of the contaminant is known or can be deduced from the spectrum, its contribution may also be eliminated arithmetically.

In determining the number of deuterium atoms incorporated into a molecule (Chap. 5) the presence of heavy water in the sample can be tolerated without effect on the accuracy of the results, as long as it is not present in such large amounts as to give rise to "$M + 2$" peaks via ion-molecule reactions (Sec. 3-1A). However, the presence of a substance exhibiting a peak in the region of the molecular weight of the deuterated compound would lead to erroneous results.

Nonvolatile impurities or compounds with vapor pressures much lower than the sample itself do not appear in the mass spectrum. Care has to be taken, however, to prevent such substances from entering the inlet system, because they would lead to the malfunctioning of the valves, pumps, or the leak.

On the other hand, if the compound is of a type which shows a high tendency for fragmentation upon electron impact and a low stability of the molecular ions, a mass spectrum with only a few peaks of low intensity at higher masses results. Then the interpretation rests on these small peaks and the larger ones at low mass. The contributions of residual solvent to the spectrum can be very confusing in such a case. Traces of impurities of higher molecular weight, exhibiting relatively strong peaks at higher masses, interfere with the correct identification of the molecular weight and of the larger fragments of the sample. A sample of high purity is then required.

Contamination with substances of high molecular weight should, therefore, always be avoided. Lubricating oils, stopcock grease, plasticizers, and silicon oil are particularly annoying and frequently encountered impurities (see Sec. 4-3).

Purity is of importance also whenever conclusions have to be drawn on the basis of peak intensities in terms of total ionization (Sec. 2-11C). For this purpose the intensities of all peaks of the mass spectrum have to be added, and the resulting sum would be in error if there were present another substance contributing peaks.

2-10. PRESENTATION OF DATA

It is difficult to present the original record as such because of its length, the large number of peaks displayed, and their widely varying intensity. For these reasons the data are frequently presented in tabular form, listing the mass number of the peaks and their intensities. The latter are expressed in relation to the most intense peak of the spectrum (often referred to as the "base peak"), which is assigned an arbitrary value of 100.

Such tables are useful in quantitative analyses, because they permit accurate computation of the contributions of individual components of a mixture to a peak at a mass number used for the estimation of another component. For the interpretation of a mass spectrum in terms of the nature of the compound giving rise to the spectrum, such tables are rather confusing, since the characteristic peaks cannot be spotted easily; in other words, such tables do not clearly exhibit the characteristics of the spectrum at a glance.

These are much clearer if the mass spectrum is presented in the form of a drawing relating the relative abundance (ordinate) of the fragments to their mass-to-charge ratio (abscissa). The relative intensities of the peaks are thus clearly recognizable, as are their masses. This kind of presentation is used throughout this book whenever a spectrum, or part of it, is depicted. Mass-to-charge ratio (m/e) appears on the abscissa, the intensity units referred to above on the left ordinate, and total ionization units on the right.

For the comparison of individual spectra, the relationship between the intensity of a given peak and the total intensity of the spectrum, i.e., the sum of the intensities of all peaks, is important. The intensity of a peak, in per cent of the "total ionization" (Σ), then indicates the extent to which the initially formed molecular ions decompose to this fragment. This type of intensity relationship is frequently required in the interpretation of spectra. To obtain this value, it is necessary to measure all the peaks for this summation. For various reasons this is frequently not possible, e.g., if the spectrum was not scanned over the entire range from m/e 1 to the molecular weight. For any comparisons one has to ensure that the mass range over which the peak intensities were summed is the same for all compounds to be compared. The lowest mass of this range is thus indicated as a subscript; i.e., Σ_{25} signifies the sum of the intensities of all peaks from m/e 25 to the molecular weight (or peak of highest mass in the spectrum). The subscript, if used in a figure, also refers to the mass at which the scan was started. Frequently the peaks at higher masses are of low intensity and have to be magnified to be recognizable in a drawing of the spectrum. The values of the per cent Σ_m scale on the ordinate refers then to those peaks which are not magnified.

For the sake of clarity, peaks due to doubly charged ions (Sec. 3-4) of odd mass are omitted. If necessary for the interpretation, both their mass and intensity are given in the caption of the figure. The same holds for metastable peaks (Sec. 3-3), the intensity of which is generally too low to be recognizable if drawn to the same scale as the normal peaks. The m/e of the maximum of a metastable peak should be mentioned in the discussion, if pertinent. In original papers it may be useful to list both doubly charged peaks and metastable peaks in a separate table. Unless otherwise stated, peaks of ≥ 0.5 per cent of the intensity of the largest peak in the spectrum are shown in the figures of this book. Wherever the intensities in the region of higher masses is rather low, this part of the spectrum will be enlarged. A slanted broken line separates the two regions of the spectrum and shows the factor of enlargement. By necessity, some of the peaks of the spectrum are lost in this kind of drawing (compare Figs. 1-4 and 3-9a). In general, however, these are not significant for the interpretation and may be neglected.

For the comparison of mass spectra of isotopically labeled with unlabeled compounds, a different form of presentation may be required, particularly if the sample consists of more than one labeled species (such as d_0, d_1, d_2, . . .) or if either the labeled or the unlabeled molecules give rise to different fragments of identical mass.

Presentation of the intensity data in terms of Σ will, under any circumstances, give a clear indication which peaks shift and to what extent (see, for example, Fig. 3-23). This form should always be used, as line drawings and/or intensity tables, if more subtle details of a fragmentation mechanism are to be discussed. In addition, correcting the data for the contribution of naturally occurring isotopes (for example, C^{13}) may be helpful.

The presentation in the more convenient form (highest peak equals 100) may give the impression that the intensities of certain peaks are markedly higher in the labeled compound. Such is the case where the highest peak in the spectrum of the unlabeled molecule is split in the labeled one (most often due to incomplete labeling). The peaks at m/e 29 in Fig. 7-8b and at m/e 91 in Fig. 7-8d, which are much higher than in Fig. 7-8a and c, may serve as an example.

2-11. TERMINOLOGY

A. Mass versus m/e

The term "m/e" (mass-to-charge ratio) will be used to refer to the position of a peak in the spectrum, while the term "mass" is used to indicate the mass of the particle; e.g., the fragment of mass 30 $[(CH_2NH_2)^+]$ gives rise to a peak at m/e 30.

B. Molecular Ion

A molecule from which one electron was removed upon electron impact, giving rise to an ion the mass of which is the same as the molecular weight, is referred to as "molecular ion." This is a departure from the current use of the terms "parent peak" or "parent." It is felt that a more precise term should be used, and although molecular ion is the longer expression, it is preferable.

C. Per Cent of Σ_m versus Per Cent of "Base Peak"

As mentioned earlier, the only meaningful way of comparing peaks in the mass spectra of different compounds is in terms of the extent to which they contribute to the spectra. It was shown that, for isomers, the total ion intensity, i.e., the ionization cross section, is equal regardless of the structure of the isomers and that this value is related only to the number and kinds of atoms present in the molecule.[8-10] For isomers, one

[8] J. W. Otvos and D. P. Stevenson, *J. Am. Chem. Soc.*, **78**, 546 (1956).
[9] G. F. Crable and N. D. Coggeshall, *Anal. Chem.*, **30**, 310 (1958).
[10] A. Hood, *Anal. Chem.*, **30**, 1218 (1958).

is therefore justified in relating the intensity of a given peak, expressed in per cent of Σ_m (sum of the relative intensities of all peaks from mass m to the molecular weight), to the probability of formation of this fragment from either one of the isomeric compounds.[11] Expressing the intensity of the peak of interest in terms of any other one in the spectrum would have no meaning in such a case. Admittedly, the measurement and summation of all the peaks in the spectrum is time-consuming, but it can be done electronically by effectively measuring the intensity of the ion beam prior to deflection in the magnetic field.[12]

Relation of the intensity of peaks to the most intense one ("base peak") is commonly used, and frequently this form of expression is employed in discussions of mass spectra. As indicated above there is no absolute physical significance inherent in such numbers, and the situation becomes confusing if more than one very intense peak is present and if the peaks are of almost equal height. Mass spectra of the same compound, when determined on different instruments or under different conditions, may have widely differing "base peaks." For all these reasons only per cent of Σ_m is used, particularly in the comparison of peaks of different spectra, unless it is specifically the intensity ratio of peaks of the same spectrum which are of importance; e.g., "The ratio of peaks at m/e 31 to m/e 59 is 1:5 in compound A but 3:1 in compound B"; on the other hand, "The peak at m/e 59 is 8.7 per cent of Σ_{27} in compound C, whereas the same peak (m/e 59) is 15.6 per cent of Σ_{27} in D."

[11] T. Aczel and H. E. Lumpkin, *Anal. Chem.*, **32**, 1819 (1960).
[12] H. E. Lumpkin and J. O. Beauxis, *Anal. Chem.*, **32**, 1815 (1960).

3. The Nature of Mass Spectra and Their Interpretation

Having obtained a usable mass spectrum of the sample, one is faced with the more formidable problem of transforming the recorded data, a large number of peaks of widely varying intensities, into meaningful information regarding the nature of the compound. The spectrum may have been determined for one of several reasons: identification of the compound with an authentic sample; quantitative analysis of a mixture the qualitative composition of which is known; or the identification or structure determination of a substance by detailed interpretation of the spectrum. The first two situations require no particular knowledge regarding the nature of the fragmentation process as long as calibration spectra of the corresponding pure compounds are available. We are, however, almost entirely concerned with the third case, and detailed discussion of the type of information that can be deduced from the peaks due to the molecular ion, the characteristic fragments, and the factors influencing their intensities is thus in order.

3-1. THE IONIZATION PROCESS

Upon bombardment of a molecule with electrons of moderate energy a number of processes may occur as the first step:

$$M + e^- = M^- \tag{3-1}$$
$$M + e^- = M^+ + 2e^- \tag{3-2}$$
$$M + e^- = M^{n+} + (n+1)e^- \tag{3-3}$$

Equations (3-1) to (3-3) illustrate the formation of negative, positive, and multiple positive molecular ions. In polyatomic molecules these may decompose further into fragments involving processes discussed in Sec. 3-2. In the mass spectra of organic molecules the formation of unipositively charged molecular ions [Eq. (3-2)] is the most important event (above the ionization potential), because it occurs much more frequently than the other reactions.

The removal of an electron from a molecule upon electron impact will occur if the bombarding electron has an energy equal to, or higher than, the ionization potential of the particular molecule. The ionization potentials of organic molecules are of the order of about 7 to 15 ev (e.g.,

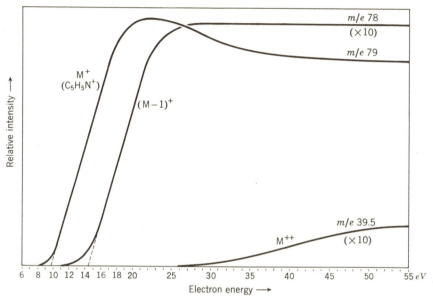

Fig. 3-1. Relationship between abundance of ions and energy of bombarding electrons in the mass spectrum of pyridine. The intensity of the signals due to the ions of *m/e* 78 and *m/e* 39.5 is shown increased for a factor of 10.

9.24 ev for benzene and 13.1 ev for methane).[1] If the energy of the electron beam employed equals the ionization potential of the molecule, complete transfer of the energy of the electron to the molecule is required for ionization to take place. This results in the formation of only a few molecular ions producing a peak of very low intensity in the mass spectrum. An increase in the electron energy increases the probability of ionization and results in a higher peak intensity. The plot of peak intensity due to the molecular ion versus electron energy, shown in Fig. 3-1, is called "ionization efficiency curve." Theoretically it rises suddenly

[1] For a collection of ionization potentials see F. H. Field and J. L. Franklin, "Electron Impact Phenomena," Academic Press, Inc., New York, 1957.

(broken line) at the electron energy corresponding to the ionization potential and levels off at about 30 to 50 ev. In the ion sources generally employed the energy spread of the electron beam is about 2 ev, which means that always some electrons are formed whose energy is higher than the mean energy of the electron beam. This produces an ionization efficiency curve of S-shaped appearance (solid line in Fig. 3-1). The slight dip in the curve for M^+ is due to the fact that the formation of fragments and of M^{++} exceeds, in this region, the increase in the formation of molecular ions.

As the electron energy is increased, the excess energy of the molecular ion will reach a value equal to, or higher than, the energy required to break a certain bond within the molecule (see Sec. 4-7), and fragmentation at that bond will result. Here again the probability of formation of these fragments increases with increasing mean energy of the electron beam, and a plot of the abundance of the fragment ions versus electron energy has a shape resembling the ionization efficiency curve of the molecule (Fig. 3-1). The onset of the curve of the fragment ion corresponds to its "appearance potential." Since all these curves level off at energies above 40 to 50 ev, an electron beam of 50 to 80 ev energy is usually used to obtain reproducible spectra. The energy transferred to the molecule during a "head-on" collision with such an electron suffices to break a bond of considerable dissociation energy or to break more than one bond. Such mass spectra are, therefore, rather complex, consisting of many peaks because of the large number of different fragments which can be formed from a polyatomic molecule. The following scheme shows the processes which follow the impact of an electron of sufficient energy upon a hypothetical molecule $ABCD$:

$$ABCD + e^- \longrightarrow ABCD^+ + 2e^- \qquad (3\text{-}2)$$

$$ABCD^+ \longrightarrow A^+ + BCD\cdot \qquad (3\text{-}4)$$

$$\longrightarrow AB^+ + CD\cdot \qquad (3\text{-}5)$$

$$B^+ + A\cdot \qquad (3\text{-}6)$$

$$A^+ + B\cdot \qquad (3\text{-}7)$$

$$\longrightarrow CD^+ + AB\cdot \text{ etc.} \qquad (3\text{-}8)$$

$$\longrightarrow AD^+ + BC\cdot \qquad (3\text{-}9)$$

$$ABCD^+ + ABCD \longrightarrow [ABCD\cdot ABCD]^+ \longrightarrow ABCDA^+ + BCD\cdot \qquad (3\text{-}10)$$

The initial removal of an electron from the molecular ion [Eq. (3-2)] has already been discussed. Equations (3-4) through (3-9) illustrate various possibilities for fragmentation of the molecular ion $ABCD^+$ leading in each case to a positively charged fragment and a neutral one. The neutral fragment may be a radical, as depicted in this scheme, but it may also be an uncharged molecule. As only the positively charged fragments are recorded on the mass spectrum, the steps in Eqs. (3-5) and (3-8) give rise to different peaks in the spectrum unless the sum of the masses of atoms A and B is equal to the sum of the masses of atoms C and D. Any one of the positively charged fragments formed can, if it consists of more than one atom, decompose further into another positively charged particle and a neutral one, provided enough energy is available for this decomposition.

The molecular ion (or a positively charged fragment) may, however, become rearranged before it decomposes, and these processes [Eq. (3-9)] lead to fragments containing atoms or groups which have not been connected with each other in this form in the original molecule. The usefulness of simple fragment ions originating in processes of this type [Eqs. (3-4) through (3-8)] for the determination of the structure of the molecule is obvious, but rearrangement processes yield ions corresponding to groups not present as such in the molecule, and it is for this reason that for a time mass spectrometry was thought to be too ambiguous for structure determinations. A prime example used in this argument was the appearance of the peak at m/e 29 in the spectrum of a hydrocarbon, neopentane, which lacks an ethyl group (mass 29). Nevertheless, the rearrangement processes which molecules containing heteroatoms undergo are rather specific and may be used very successfully for the interpretation of the mass spectrum once the mechanism and the structural requirements for the rearrangement are understood. This situation closely resembles one with which the organic chemist is quite familiar: the high tendency of terpenes and related compounds to undergo acid-catalyzed rearrangements considerably hampered work in this area and led to many erroneous results in earlier times.

As the ions are formed in relatively low yield, there are always present a large number of un-ionized molecules which occasionally may collide with an ion formed upon electron impact. During such a collision an atom or a group may be abstracted from the neutral molecule by the positive ion, resulting in a particle the total mass of which is larger than the mass of the molecule under consideration, as shown in Eq. (3-10). As a second-order reaction this process is proportional to the product of the concentrations of the ion and of the uncharged molecule, in contrast to the unimolecular decomposition of the molecular ion [Eqs. (3-4) through (3-9)]. The yields of such ion-molecule reactions [Eq. (3-10)] are therefore proportional to the square of the sample concentration ($=$ pressure). For the sample concentration usually employed in mass spectrometry, the occurrence of such a reaction is negligible, with the exception of the abstraction of a hydrogen atom by the molecular ion, a process which is discussed in detail in Sec. 3-1A. Any such peaks due to collision reactions [Eq. (3-10)] may be recognized by their dependence on the square of the pressure or, more accurately speaking, on the product

$$[ABCD^+] \times [ABCD]$$

A. Molecular Weight

If the molecular ion formed in the reaction in Eq. (3-2) is accelerated and deflected in the mass spectrometer, it will give rise to a peak in the spectrum at the mass of the molecular weight. It is expected to correspond to the peak of highest mass in the spectrum if collision processes [Eq. (3-10)] can be neglected. For this reason mass spectrometry is believed to be an accurate and unambiguous method for the determination of the molecular weight of an organic molecule. This is not necessarily so, and the characteristics of the molecular ion and the peak will be discussed in detail because of the great importance of the correct molecular weight in determining the structure of an organic molecule and for correct interpretation of the mass spectrum.

The intensity of the peak corresponding to the molecular weight of the compound represents the number of molecular ions arriving at the collector, not the number of molecular ions originally formed in the ion source. Only those ions having a lifetime long enough to be fully accelerated (about 10^{-5} sec) will be recorded at the corresponding mass. If they decompose in a shorter time, the daughter ions will appear in the spectrum. The relative number of molecular ions surviving long enough will depend on their stability versus their tendency to form fragments. In an unfavorable case, the decomposition of the molecular ion may be so fast that only very few such ions arrive at the collector, not enough to produce a visible peak.

In general it can be said that only in 80 to 90 per cent of the cases will the molecular weight of the compound be easy to determine from the mass spectrum. To the remaining group belong compounds which give rather small peaks of that kind, and care has to be taken not to confuse them with peaks due to impurities or fragments. In the most unfavorable cases, where virtually no peak is found for the molecular ion, the molecular weight can be determined indirectly (see page 58 and Sec. 4-4).

The stability of the molecular ion is increased by the presence in the molecule of π-electron systems from which the loss of one electron is more easily accommodated than from a σ bond. Cyclic structures also give rise to more intense peaks at the molecular weight, because in such molecules the cleavage of one bond does not lead to a fragment of lower mass. On the other hand, if functional groups are present which either weaken bonds or stabilize fragments better than the molecular ion, fragmentation of the molecule will be greatly facilitated and the majority of (or all) the molecular ions will be lost through such decompositions. On the basis of these considerations and the factors governing the stability of fragments (Sec. 3-2), the more common types of organic molecules can be arranged in the following approximate order of decreasing stability of the molecular ion:

Aromatic compounds—conjugated olefins—alicyclic compounds—sulfides—unbranched hydrocarbons—mercaptans—ketones—amines—esters—ethers—carboxylic acids—branched hydrocarbons—alcohols

Both the stabilization of the positive charge in the molecular ion due to the presence of groups containing π-electron systems and the tendency toward fragmentation of certain bonds (Sec. 3-2) influence the intensity of the molecular-ion peak, and both these properties are therefore additive. This is shown in Table 3-1, which gives the intensity of the molecular-ion peak in per cent Σ for a variety of compounds of roughly equal size.

Owing to the presence of easily ruptured bonds a side chain attached to the aromatic system reduces considerably the intensity of M^+ (compare naphthalene and the butyl benzenes).

Both alloocimene and myrcene contain three double bonds, but their arrangement is such that a C—C bond (a) is present in myrcene which is allylic to two π-electron systems. Fragmentation of that bond is facilitated, and the M^+ intensity is thus lower than in alloocimene which is fully conjugated.

$$\begin{array}{cc}
\underset{\text{allo-Ocimene}}{\overset{\displaystyle \text{H}_3\text{C}}{\underset{\displaystyle \text{H}_3\text{C}}{>}}\text{C=CH}-\text{CH=CH}-\overset{\displaystyle \text{CH}_3}{\underset{|}{\text{C}}}=\text{CH}-\text{CH}_3} & \underset{\text{Myrcene}}{\overset{\displaystyle \text{H}_3\text{C}}{\underset{\displaystyle \text{H}_3\text{C}}{>}}\text{C=CH}-\text{CH}_2\overset{a}{-}\text{CH}_2-\overset{\displaystyle \overset{\displaystyle \text{CH}_2}{\|}}{\text{C}}-\text{CH=CH}_2}
\end{array}$$

The greater stability exhibited by cyclic molecules (decalin versus decane, decalol versus decanol) is due to the fact that two bonds have to be broken in such molecular ions to lead to fragmentation.

Since branching favors fragmentation, n-decane has a more pronounced M^+ peak than 3,3,5-trimethylheptane.

Table 3-1. Abundance of Molecular Ion for Various Compounds

Compound	Abundance, per cent Σ
Naphthalene	44.3
Quinoline	39.6
n-Butylbenzene	8.26
trans-Decalin	8.22
tert-Butylbenzene	7.00
Alloocimene	6.40
Diamyl sulfide	3.70
n-Decane	1.41
n-Decylmercaptan	1.40
Diamylamine	1.14
Methyl nonanoate	1.10
Myrcene	1.00
Cyclododecane	0.88
3-Nonanone	0.50
n-Decylamine	0.50
Diamyl ether	0.33
cis-cis-2-Decalol	0.08
3-Nonanol	0.05
Linalool	0.04
3,3,5-Trimethylheptane	0.007
n-Decanol	0.002
Tetrahydrolinalool	0.000

Heteroatoms favor fragmentation (n-decylmercaptan, n-decyl amine and n-decyl alcohol versus n-decane) but this effect is almost offset in the mercaptan perhaps because of the much higher ionization cross section [2] of sulfur.

Combination of a hydroxyl group with a highly branched carbon chain leads to disappearance of the M^+ peak (n-decanol versus tetrahydrolinalool). Introduction of π bonds increases it again (linalool versus tetrahydrolinalool).

[2] J. W. Otvos and D. P. Stevenson, *J. Am. Chem. Soc.*, **78**, 546 (1956).

$$CH_3-\underset{\underset{}{\overset{\overset{CH_3}{|}}{C}H}}-CH_2-CH_2-CH_2-\underset{\underset{OH}{|}}{\overset{\overset{CH_3}{|}}{C}}-CH_2-CH_3$$

Tetrahydrolinalool

$$CH_3-\overset{\overset{CH_3}{|}}{C}=CH-CH_2-CH_2-\underset{\underset{OH}{|}}{\overset{\overset{CH_3}{|}}{C}}-CH=CH_2$$

Linalool

The compounds listed in Table 3-1 have been selected to represent as far as possible the same molecular size. The two lowest members of a homologous series always have an atypically intense M^+ peak, and in most groups there is also a gradual change in relative M^+ intensity with molecular weight.

Because of the high sensitivity of mass spectrometers and the reproducibility of the spectra, a peak with an intensity of 1 per cent of Σ is clearly visible and easily identifiable. The determination of the molecular weight is no problem at all if the corresponding peak is of such intensity and if the compound is a pure substance. Even peaks ten times smaller can still be detected with confidence unless a very small sample is used. The determination of the molecular weight of a compound with a molecular ion which gives rise to a peak of still lower intensity may be quite difficult or impossible to accomplish directly but may be accomplished by an indirect method (page 58). Highly branched alcohols (Table 3-1) are a good example of this group.

In order to identify the peak at highest mass (disregarding the isotope peaks described in Sec. 3-1B) as the molecular weight of the compound, one has to ascertain that this peak exhibits all the characteristics of a molecular ion and is not a fragment or due to an impurity or another component in the sample. Furthermore, the appearance of peaks at masses higher than the molecular weight of the compound arising from ion-molecule collisions discussed earlier has to be kept in mind.

Previously it was mentioned that the formation of fragments requires energy in excess of the ionization potential of the molecule, and Fig. 3-1 indicates that the intensity of the molecular-ion peak would decrease less than the intensity of fragment peaks if one were to scan the spectrum repeatedly at lower and lower electron energy. In other words, the abundance of the molecular ion, expressed in per cent Σ, increases with decreasing electron energy (see Fig. 4-1). This technique is, however, useful only in order to distinguish fragment peaks of an impurity of higher molecular weight from the molecular-ion peak of the major component, because the overall intensity of all the peaks decreases with decreasing electron energy. A substance not exhibiting a visible molecular-ion peak at 70 ev will also not show any peak at that mass at lower energies.

The mass of a given peak can be used to distinguish between the molecular ion and a fragment, because the molecular weight of a compound consisting of the elements usually encountered in organic molecules will always be an even number unless the molecule contains an odd number of nitrogens, whereas simple fragments of such molecules will always have odd mass numbers. Exceptions are rearrangement peaks (Sec. 3-2B), which are frequently formed by the elimination of a neutral molecule and thus produce a fragment of even mass number if derived from an even-numbered mass.

Finally, the difference in mass between the supposed molecular weight and the next lower fragment peak of appreciable intensity can be used for the characterization of the molecular-weight peak. This mass difference must correspond to the loss of a group by cleavage of a bond in a favored fragmentation process. The fragmentations giving rise to peaks of reasonable intensity are discussed in Sec. 3-2, and it follows, for example, that a peak which would appear three mass numbers below the one considered to be due to the molecular ion would have to arise by elimination of three hydrogen atoms from the molecule. Although a process of this kind cannot be excluded a priori (e.g., in certain molecules which can yield a highly stabilized conjugated ion by loss of one hydrogen atom followed by loss of a hydrogen molecule), such mass differences are always suspect, and it is more reasonable to assume that both peaks are due to fragment ions formed by loss from the molecule of two different groups with a mass difference of 3 mass units. Such is the case frequently with alcohols, which have the tendency to lose an alkyl group, e.g., methyl, or a molecule of water; a specific example will be discussed on page 58.

The final identification of the molecular-weight peak must always be accompanied by a partial interpretation of the spectrum itself sufficient for recognizing the general group to which the compound belongs, unless this is known beforehand. It is important to ascertain that the intensity of the peak considered to be due to the molecular ion is of the magnitude expected for this type of molecule. If the peak is very intense, for example, but the remaining part of the spectrum indicates that the compound is a branched amine, then it is quite possible that one has chosen a fragment of the molecule that still contains the nitrogen atom but not the molecular ion itself.

We have already mentioned that ions arising via an ion-molecule collision[3] [Eq. (3-10)] may appear at masses higher than the molecular weight of the compound and thus interfere with the determination of the correct molecular weight. Particles formed by abstraction of a group of atoms from a neutral molecule have very low abundance under the conditions normally used to obtain a mass spectrum. Only at unusually high sample pressures ($> 5 \times 10^{-1}$ Hg mm in the reservoir) so-called "secondary spectra" of significant intensity are obtained which, in fact, contain a number of peaks higher than the molecular weight of the compound, up to trimers or even tetramers.[4] With the much lower sample pressures used for determining mass spectra in general, only the abstraction of a hydrogen radical from a neutral molecule by the molecular ion, giving rise to a peak at mass $M + 1$, is of practical importance. It can be recognized as a peak arising from an ion-molecule collision by the proportionality of its intensity to the square of the pressure of the sample or by the effect which certain changes in the ionizing conditions have on the ratio of its intensity to the intensity of the other peaks in the spectrum. The rate of formation of such an "$M + 1$" peak * is proportional to the product $[M^+][HX]$, where HX may equal M, and the intensity of the "$M + 1$" peak will, therefore, depend on the concentration of the species and on the time interval during which the reaction can occur.[3,5,6] The "$M + 1$" peak is for these reasons sensitive to changes in sample pressure or in the potential gradient in the ion source. The intensity of that peak will increase relatively to the intensity of the other peaks if the pressure is increased. An increase in repeller potential will decrease the residence time of the ions within the ion source and thus decrease the number of collisions.

The "$M + 1$" peak has particular significance for those types of compounds in which the molecular ion is very unstable and has a high tendency to decompose, while the corresponding protonated molecule, on the other hand, is a very stable entity (e.g., an oxonium or ammonium ion). Such a situation leads to a very small or negligible peak at the mass

---

* The quotation marks denote a peak 1 mass unit higher than the molecular weight due to such a collision process, as distinct from a peak of the same nominal mass due to isotopic molecules (see Sec. 3-1B).

[3] For a recent review, see F. W. Lampe and F. H. Field, *Tetrahedron*, 7, 189 (1959).

[4] F. H. Field, *J. Am. Chem. Soc.*, 83, 1523 (1961).

[5] F. W. McLafferty, *Anal. Chem.*, 29, 1782 (1957).

[6] J. H. Beynon, G. R. Lester, R. A. Saunders, and A. E. Williams, *Trans. Faraday Soc.*, 57, 1259 (1961).

of the molecular ion but to an appreciable peak 1 mass unit higher. This is the case for ethers, esters, amines, amino esters, and nitriles, the molecular weight of which can be determined [5] in this way with a high degree of confidence in spite of their usually low-intensity molecular-ion peak. Rather than using spectra of a small and of a large sample for the detection of the "$M + 1$" peak, it is simpler and more practical to change the potential in the ionization region in the source. With the CEC 21-103C

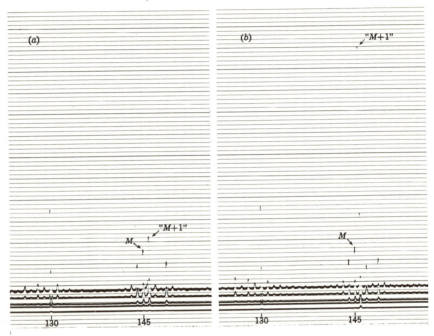

Fig. 3-2. Change in the relative intensity of the "$M + 1$" peak of valine ethyl ester ($C_7H_{15}NO_2$) upon switching the ion source from "focused" (a) to "nonfocused" (b) and increasing the ionizing current from 9 to 40 μamp.

mass spectrometer (the type used in the author's laboratory) this is achieved simply by scanning the molecular-weight region of the spectrum first with the ion-source controls set to "focused." The scan is repeated after switching to "nonfocused" and increasing the ionizing current to give the same intensity of the "normal" peaks. In this instrument, the positive potential applied to the repeller plates (Fig. 1-3) is simultaneously reduced with the focus potential when the controls are set to "nonfocused."

Figure 3-2 shows part of the mass spectrum of valine ethyl ester

[(CH$_3$)$_2$CHCH(NH$_2$)CO$_2$C$_2$H$_5$, mol. wt 145] scanned under such conditions. The much increased intensity of the peak at m/e 146 is a clear indication that it arises via such a collision process and that the molecular weight is 145. All other peaks remain exactly the same because of the high reproducibility of mass spectra and because exactly the same sample (including background and impurities) is scanned both times. For example, the peak at m/e 149 in Fig. 3-2 is due to a trace of diffusion-pump fluid. This degree of reproducibility is particularly important if small samples are to be used. A further characteristic of such "$M+1$" peaks is their shape, as they seem to be wider, especially on the low-mass side. Thus they may also be recognized by their apparent lower resolution,

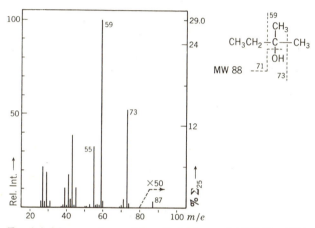

Fig. 3-3. Mass spectrum of 2-methyl-2-butanol (API No. 656).

especially if the molecular weight is high, because at higher masses the height of the valley between peaks is very sensitive to peak width. These "$M+1$" peaks are thus very helpful in the determination of the molecular weight of a compound, but they can give rise to difficulties in quantitative analyses or in determining stable isotopes in the molecule (see Sec. 5-1).

There are still many molecules which fail to exhibit a peak at the molecular weight or 1 mass unit higher. In such cases it is sometimes possible to arrive at the molecular weight of the compound by the partial interpretation of the mass spectrum. As an example, for such a case, the mass spectrum shown in Fig. 3-3 will be discussed. There is a very intense peak at m/e 59, but the peak of highest mass and of appreciable intensity is found at m/e 73 (the peak at m/e 74 is due only to heavy isotopes, as discussed in Sec. 3-1*B*, while the one at m/e 87 is of such low intensity that it has to be regarded with caution) and small peaks at m/e 71 and at m/e 70. Mass 73 is eliminated as the molecular weight for a number of reasons: First, the odd number would imply the presence of one nitrogen atom, but this is impossible, for no other characteristic peaks appear in the spectrum, which would indicate that the compound was an amine, nitrile, or another nitrogen-containing molecule. The correctness of this statement will become obvious later when the type of fragmentation to be expected of such molecules will be discussed in detail (Sec. 3-2). Second, there is a strong peak at m/e 59, which corresponds to 14 mass units less than 73. The loss of CH_2 would imply the formation of a carbene and transfer of a hydrogen atom, which would require considerable energy and is never observed to any appreciable extent. Therefore, if mass 73 were the molecular weight of the compound, mass 59 would have to be the molecular ion of a lower homolog, thus indicating the presence of a mixture. While this could not be excluded in the absence of other information, the peaks at m/e 71 and m/e 70 are a strong indication that mass 73 is not the molecular weight but a fragment of the compound, because otherwise those two peaks would correspond to the loss of two and three hydrogens, respectively, which does not happen often. Although none of these arguments definitely excludes molecular weight 73 for the compound in question, the spectrum can more easily be interpreted in terms of a unique structure, if we assume all those peaks to be fragments. The difference of 3 mass units between mass 73 and mass 70 can be explained satisfactorily if we assume that mass 73 is a fragment due to the loss of a methyl group and that mass 70 arises by the elimination of water from the molecule. These assumptions immediately remove the difficulty we had in explaining the mass difference of 14 units between mass 73 and mass 59, because it follows that the latter peak is due to the loss of an ethyl group from the molecular ion. Addition of these masses ($59 + 29$, $70 + 18$, $73 + 15$) leads to mass 88 as the molecular weight of the compound in question, and the peak at m/e 71 is then due to the loss of 17 mass units (OH), while the small peak at m/e 87 corresponds to the loss of hydrogen. Arguments of this type can frequently be used to establish the molecular weight of the compound, or at least to make certain values plausible and eliminate others.

Another indirect way to determine the molecular weight is based on the rate of effusion of the molecule through the leak of the mass spectrometer. It will be discussed in Sec. 4-4.

B. Isotope Peaks

In the previous discussions we have been concerned with one peak, the mass of which corresponds to the molecular weight of the compound, but have neglected two important facts: First, the mass spectrum of any organic compound shows that it is composed of different molecular species, namely, those consisting only of the lightest isotopes of the elements present in the compound (it is this "monoisotopic" peak to which we will refer throughout the book) and other species containing one or more heavy isotopes. Secondly, the molecular weight is not the one which we would calculate on the basis of the atomic weight on the chemical scale but rather is the sum of the isotopes specified in the formula (always the lightest naturally occurring isotope unless stated otherwise).

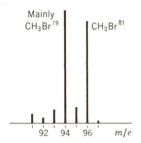

Fig. 3-4. Mass spectrum of methyl bromide in the region of the molecular weight.

Although this mass difference is insignificant for compounds not containing halogens or large organic molecules, we have to keep in mind that the molecular weight of methyl bromide, for example, is either 94 or 96 but not 95. The mass spectrum of methyl bromide in the region of its molecular weight is shown in Fig. 3-4. The significance of those isotope peaks goes, however, far beyond these effects, inasmuch as they permit us to obtain valuable information about the elemental composition of the molecule. Figure 3-4 shows, for example, that it is easy to recognize the presence of a bromine atom in the molecule, because the mass spectrum will exhibit one or more such doublets due to the presence of Br^{79} and Br^{81}, which occur in nature in a ratio of about 1:1. Careful measurement of the intensity of these isotope peaks and comparison with the intensity of the monoisotopic peak of the same species permits the calculation of the number of various atoms of a given element in the molecule. (The present discussion is concerned with the molecular ions, but the same holds true throughout for fragment ions as well.) Table 3-2 gives the natural abundances of the isotopes for the elements commonly encountered in organic molecules.

Table 3-2. Natural Abundance·of the Isotopes of Some Elements *

Element	Abundance, per cent						
Hydrogen	99.985 H^1,	0.015 H^2					
Carbon	98.893 C^{12},	1.107 C^{13}					
Nitrogen	99.634 N^{14},	0.366 N^{15}					
Oxygen	99.759 O^{16},	0.037 O^{17},	0.204 O^{18}				
Fluorine	100 F^{19}						
Silicon	92.21 Si^{28},	4.70 Si^{29},	3.09 Si^{30}				
Phosphorus	100 P^{31}						
Sulfur	95.0 S^{32},	0.76 S^{33},	4.22 S^{34},	0.14 S^{36}			
Chlorine †	75.77 Cl^{35},	24.23 Cl^{37}					
Bromine	50.537 Br^{79},	49.463 Br^{81}					
Iodine	100 I^{127}						

* "Best values" listed (except chlorine) in U.S. Atomic Energy Commission, "Nuclear Data Tables," National Research Council, Washington, 1959.
† W. R. Shields, E. L. Garner, and V. H. Dibeler, *J. Am. Chem. Soc.*, **84**, 1519 (1962).

The abundance of the molecules having a molecular weight of 1, 2, 3, 4, or more units higher than the weight of the monoisotopic molecule depends on the number of atoms present and on the relative abundance of the isotopes in these elements. For C^{13} it is about 1.1 per cent, and this is illustrated by the mass spectrum of methane, which shows a peak at mass 17, which is about 1.1 per cent as intense as the peak at mass 16. The natural abundance of deuterium is so low that it can be neglected as long as there are only a few hydrogen atoms in the molecule. In ethane, each one of the two carbon atoms has 1.1 per cent chance to be carbon-13, and one finds that mass 31 in ethane is about 2.2 per cent as intense as the peak at mass 30, and for larger molecules the intensity of the peak at $(M + 1)$, expressed in per cent of the intensity at M, increases correspondingly. Considerable information about the number of carbon atoms present in the molecule can thus be obtained from the ratio of the intensity of the monoisotopic ion of the molecule to that of the peak found 1 mass unit higher. This ratio can be calculated with considerable accuracy by using standard natural abundances of the isotopes, but the calculation is rather complex. The abundance of the molecular species 1 mass unit heavier than the monoisotopic molecule for a compound containing carbon, hydrogen, nitrogen, and oxygen may be based on Eq. (3-11):[7]

$$\frac{P_{M+1}}{P_M} = w\left(\frac{c}{100-c}\right) + x\left(\frac{h}{100-h}\right)$$

$$+ y\left(\frac{n}{100-n}\right) + z\left(\frac{o_1}{100-o_1-o_2}\right) \qquad (3\text{-}11)$$

where P_M = abundance of molecules containing no heavy isotopes

$P_M + 1$ = abundance of molecules containing one H^2, C^{13}, N^{15}, or O^{17} atom

w, x, y, z = number of carbons, hydrogens, nitrogens, and oxygens present

c, h, n, o_1, o_2 = abundance of C^{13}, H^2, N^{15}, O^{17}, and O^{18}, respectively

Although this equation would still be manageable, the calculation of the abundance of the molecules 2 mass units heavier than the monoisotopic molecule, owing to the presence of any combination of two atoms of H^2, C^{13}, N^{15}, or O^{17} or of one atom of O^{18}, involves an equation [7] about five times as long as Eq. (3-11) and is, therefore, not very handy for speedy calculation by slide rule.

Fortunately the calculation of such abundances with high accuracy is in general not necessary. There is no point in obtaining these values to more significant numbers than is warranted by the accuracy of the measurement on the record given by the mass spectrometer. Furthermore, we have to keep in mind the fact that the natural abundance of stable isotopes changes to a certain degree according to the origin of the molecule. Even small variations in the isotope abundance of those elements present in large numbers in the molecule will change the ratio of the abundance of P_M and P_{M+1} to an extent that makes high accuracy in the calculation of these ratios irrelevant. Unfortunately, the natural abundance of C^{13} varies about 4 per cent (see Fig. 3-5).[8] The C^{13}/C^{12} ratio is thus about 0.01118 for the average atmospheric carbon dioxide, while it is 0.01082 in the lower extreme of terrestrial plants, corresponding to 1.1056 per cent and 1.0704 per cent, respectively, for the abundance of C^{13}. The value for C^{13} in Table 3-2 is the average of two limestones.[9]

The use of more accurately calculated abundances of the species P_{M+1}

[7] J. H. Beynon, "Mass Spectrometry and Its Application to Organic Chemistry," Elsevier Publishing Company, Amsterdam, 1960.
[8] R. Park and H. N. Dunning, *Geochim. et Cosmochim. Acta*, **22**, 99 (1961).
[9] A. O. Nier, *Phys. Rev.*, **77**, 789 (1950).

and P_{M+2} which are available [7,10] for a considerable but still limited number of combinations is justified only if the abundance of C^{13} in the particular sample is known with comparable accuracy. Frequently this will not be the case with a wide variety of organic compounds. A commercially available amino acid may come from animal proteins and have a low C^{13} content, or it may have been produced by synthetic processes originating partly or entirely from atmospheric CO_2 or limestone and therefore have a high C^{13} content. A simple calculation shows that the ratio P_{M+1}/P_M is about the same both for a compound containing 35 C atoms derived from atmospheric CO_2 and for one containing 36 C atoms originating from terrestrial lipids.

Accurate values for the abundances of P_{M+1} and P_{M+2} have received considerable attention in the petroleum industry for use in the quantitative analysis of complex hydrocarbon mixtures. This is an area where, because of the narrow range of the C^{13} abundance in terrestrial petroleum, the use of more precise values is most applicable (see Fig. 3-5).

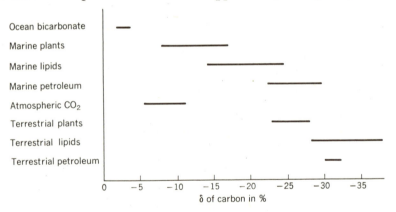

Fig. 3-5. Variations in the natural abundance of C^{13}. (*From Ref. 8.*) The unit of the abscissa is δ (in. per mil) $= \dfrac{C^{13}/C^{12} \text{ of sample} - C^{13}/C^{12} \text{ of standard}}{C^{13}/C^{12} \text{ of standard}}$

A very much simplified and somewhat empirical scheme may be used instead of Eq. (3-11) for the calculation of the intensity of the heavier molecular species of organic molecules, which in general consist of three groups of elements:

1. Elements with heavy isotopes of low abundance but possibly present in a considerable number in a molecule: carbon, hydrogen, nitrogen, and oxygen

[10] D. R. McAdams, "Isotope Correction Factors for Mass Spectra of Petroleum Fractions," Esso Research Laboratories, Baton Rouge, La., 1957.

2. Elements with isotopes of relatively high abundance but occurring in small numbers in organic molecules: sulfur, silicon, chlorine, and bromine

3. Monoisotopic elements: fluorine, phosphorus, iodine

For an approximation of the abundance of the heavier species, one may treat these three groups of elements in a molecule separately and add the results together. The values obtained in this way are in general sufficiently accurate to permit drawing important conclusions as to the composition of the molecules. In the relatively few cases where the accuracy by which the intensity of these peaks can be measured warrants the use of more precise values, published tables [7,10] of abundance ratios should be consulted.

The two most important elements of group 1 are carbon and hydrogen, since they contribute most to the molecular weight, and the molecular species 1 mass unit heavier than the majority of the molecules will be due to the presence of one atom of C^{13} or of one atom of deuterium.

The value expected for $(P_{M+1}/P_M)100$, i.e., the intensity of P_{M+1} expressed in per cent of the intensity of P_M, may be calculated simply as follows (based on a δ value of -30 as the average of the C^{13} abundance in terrestrial plants, lipids, and petroleum, the major sources of organic compounds):

$$1.09 \times \text{number of C atoms present} \tag{3-12}$$
or
$$1.10 \times \text{number of CH groups present} \tag{3-13}$$
or
$$1.12 \times \text{number of CH}_2 \text{ groups present} \tag{3-14}$$

Depending on the degree of saturation that the compound in question seems to have, one will use any one of the three values or an interpolated one and in this way also account for the natural abundance of deuterium in one single operation. If a considerable number of carbon atoms are present in the molecule, its peak at $M+2$ due to the presence of two atoms of carbon-13, or the presence of one atom of carbon-13 and one of deuterium, will become appreciable. Its value (in per cent of M^+ intensity) can simply be approximated, for example, by

$$\frac{(1.10 \times \text{number of CH groups present})^2}{200} \tag{3-15}$$

Table 3-3 compares some values obtained on the basis of the approximations outlined above with the values obtained by more accurate treatment involving complex calculations. The values for the intensities of the

$M + 1$ peak are in very good agreement; although those for the $M + 2$ peak obtained from Eq. (3-15) are a little higher than the ones calculated more accurately, the difference is still below 0.2 per cent of the intensity of M^+ in molecules with up to 30 carbon atoms, implying that the accuracy is sufficient for the most common use of the $M + 2$ peak, namely, the detection of oxygen atoms. The values for the contributions of carbon and hydrogen to P_{M+1} and P_{M+2} having been obtained, 0.36 per cent of P_M is added to P_{M+1} for each nitrogen atom present, and 0.20 per cent is added to P_{M+2} for each oxygen atom.

Table 3-3. Intensities of Isotope Peaks of Mass $M + 1$ and $M + 2$ (in Per Cent of Intensity of M)

Composition	Mass	Approximated value	Calculated	
			Ref. 7	Ref. 10
C_5H_{12}	$M + 1$	5.6	5.595	5.5855
	$M + 2$	0.15	0.1273	0.1267
$C_{10}H_{12}$	$M + 1$	11.0	10.998	10.9910
	$M + 2$	0.60	0.5464	0.5455
$C_{15}H_{24}$	$M + 1$	16.80	16.593	16.5765
	$M + 2$	1.41	1.289	1.2861
$C_{20}H_{42}$	$M + 1$	22.40	. . .	22.25
	$M + 2$	2.51	. . .	2.3587
C_9H_8O	$M + 1$	9.90	9.893	9.8899
	$M + 2$	0.69	0.6372	0.6369
$C_8H_8N_2$	$M + 1$	9.52	9.536	. . .
	$M + 2$	0.39	0.4065	. . .
$C_{20}H_{26}ON_2$	$M + 1$	22.72	. . .	. . .
	$M + 2$	2.62	. . .	. . .

By the method outlined above, it is possible to calculate the intensity ratios of the peaks at M, $M + 1$, and $M + 2$ expected for a given molecule containing carbon, hydrogen, oxygen, and nitrogen.

The isotope distribution of molecules containing elements of group 2 mentioned earlier do not require the use of approximations, because they are present in organic molecules usually only in small numbers; approximations would give rather inaccurate results because of the considerable abundance of heavy isotopes in this group. Such a case is treated in terms of the binomial expansion:

$$(a+b)^n \qquad (3\text{-}16)$$

where a = relative abundance of light isotopes
  b = relative abundance of heavy isotopes
  n = number of atoms of this element present in molecule

For an ion containing three chlorine atoms $a \approx 3$, $b \approx 1$ (the natural abundance of Cl^{35} = 75.8 per cent and Cl^{37} = 24.2 per cent), and $n = 3$. Since $(a+b)^3 = a^3 + 3a^2b + 3ab^2 + b^3$, the intensity ratios of the peaks at mass x, $x+2$, $x+4$, and $x+6$ will be 27:27:9:1.

These intensity ratios can be calculated for ions containing different elements as well, for example, two chlorine atoms and one bromine. In the evaluation of the product $(a+b)^2(c+d)$, where a, b, c, and d are the abundances of Cl^{35}, Cl^{37}, Br^{79}, and Br^{81}, respectively, care has to be taken to use the correct proportions, namely, 0.758 and 0.242, 0.505 and 0.495, or, less accurately, 3:1:2:2 (but not 3:1:1:1 because of the $\approx 1:1$ ratio of the bromine isotopes). From the above product, which is

$$a^2c + 2abc + b^2c + a^2d + 2abd + b^2d$$

and keeping in mind that both b and d indicate the presence of an atom 2 mass units heavier than a and c, the intensity distribution of the peaks at mass x, $x+2$, $x+4$, $x+6$ is found to be about 18:30:14:2. Here again more accurate results are obtained by the use of the more precise abundances given in Table 3-2, but it is warranted only if these isotope ratios are correct for the particular sample under investigation. Also, considerable variations may occur in the abundance of the isotopes of these elements. Furthermore, it is not necessary to obtain more accurate values, because the multiplet most similar to Cl_2Br would be that of Br_2, requiring a triplet of the ratio 1:2:1, which can be easily distinguished.

Calculations of this kind are also very useful in determining the extent of incorporation of other stable isotopes (H^2, C^{13}, N^{15}, and O^{18}) into different parts of a molecule, as outlined in Chap. 5.

The mass spectra of molecules containing elements of group 2 exhibit very characteristic multiplets of peaks, examples of which are shown in Fig. 3-6. The presence of such elements in a molecule and their number can, therefore, easily be deduced from a consideration of the multiplets of peaks separated by 2 mass units. The elements of group 1, discussed above, contribute substantially only to the species 1 mass unit higher than the major molecular species. Simple addition of the intensities calculated for these two groups will give a reasonably correct picture. Figure 3-7 shows the carbon isotope peak between the chlorine isotope peaks quite clearly.

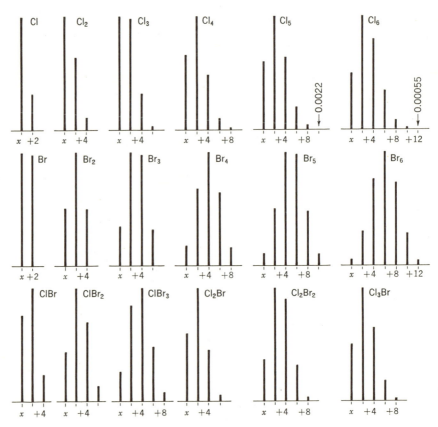

Fig. 3-6. Characteristic multiplets of peaks, spaced 2 mass units apart, because of the presence of one or more halogen atoms in a molecule or fragment (x refers to the mass of the species containing only light isotopes). The numbers indicate the intensity (in terms of the most prominent peak of the group) of those species of which the abundance is too low to be shown graphically.

The presence of elements of group 3 may also be recognized from the mass spectrum of the compound, because they give rise to a low intensity of the isotope peaks due to the presence of carbon. A molecule of mass 142, which shows only 1.1 per cent of the species of mass 143, can contain at the most only one carbon atom, while the rest of its mass must be due to a monoisotopic element; iodine is the most obvious choice. The substance therefore must be methyl iodide, which is confirmed by a peak at mass 127.

The calculation of the intensity of the heavier molecular species of a certain compound of known composition is of less interest than the reverse

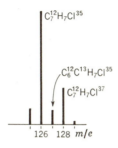

Fig. 3-7. Mass spectrum of benzyl chloride in the region of the molecular weight. The isotopic composition of the major species contributing is indicated; the isotope peak of the fragment of mass 125 and the contributions of species containing D, $C^{12}D$, or C_2^{13} are neglected.

process, the deduction of the elemental composition. Table 3-4 summarizes the intensities of the peaks at $M+1$ and $M+2$ (in per cent of the intensity of M) for three compounds of molecular weight 132. An indication of the number of carbon atoms present in the molecule is given by the intensity of the peaks at $M+1$, which upon division by 1.1 gives

Table 3-4. Dependence of P_{M+1}/P_{M+2} Ratio on Elemental Composition

Empirical formula	Molecular weight	P_{M+1}°	P_{M+2}°	P_{M+1}/P_{M+2}
$C_{10}H_{12}$	132	11.0	0.60	18.4 (20.1)†
C_9H_8O	132	9.90	0.69	14.3 (15.5)
$C_8H_8N_2$	132	9.52	0.39	24.4 (23.4)

° From Table 3-3, col. 3.
† Values in parentheses calculated from Table 3-3, col. 4.

an upper limit for the number of carbon atoms possibly present; the peak at $M+2$ is a measure of the number of sulfur atoms, if any, in the molecule and also of oxygen if the peaks are intense enough to be measured with the required accuracy. In combination with the molecular weight of the compound, such considerations frequently permit the deduction of the elemental composition of the molecule in question. An additional criterion,[11] the ratio of $(M+1)/(M+2)$, is given in Table 3-4. It is particularly useful for an evaluation of the number of oxygen atoms present, but this ratio is also very sensitive to a contribution of an impurity to the intensity of the $M+2$ peak.

Obviously there are a number of limitations to this method of determining the elemental composition of an organic molecule. First, if the compound belongs to a group which does not give molecular ions of considerable intensity, an accurate measurement of the abundance of the heavier molecules is not possible. Secondly, impurities present in the compound and contributing to any one of those masses may give rise to errors. Those, of course, can be only positive errors, unless the contaminant contributes a great deal to the intensity of the monoisotopic peak (M). Small contributions to the $M+1$ peak and even smaller ones to the $M+2$ peak may make it impossible to apply the method outlined above. Third, if the compound has a tendency to give rise to "$M+1$" peaks due to ion-molecule reactions, the intensity of this peak cannot be used to deduce the number of carbon atoms present in the molecule. It is important to note, however, that a given formula can be excluded if the isotope peaks calculated exceed the ones measured on the spectrum, if one deals at all with a compound that has not undergone isotopic fractionation. Frequently the intensity ratios should be measured on spectra obtained by using low-energy electrons; the contribution of fragments of impurities is minimized, and so are the contributions of the isotope peaks of the fragment of mass $M-1$ due to loss of hydrogen from the molecular ion. The latter contributions can also be eliminated by calculation.

The major requirement for the successful application of the principle outlined in this section for the determining the elemental composition of the substance is a peak for the molecular ion sufficiently intense to give accurately measureable peaks of $M+1$ and $M+2$, a pure sample and sufficient resolution. In a number of cases the intensity of the molecular-weight peak can be increased by conversion to a more suitable derivative (Sec. 4-5). The ultimate method for the determination of the elemental composition is, of course, accurate mass measurement with a mass spectrometer of high resolving power as discussed in Sec. 4-6. The isotope-peak method described above should not be overemphasized but also should not be neglected wherever applicable.

It should be repeated that the distribution of the heavier species holds just as well for fragments as for molecules, and the composition of fragment ions may also be deduced in the manner outlined above. Fre-

---

[11] J. H. Beynon, *Mikrochim. Acta*, **1956**, 437.

quently, other fragments of the molecule have masses coinciding with the ones due to the presence of heavy isotopes in another fragment, and in such a situation it is impossible to use this approach. It is in any case worthwhile to scan this group of peaks repeatedly while decreasing the energy of the bombarding electrons. If the intensity ratios of the peaks in question remain the same over a wide range of electron energy near the appearance potential of the fragment, one can assume that the peaks are due to different isotopic species of the same fragment. Most often, different fragments would have different appearance potentials, and therefore one would disappear from the spectrum at still higher electron energy than another.

In many of the figures in this book mass spectra are shown which are good examples of the appearance of such isotope peaks, both in the region of the molecular weight and of certain characteristic fragments; the presence of sulfur or halogens in some of the compounds can easily be spotted.

The above discussion has been limited to isotopes present in their natural abundance. Obviously, the mass spectrum will be greatly altered by the presence of heavy isotopes in higher concentration. This very important aspect will be discussed in detail in Chap. 5.

3-2. FRAGMENTATION

For the correct interpretation of the mass spectrum of an organic molecule in terms of its structure or for the reverse process, the prediction of the major features of the spectrum of such a molecule, a detailed knowledge of the fragmentation processes giving rise to the spectrum is imperative. The major part of the literature that has been published concerning such processes seems to originate from three groups of workers representing three different approaches: First, there is the approach of physicists and physical chemists, who are interested in investigating the basic aspects of electron impact and who study these phenomena on atoms or small molecules consisting of relatively few atoms. Secondly, there is the analytical approach, characterized by the collection of the mass spectra of a group of compounds containing a single functional group, the search for common trends ("structure correlations"), and the designing of a scheme, or set of rules, that applies to most of the intense peaks of the spectra presented, to be used for identifying closely related compounds of this class. Most of the work reported in Refs. 22 to 65 belong in this category. The third approach is that of investigating single compounds or a few related ones commonly of uncomplicated and known structure. In these investigations a detailed tabulation of the presumed nature of all the fragments formed from the molecule is presented along with a detailed discussion of the posssible formation of some minor peaks of unexpected mass.

All these investigations have added considerably to our present knowledge of the mass spectra of organic molecules. Most of them, however, have been limited to aspects of mass spectrometry without applying the results to the solution of problems in organic chemistry. The first approach, the entirely theoretical one, is presently still too far removed from the possibility of studying complex molecules. The work of those using the second approach is frequently hampered or breaks down if an additional functional group is introduced into the molecule; only little work has been done (Refs. 25, 42, 43, 46, 52, 53, 55) on types of compounds containing two or more different functional groups (not counting aromatic rings). The third approach, while important for the deeper understanding of electron-impact-induced fragmentation, sometimes leads to more confusion than understanding, particularly on the part of those who are less familiar with the interpretation of mass spectra.

It is felt that it is necessary in mass spectrometry, just as it was and still is in UV, IR, and NMR spectroscopy, to use a somewhat empirical approach for the interpretation of these complex spectra. For this purpose, in contrast to the three methods described above, it is not feasible to catalog the vast variety of organic molecules as hydrocarbons, alcohols, aldehydes, ketones, etc.; rather, it is necessary to think in terms of the entire molecule, which first is ionized and then undergoes fragmentation, and not of a particular functional group isolated from the rest. Consideration of the mutual interactions of all atoms and groups within such complex molecules is necessary for the correct interpretation of a mass spectrum.

An attempt is made in this chapter to summarize the more important modes of fragmentation of complex organic molecules in the light of carbonium-ion chemistry, a view particularly appealing to the organic chemist; the mutual influence and competition exerted by the various functional groups present in the same molecule will be emphasized, because of the importance of these effects in the fragmentation of larger, polyfunctional molecules.

Another item to be taken over from organic chemistry is thinking in terms of mechanisms. Just as "drawing boxes" (for example, around any two hydrogen atoms and one oxygen atom, a method full of pitfalls for the explanation or prediction of reactions occurring with elimination of

H_2O) has long given way to depicting the mechanism in the form of electrons moving over an energetically favorable path, so the liberal use of wiggled lines to indicate cleavage of more than one bond, for the purpose of creating on paper a particle of the desired mass, has to give way to a more selective approach which delineates the fragmentation of the molecule by moving the valence electrons available in the energetically most favored manner without creating many particles having unshared electrons. Aside from some earlier isolated examples,[12] McLafferty [13-15] has first used the mechanistic approach more widely in the correlation of mass spectra of certain compound types. The situation is obviously complicated by the fact that the energies involved in electron-impact reactions, in contrast to conventional chemical reactions, are rather high and cannot be dissipated to an appreciable extent by collisions.

In the discussion of fragmentation processes in this chapter and the remaining part of the book, mechanisms and detailed structures with concrete bonds are depicted. This is done mainly in order to describe the approximate path the fragmentation takes, the distribution of the atoms in the fragments, and the source of stabilization of the positive charge. We need to be fully aware that we are dealing with particles in an excited state rather than particles in the ground state, but since virtually nothing is known about the nature of the former, we have to use the latter as one of the crutches we so often use in the presentation of phenomena either to save time or to gloss over our ignorance, as in the use of a line to connect two atoms.

It may be appropriate here to mention briefly the present status of the theory of mass spectra. A very recent paper [16] on a comprehensive study of the mass spectra of C_2 to C_8 hydrocarbons produced by photoionization begins with the statements "The ionization and dissociation of diatomic molecule is rather well understood. . . . By contrast, the case of polyatomic molecules is not well understood" and ends saying "The conclusions reached in this paper are seemingly all negative." While these statements do not seem very encouraging, in the same paper many current problems are pointed out the solution of which would contribute to the formulation of a theory adequately describing the processes occurring in the ion source of the mass spectrometer.

[12] C. S. Cummings and W. Bleakney, *Phys. Rev.*, **58**, 787 (1940).

[13] F. W. McLafferty, *Appl. Spectroscopy*, **11**, 148 (1957).

[14] F. W. McLafferty, in J. D. Waldron (ed.), "Advances in Mass Spectrometry," p. 355, Pergamon Press, London, 1959.

[15] F. W. McLafferty, *Anal. Chem.*, **31**, 477 (1959).

[16] B. Steiner, C. F. Giese, and M. G. Inghram, *J. Chem. Phys.*, **34**, 189 (1961).

The only theory ever put forward in this area, one strongly criticized in the paper by Steiner et al.,[16] is the "statistical theory of mass spectra" of Eyring et al.[17] It assumes that (1) any one of the valence electrons is removed from the molecule with the same probability as the others; (2) the energy excess is free to travel about rapidly in the molecule; and (3) whenever energy sufficient for fragmentation is concentrated at a given bond, the bond will break. By applying the principles of absolute-rate theory, the mass spectra of molecules as complicated as propane, propane-2,2-d_2 and n-butane have been calculated and found to agree well with the experimental ones. More recently a number of investigators working with slightly more complicated compounds were not able to obtain more than qualitative agreement of the calculated mass spectra with the experimentally determined ones,[18] nor were the peak intensities of the order of magnitude of the ones calculated when electron energies near the appearance potential of the fragment were used.[19]

A considerable rephrasing of the theory seems to be needed to reconcile the data available at the present time. For this reason and because this book is directed to an area at present far beyond the limit of theoretical treatment, these theories are not discussed in more detail here. The reader interested in the present status of the theory is referred to some of the more comprehensive original papers [17,20,21] and those to be published by these writers in the near future.

Earlier in this chapter it was mentioned that the molecular ion may decompose into fragments if the bombarding electron transfers energy in excess of the ionization potential of the molecule and if this excess energy suffices for breaking a bond. The fragmentation scheme on page 48 indicates the multitude of fragments obtainable from a relatively small molecule; this is the reason for the complexity of mass spectra and for the great number of peaks that make them so highly characteristic for a given compound. The fact that a mass spectrum of an organic molecule exhibits a peak for almost each mass which can conceivably be constructed from any number of the atoms present in the molecule would seem to be a disadvantage in using mass spectra to determine the structure of the

[17] H. M. Rosenstock, M. B. Wallenstein, A. L. Wahrhaftig, and H. Eyring, *Proc. Natl. Acad. Sci. U.S.*, **38**, 667 (1952).

[18] W. A. Chupka, *J. Chem. Phys.*, **30**, 191 (1959).

[19] L. Friedman, F. A. Long, and M. Wolfsberg, *J. Chem. Phys.*, **26**, 714 (1957).

[20] A. Kropf, E. M. Eyring, A. L. Wahrhaftig, and H. Eyring, *J. Chem. Phys.*, **32**, 149 (1960).

[21] H. M. Rosenstock and M. Krauss, in R. M. Elliott (ed.), "Advances in Mass Spectrometry," vol. II, Pergamon Press, London, 1962.

compound. The very great differences in the intensities of those peaks, however, provide an additional criterion. The mass spectrum of ethanol (Fig. 3-8), for example, consists of about 30 peaks (some of which are of too small a mass or too low an intensity to appear in the figure), but 80 per cent of the sum of the intensities of all peaks are due to only six fragments (i.e., mass 15, 27, 29, 31, 45, and 46), the remaining 24 peaks being of low or almost negligible intensity. It is primarily these intense peaks (see page 78 for definition) that are used for interpreting the mass spectrum of an organic compound, because the high intensity indicates a high probability of formation of the particular fragment and thus implies that it arises by an energetically favorable process. On the other hand,

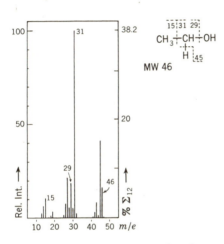

Fig. 3-8. Mass spectrum of ethanol.

a particle formed with low probability, therefore giving rise to only a very small peak, may be formed by a complex process involving the rupture of a number of bonds and is therefore not very characteristic of the structure. The fragment of mass 24 in the spectrum of ethanol must be formed by the rupture of six bonds, and its only significance is the indication that the molecule does contain at least two carbon atoms. An attempt to explain the formation of all the peaks in a mass spectrum is therefore neither sensible nor feasible, nor is such an explanation necessary for the successful interpretation of the mass spectrum. This situation is somewhat similar to the significance of the "fingerprint region" in IR spectra.

A large number of mass spectra are available in published form. Listed below are those papers dealing with particular groups of compounds and containing complete spectra (presented either graphically or as a list of intensities). These papers are listed here because they contain, collectively, most of the published data on the mass spectra of compounds of known structure. The inclusion of a paper in this group should not imply that the particular investigation is historically the first one or that it contains the best discussion of the fragmentation processes; these processes receive an amount of attention that differs widely over the entire list, ranging from detailed discussions to none at all.

Classes of Organic Compounds Which Have Been the Subject of Mass Spectrometric Investigations

Aliphatic hydrocarbons [22,23]	Aromatic esters and acids [45,46]
Alkylbenzenes [24]	Quinones and polycyclic ketones [47]
Olefins [22,25]	Phenols and aromatic alcohols [48]
Aliphatic alcohols [26]	Furanes [49]
Steroids [27,27a]	Aliphatic amines [50]
Aliphatic ethers [5]	Aliphatic amides [51]
Vinyl ethers [25]	Amino esters [52]
Aromatic ethers [28]	Formamido esters [53]
Acetals [29]	Aliphatic nitriles [53a]
Aliphatic aldehydes [30]	Nitroalkanes [54]
Aromatic aldehydes [31]	Nitrobenzenes [55]
Aliphatic ketones [32]	Alkylpyridines [56]
Cyclic ketones [33]	Alkylprazines [57]
Aliphatic esters [34-37]	Alkylindoles [58]
Aliphatic esters (dibasic) [38,39]	Alkyl mercaptans [59]
Aliphatic esters (alkyl-substituted) [40,41]	Dialkylsulfides [59]
Aliphatic esters (unsaturated) [42]	Thiophenes [60-62]
Aliphatic esters (hydroxy-, oxo-, epoxy-, and methoxy) [43]	Fluorocarbons [63]
	Halogenated compounds [64]
Lactones [44]	Silylethers [65]

[22] American Petroleum Institute, Research Project 44.

[23] M. J. O'Neal and T. P. Wier, *Anal. Chem.*, **23**, 830 (1951).

[24] S. Meyerson, *Appl. Spectroscopy*, **9**, 120 (1955).

[25] F. W. McLafferty, *Anal. Chem.*, **31**, 2072 (1959).

[26] R. A. Friedel, J. L. Shultz, and A. G. Sharkey, *Anal. Chem.*, **28**, 926 (1956).

[27] S. S. Friedland, G. H. Lane, Jr., R. T. Longman, K. E. Train, and M. J. O'Neal, Jr., *Anal. Chem.*, **31**, 169 (1959).

[27a] H. Budzikiewicz and C. Djerassi, *J. Am. Chem. Soc.*, **84**, 1430 (1962).

[28] J. M. Wilson, *Experientia*, **16**, 403 (1960).

[29] R. A. Friedel and A. G. Sharkey, *Anal. Chem.*, **28**, 940 (1956).

[30] J. A. Gilpin and F. W. McLafferty, *Anal. Chem.*, **29**, 990 (1957).

[31] T. Aczel and H. E. Lumpkin, *Anal. Chem.*, **33**, 386 (1961).

[32] A. G. Sharkey, J. L. Schultz, and R. A. Friedel, *Anal. Chem.*, **28**, 934 (1956).

As noted earlier in this section, the fragmentation processes will be presented on a general basis, with emphasis on the mutual effects and competition of various functional groups, rather than as a discussion of one group after the other, which would not contribute to the basic understanding of the entire subject.

The energy required for the production of a certain fragment from the molecular ion will depend primarily on the energy of the bond to be broken, on the energy content (stabilization) of the positive ion formed, on the energy content (stabilization) of the neutral fragment, which may

---

[33] J. H. Beynon, R. A. Saunders, and A. E. Williams, *Appl. Spectroscopy*, **14**, 95 (1960).

[34] A. G. Sharkey, J. L. Shultz, and R. A. Friedel, *Anal. Chem.*, **31**, 87 (1959).

[35] J. H. Beynon, R. A. Saunders, and A. E. Williams, *Anal. Chem.*, **33**, 221 (1961).

[36] R. Ryhage and E. Stenhagen, *Arkiv Kemi*, **13**, 523 (1959).

[37] *Ibid.*, **14**, 483 (1959).

[38] *Ibid.*, p. 497.

[39] R. E. Kourey, B. L. Tuffly, and V. A. Yarborough, *Anal. Chem.*, **31**, 1760 (1959).

[40] R. Ryhage and E. Stenhagen, *Arkiv Kemi*, **15**, 291 (1960).

[41] *Ibid.*, p. 333.

[42] B. Hallgren, R. Ryhage, and E. Stenhagen, *Acta Chem. Scand.*, **13**, 845 (1959).

[43] R. Ryhage and E. Stenhagen, *Arkiv Kemi*, **15**, 545 (1960).

[44] L. Friedman and F. A. Long, *J. Am. Chem. Soc.*, **75**, 2832 (1953).

[45] F. W. McLafferty and R. S. Gohlke, *Anal. Chem.*, **31**, 2076 (1959).

[46] E. M. Emery, *Anal. Chem.*, **32**, 1495 (1960).

[47] J. H. Beynon and A. E. Williams, *Appl. Spectroscopy*, **14**, 156 (1960).

[48] T. Aczel and H. E. Lumpkin, *Anal. Chem.*, **32**, 1819 (1960).

[49] J. Collin, *Bull. soc. chim. Belges*, **69**, 575 (1960).

[50] J. Collin, *Bull. soc. roy. sci. Liège*, **21**, 446 (1952).

[51] J. A. Gilpin, *Anal. Chem.*, **31**, 935 (1959).

[52] K. Biemann, J. Seibl, and F. Gapp, *J. Am. Chem. Soc.*, **83**, 3795 (1961).

[53] K. Heyns and H.-F. Grützmacher, *Z. Naturforsch.*, **16b**, 293 (1961).

[53a] F. W. McLafferty, *Anal. Chem.*, **34**, 26 (1962).

[54] J. Collin, *Bull. soc. roy. sci. Liège*, **23**, 201 (1954).

[55] J. Momigny, *Bull. soc. roy. sci. Liège*, **25**, 93 (1956).

[56] K. Biemann and G. Spiteller. (To be published.)

[57] K. Biemann and J. Seibl. (To be published.)

[58] J. H. Beynon and A. E. Williams, *Appl. Spectroscopy*, **13**, 101 (1959).

[59] E. J. Levy and W. H. Stahl, *Anal. Chem.*, **33**, 707 (1961).

[60] I. W. Kinney and G. L. Cook, *Anal. Chem.*, **24**, 1391 (1952).

[61] K. I. Zimina, A. A. Polyakova, R. A. Khmel'nitskiï, and R. D. Obolentsev, *Zhur. Obshchei Khim.*, **30**, 1264 (1960).

[62] V. Hanus and V. Cermak, *Collection Czechoslov. Chem. Commun.*, **24**, 1602 (1959).

[63] F. L. Mohler, V. H. Dibeler, and R. M. Reese, *J. Research Natl. Bur. Standards*, **49**, 343 (1952).

[64] F. W. McLafferty, *Anal. Chem.*, (a) **34**, 2 (1962); (b) **34**, 16 (1962).

[65] A. G. Sharkey, R. A. Friedel, and S. H. Langer, *Anal. Chem.*, **29**, 770 (1957).

be a radical or a neutral molecule, and finally on the steric arrangement of the atoms in the molecule, a factor which is significant mainly for rearrangement processes.

The most important of these factors seems to be the stabilization of the positive charge of the fragment. Its formation will be enhanced even further if in the fragmentation process a particularly stable radical or, better, a neutral molecule is produced. Almost all the fragmentation processes leading to intense peaks in the mass spectra of organic molecules can be summarized as follows:

Simple cleavage:

Type A_1:
$$\left[-\overset{|}{\underset{|}{C}}-\overset{|}{\underset{|}{C}}- \right]^+ \longrightarrow -\overset{|}{\underset{|}{C}}{}^+ \quad \cdot\overset{|}{\underset{|}{C}}- \tag{3-17}$$

$$(CH_3{}^+ < RCH_2{}^+ < R_2CH^+ < R_3C^+)$$

Type A_2:
$$-\overset{|}{\underset{|\ \gamma}{C}}\overset{\frown}{-}\overset{|}{\underset{|\ \beta}{C}}\overset{\curlyvee}{-}\overset{|}{\underset{|\ \alpha}{C}}{}^+ \longrightarrow -\overset{|}{\underset{|\ \gamma}{C}}{}^+ + \overset{|}{\underset{|}{C}}=\overset{|}{\underset{|}{C}} \tag{3-18}$$

Type A_3:
$$\left[\overset{|}{\underset{|}{C}}=\overset{|}{\underset{|}{C}}-\overset{|}{\underset{|}{C}}-\overset{|}{\underset{|}{C}}- \right]^+ \longrightarrow \overset{|}{\underset{|}{C}}=\overset{|}{\underset{|}{C}}-\overset{|}{\underset{|}{C}}{}^+ + \cdot\overset{|}{\underset{|}{C}}- \tag{3-19}$$

$$\downarrow$$

$$^+\overset{|}{\underset{|}{C}}-\overset{|}{\underset{|}{C}}=\overset{|}{\underset{|}{C}}$$

Type A_4:
$$\left[\langle\bigcirc\rangle-CH_2-\overset{|}{\underset{|}{C}}- \right]^+ \longrightarrow \left(\langle\bigcirc\rangle-CH_2{}^+ \right) \longrightarrow$$

$$\tag{3-20}$$

Type A_5:
$$\left[-\overset{|}{\underset{|}{C}}-X \right]^+ \longrightarrow -\overset{|}{\underset{|}{C}}{}^+ + \cdot X \ (X = \text{halogen, OR, SR, NR}_2, R = H \text{ or alkyl}) \tag{3-21}$$

Type B:
$$\left[R-\overset{|}{\underset{|X}{C}}-R \right]^+ \longrightarrow R\cdot + {}^+\overset{|}{\underset{\curvearrowleft X}{C}}-R \longleftrightarrow \overset{|}{\underset{X^+}{C}}-R \tag{3-22}$$

Type C:
$$\left[R-\overset{\|}{\underset{|O|}{C}}-R \right]^+ \longrightarrow R-\overset{+\frown}{C}{=}\underline{O} \longleftrightarrow R-C{\equiv}O|^+ \tag{3-23}$$

Type D:
$$\left[\right]^{+} \longrightarrow \left[\right]^{+} + \ \underset{C}{\overset{C}{\underset{|}{\overset{|}{C}}}} \qquad (3\text{-}24)$$

Rearrangements:

Type E_1:
$$\left[\begin{array}{c} C\!-\!X \\ | \\ C_n \\ | \\ C\!-\!H \end{array}\right]^{+} \longrightarrow \left[C_n \overset{C}{\underset{C}{\diagdown}}\right]^{+} + \ HX \quad (n = 0,1,2,3 \ldots) \qquad (3\text{-}25)$$

Type E_2:
$$\left[\overset{B}{\diagup}\ (D\!-\!R)\overset{}{\underset{A\diagdown H}{}}\right]^{+} \longrightarrow \left[\overset{B}{}\overset{}{\underset{A}{}}\right]^{+} + \ \underset{H}{\overset{D\!-\!R}{|}} \qquad (3\text{-}26)$$

Type F:
$$\overset{H}{\overset{\frown}{}}\ -\overset{|}{\underset{|}{C}}-\overset{|}{\underset{|}{C}}-\overset{|}{\underset{X}{C}}{}^{+} \longrightarrow \ \overset{\diagdown}{\diagup}C\!=\!C\overset{\diagup}{\diagdown} + \ \overset{|}{\underset{X}{C}}H^{+} \quad (X = O, S, N, R, H) \qquad (3\text{-}27)$$

Type G:
$$\overset{H}{\overset{\frown}{}}\ -\overset{|}{\underset{|}{C}}-\overset{|}{\underset{|}{C}}-\overset{+}{X}\!=\!C\overset{\diagup}{\diagdown} \longrightarrow \ \overset{\diagdown}{\diagup}C\!=\!C\overset{\diagup}{\diagdown} + \ H\overset{+}{X}\!=\!C\overset{\diagup}{\diagdown} \quad (X = O, S, N) \qquad (3\text{-}28)$$

Type H:
$$\left[\begin{array}{c} \overset{H}{\frown} \\ Z \quad B \\ \diagdown \quad \| \\ Y \quad C \\ \diagdown \diagup \diagdown \\ X \quad A \end{array}\right]^{+} \longrightarrow \ \underset{Y}{\overset{Z}{\|}} \ + \left[\begin{array}{c} H\diagdown B \\ | \\ X\!\!=\!\!\overset{C}{\diagdown}A \end{array}\right]^{+} \qquad (3\text{-}29)$$

Here and henceforth, a structure in brackets with a plus sign denotes a molecule less one electron, i.e., a molecular ion or a fragment ion with no free valence.

Types A through D are fragmentation processes requiring the cleavage of one or two (Type D) bonds; such process will be referred to as "simple cleavage." Types E through H involve the migration of a hydrogen atom from one part of the molecule to another during the fragmentation process, termed "rearrangement." In the following sections these fragmentation processes will be discussed one by one in detail, with particular emphasis on the influence exerted upon the intensity of the resulting peaks by the structure of the molecule and by other groups present. The classification of fragmentation processes as Types A through H is mainly for convenience in referring to the process throughout the book and may be helpful in grouping related processes.

A. Simple Cleavage

Type A. Combined in this group are fragmentation processes involving the cleavage of a single bond with retention of the positive charge at a carbon atom, where it is stabilized by hydrocarbon groups [saturated (A_1, A_2) or unsaturated (A_3, A_4)] attached to that carbon atom rather than by a heteroatom.

Type A_1

$$\left[-\overset{\mid}{\underset{\mid}{C}}-\overset{\mid}{\underset{\mid}{C}}- \right]^{+} \longrightarrow -\overset{\mid}{\underset{\mid}{C}}{}^{+} \quad \cdot\overset{\mid}{\underset{\mid}{C}}- \tag{3-17}$$

The increase in stabilization of a carbonium ion with alkyl substitution leads to a preferred fragmentation of hydrocarbon chains at the branching points. The mass spectrum of a straight-chain hydrocarbon has a very typical appearance. As an example, the spectrum of hexadecane is shown in Fig. 3-9a. Such spectra exhibit peaks at mass C_nH_{2n+1} with a maximum intensity at $n = 3$, 4, or 5. Those peaks are accompanied by smaller ones 1, 2, or 3 mass units lower and, of course, the C^{13}-isotope peak 1 mass unit higher. Beyond the intensity maximum in the low-mass region, the height of these peaks decreases steadily down to the fragment which corresponds to the loss of an ethyl group and to only a very small peak owing to the loss of a methyl group, while the peak due to the molecular ion is somewhat more intense than the peaks for the larger fragments. The appearance of this spectrum shows also that peaks in the upper mass range are always of much lower intensity than those due to smaller fragments arising by principally the same process. This is due not only to instrumental factors, i.e., that the mass spectrometer discriminates against higher masses, but also to the fact that larger fragments still contain many bonds which can be cleaved during secondary fragmentation processes. Smaller fragments, on the other hand, either contain fewer such bonds or have arisen via a multistep fragmentation process which gave rise to a fragment lacking enough excess energy to decompose further. This situation must be kept in mind henceforth when "intense" peaks are discussed. It does not necessarily imply that a given peak is more intense than another one in an absolute sense but rather in a relative sense, since it may occur in the region of higher masses. To avoid this ambiguity the expression "characteristic peaks" is preferable, implying that the peak in question is much more intense than others in a particular mass region.

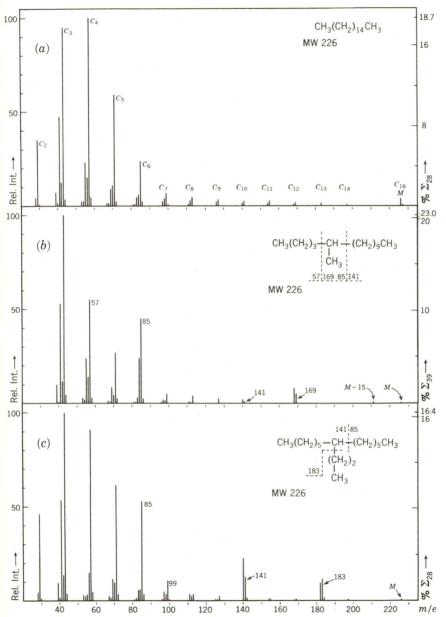

Fig. 3-9. Mass spectra of isomeric C_{16} hydrocarbons. (a) n-Hexadecane; (b) 5-methyl-pentadecane [*from data of J. P. Wibaut and H. Brand, Rec. trav. chim.*, **80,** 97 (1961)]; (c) 7-n-propyltridecane (API No. 591).

From the mass spectrum of a branched hydrocarbon one can deduce the position and the size of the alkyl branch, as illustrated in Figs. 3-9b and c and 3-10. The position of the highly substituted carbon atom in 5-methylpentadecane (Fig. 3-9b) is indicated by the relatively intense peaks, as compared with the unbranched isomer (Fig. 3-9a), at m/e 85 and 169, which are due to cleavage of a bond at the branching point and retention of the positive charge on the more highly substituted carbon atom. These fragments also have a tendency to lose a hydrogen atom, giving rise to a doublet of peaks in this region of the spectrum. The virtual absence of a small peak at m/e 155 shows that a C_{11} fragment is formed only with difficulty and that the branch is a methyl group. This is also suggested by the molecular weight (226, i.e., $C_{16}H_{34}$), which indicates that the two large fragments ($C_{12}H_{25}$ and C_6H_{13}) arising by cleavage of bonds at the branching point must have two carbon atoms in common, leaving only one for the substituent. Lastly, the appearance of an $M - 15$ peak (mass 211) much larger than in hexadecane points out that there is a methyl group present in the compound corresponding to the mass spectrum in Fig. 3-9b and that this methyl group is lost much more easily than in the unbranched hydrocarbon.

The structure of another C_{16} isomer, the mass spectrum of which is shown in Fig. 3-9c, can be deduced in a similar fashion. The presence of only one doublet at m/e 140, 141 points to a symmetrically branched molecule in which two C_6 chains are attached to the highly substituted carbon atom. The remaining smaller side chain, which has to be attached to C-7, must contain three carbon atoms, as deduced from the fact that the fragments of m/e 99, 113, and 127 are smaller than the neighboring peaks in this homologous series of fragments. These masses cannot arise by cleavage of only one carbon-carbon bond and should, therefore, not be present at all. The peak at m/e 99 is due to a process of Type F, namely, the migration of a hydrogen atom and elimination of propylene from the fragment of mass 141:

$$\left[\begin{matrix} C_6H_{13}-CH-C_3H_7 \\ | \\ C_6H_{13} \end{matrix}\right]^+ \longrightarrow C_6H_{13}-\overset{+}{C}H-CH_2-\overset{H}{\overset{|}{C}H}-CH_3 \longrightarrow C_6H_{13}-CH_2^+$$

$$m/e\ 141 \qquad\qquad\qquad\qquad m/e\ 99$$

It is very important to keep this process in mind and not to assume the presence of a C_7 fragment in the molecule because of the presence of a peak at m/e 99.

Occasion to determine the structure of a plain hydrocarbon for its own sake will scarcely arise unless one is concerned with the chemistry of petroleum. The preferred cleavage of carbon-carbon bonds at highly substituted carbon atoms must be considered also in the interpretation of a mass spectrum of a compound containing the hydrocarbon substituent in addition to a functional group. However, whether the fragments due to cleavage of Type A_1 will be significant or whether the functional group will dominate the fragmentation process to such an extent that the influence of a highly substituted carbon atom elsewhere in the molecule will no longer be expressed in the mass spectrum will depend on the nature of the functional group. It may be necessary to remove the functional groups from the molecule by chemical means and to deduce the aliphatic carbon skeleton of the original molecule from the mass spectrum of the hydrocarbon obtained in this manner. The highly substituted carbon atoms are then the only remaining factors which can influence the mode of fragmentation of the molecule, and the mass spectrum therefore will clearly exhibit the nature and points of attachment of the alkyl groups, at least as long as there are not too many such points of branching present along the chain.

This approach has recently been used, for example, in the elucidation of the structure of the antibiotic fungichromine.[66] Removal of all the oxygen functions and saturation of all multiple bonds yielded a hydrocarbon the structure of which permitted not only determination of the number of carbon atoms of the original compound but also elucidation of the carbon skeleton of the antibiotic. The spectrum of this hydrocarbon is shown in Fig. 3-10, in which 35 carbon atoms in all are present in the form of a C_{33} chain substituted at C-7 and C-21 with a methyl group in each. These conclusions could not be obtained from any less completely degraded derivative of fungichromine, first, because the volatility of those derivatives would have been much lower and, secondly, because the functional groups would have dominated the fragmentation process to an extent which could have overshadowed the influence of the methyl group at a carbon atom far removed from the functional group. It should be noted (Fig. 3-10) that there is no noticeable peak at m/e 492 corresponding to the molecular weight of the saturated C_{35} hydrocarbon. The peak at m/e 490 ("$M - 2$") is most probably due to contaminating olefin, the molecular ion of which is relatively much more intense (see Table 3-1).

Type A_2

$$-\overset{|}{\underset{|\,\gamma}{C}}-\overset{|}{\underset{|\,\beta}{C}} \cdot \overset{|}{\underset{|\,\alpha}{C}}{}^{+} \longrightarrow -\overset{|}{\underset{|\,\gamma}{C}}{}^{+} + \overset{|}{\underset{|}{C}}=\overset{|}{\underset{|}{C}} \qquad (3\text{-}18)$$

[66] A. C. Cope et. al., *J. Am. Chem. Soc.* (In press.)

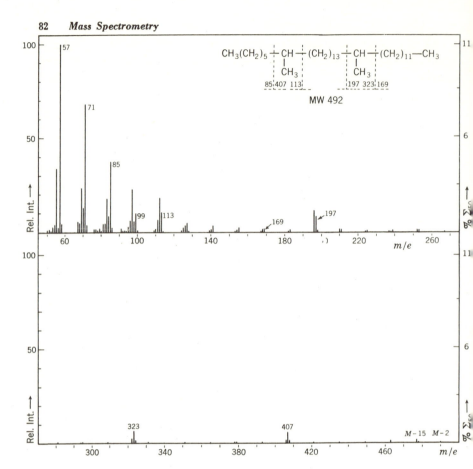

Fig. 3-10. Mass spectrum of 7,21-dimethyltritriacontane (lower part is continuation of upper part).

Hydrocarbon fragments of mass C_nH_{2n+1} may also arise by further decomposition of larger hydrocarbon fragments via elimination of an olefin molecule. While this process constitutes the path by which hydrocarbon molecules could decompose into small fragments, it was recently shown by experiments with isotopically labeled hydrocarbons that this mode of fragmentation is not responsible to an appreciable extent for the accumulation of smaller fragments.[67]

A variation is the elimination of carbon monoxide as the neutral particle from fragments of Type C:

$$R\text{—}\overset{+}{C}{\equiv}O| \longrightarrow R^+ + |C{\equiv}O|$$

[67] J. H. Beynon, R. A. Saunders, A. Topham, and A. E. Williams, *J. Phys. Chem.,* **65**, 114 (1961).

All these fragments could, in most cases, also arise by direct cleavage of the appropriate bond, but the occurrence of Type A_2 is evident in some spectra (for example in Fig. 3-17a) on the basis of metastable peaks (Sec. 3-3).

Type A_3

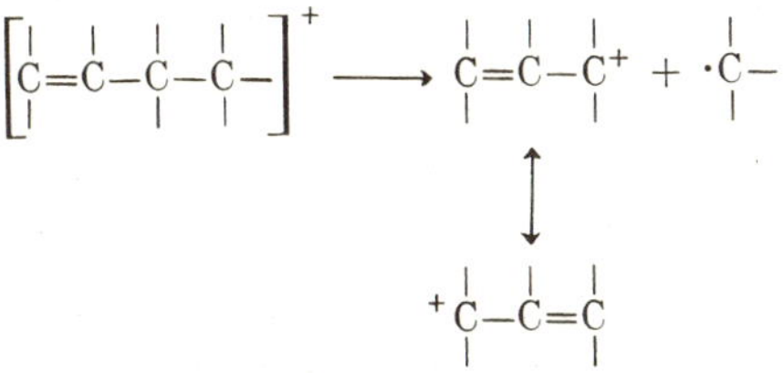

$$\left[\begin{array}{c} | \ \ | \ \ | \ \ | \\ C=C-C-C- \\ | \ \ | \ \ | \ \ | \end{array}\right]^+ \longrightarrow \begin{array}{c} | \ \ | \ \ | \\ C=C-C^+ \\ | \ \ | \ \ | \end{array} + \begin{array}{c} | \\ \cdot C- \\ | \end{array} \qquad (3\text{-}19)$$

$$\uparrow\downarrow$$

$$\begin{array}{c} \ \ | \ \ | \ \ | \\ ^+C-C=C \\ | \ \ | \ \ | \end{array}$$

The resonance stabilization of an allyl cation leads to increased probability of the fragmentation of a carbon-carbon bond β to a double bond. This factor would be expected to lead to considerable and significant differences in the mass spectra of isomeric olefins; unfortunately, this is often not the case. In contrast, double-bond isomers give rather similar, sometimes almost identical, mass spectra; only if the double bond is in close proximity to a functional group are some differences observed. It seems that the double bond in the molecular ion is rather mobile and can migrate with extreme ease via successive shifts of hydride ions and hydrogen radicals. Such a process in effect leads to the conversion of the molecular ion of olefin X to the molecular ion of olefin Y and vice versa:

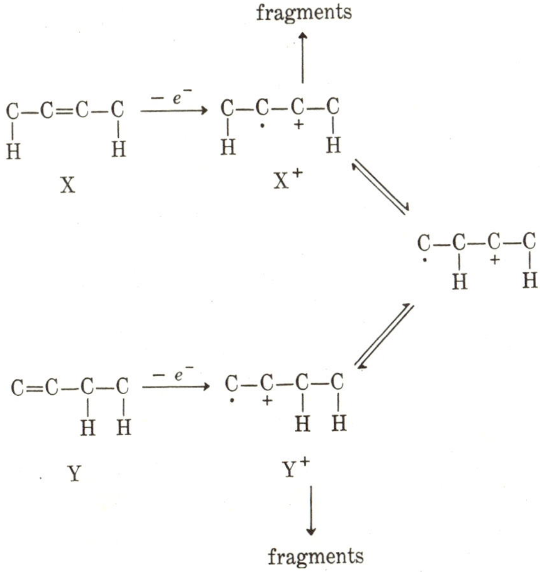

Further decomposition of those molecular ions leads, then, to the same fragments, regardless of whether the molecular ion Y^+ came directly from molecule Y or indirectly from molecule X. A good example is found in the various octadecenoic acids and their esters.[42] The mass spectra of the methyl esters of the $\Delta^{6,7}$- (petroselinic), $\Delta^{9,10}$- (oleic), and $\Delta^{17,18}$-octadecenoic acids are virtually identical, and only the $\Delta^{2,3}$ and $\Delta^{3,4}$ isomers differ appreciably from the others. In these two isomers the presence of the double bond prevents the rearrangement of Type H from occurring; furthermore, the migration of the double bond to a position farther removed from the ester group may be energetically unfavorable in the $\Delta^{2,3}$ isomer because of the loss of conjugation, and in the $\Delta^{3,4}$ isomer because of the tendency of the double bond to migrate to the 2,3 position rather than away from the carbonyl group.

Locating a double bond in a molecule, especially in aliphatic ones, on the basis of its mass spectrum is therefore frequently not a simple task; it sometimes requires conversion of the double bond into a functional group or specific saturation with deuterium [68] (Chap. 5).

Migration of a double bond in the ions derived from cyclic molecules seems to be less facile, as indicated by a greater difference in the spectra of isomeric cyclic olefins. The fragments formed via Type D from isomeric molecules support this statement. The hydrogen migration outlined above is for steric reasons more inhibited, especially in polycyclic structures.

Type A$_4$. Considerable stabilization of the carbonium ion is also provided by a neighboring aromatic system expressed by the high tendency to cleavage of a carbon-carbon bond beta to an aromatic ring.

For alkyl benzenes the resulting ion has been shown [69] to be the tropylium ion (1) rather than the less symmetrical benzyl ion (2)

on the basis of the mass spectra of alkylbenzenes labeled with deuterium and C^{13}, and energy considerations. Meyerson was able to show that the

[68] Ng. Dinh-Nguyen, R. Ryhage, and S. Ställberg-Stenhagen, *Arkiv Kemi*, 15, 433 (1960).

[69] P. N. Rylander, S. Meyerson, and H. M. Grubb, *J. Am. Chem. Soc.*, 79, 842 (1957).

mass spectra of monodeuterotoluenes, labeled in the α, o, m, or p position, are virtually identical, implying that all hydrogen atoms in toluene become equivalent in the molecular ion. Rearrangement of the molecular ion prior to fragmentation is proposed as an explanation of the fact that the $C_7H_7^+$ fragment formed has a higher appearance potential than would be expected on the basis of the strength of the benzyl bond.

Furthermore, the tropylium-ion hypothesis explains why methyl is easily lost from the xylenes (3), which exhibit an intense peak at m/e 91 ($M - 15$), while toluene does not lose a methyl group to an appreciable extent: If xylene first rearranges to methyl cycloheptatriene (4) and loss of methyl follows,

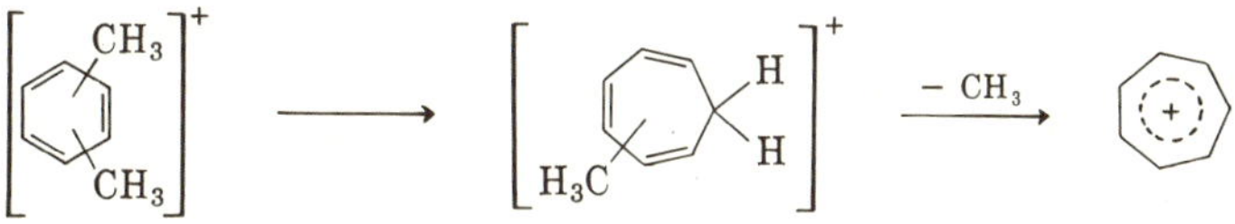

$$(3) \qquad\qquad (4) \qquad\qquad (1)$$

the stable tropylium ion (1) is formed, while the less favorable phenyl ion would be obtained by loss of methyl from toluene. This effect is also noted with other di- or polyalkylated aromatic systems, which give rise to intense peaks due to the loss of an entire substituent rather than cleavage of Type A_3. In determining the size of such substituents this effect of polysubstitution must be kept in mind.

Similar ring expansions have been postulated for the furfuryl and thenyl ions formed by fragmentation of alkylfuranes [49] and alkylthiophenes: [62]

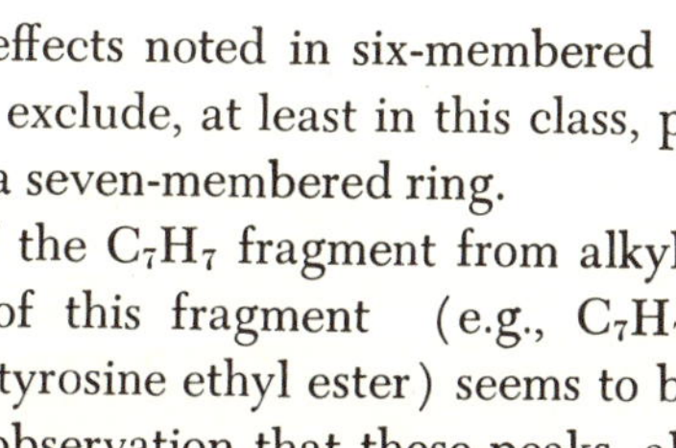

The substituent effects noted in six-membered nitrogen heterocyclics (Sec. 3-2C) seem to exclude, at least in this class, prior rearrangement of the molecular ion to a seven-membered ring.

The formation of the C_7H_7 fragment from alkyl-substituted benzenes and of derivatives of this fragment (e.g., C_7H_7O) from substituted alkylbenzenes (e.g., tyrosine ethyl ester) seems to be somewhat involved, as indicated by the observation that these peaks, although of high intensity if 70-volt electrons are used, disappear almost completely at low electron energies. In their stead a peak 1 mass unit higher appears, arising through the rearrangement of Type H if the structural requirements for this rearrangement are fulfilled. This technique can be used to distinguish such fragments due to cleavage of a bond beta to a benzene ring from other fragments of the same mass.

From appearance potential studies (Sec. 4-7) of the ions $R\text{-}C_7H_6{}^+$ arising from substituted benzyl compounds (such as benzyl halides) it was concluded that these ions in fact have the tropylium structure, as there was no difference found between meta and para isomers if R was CH_3, F, or OH. The ion $(CH_3OC_7H_6)^+$ derived from *p*-methoxybenzylchloride had, however, an appearance potential 1.15 ev lower than the one derived from the meta isomer, indicating the formation of nonidentical ions which thus have the benzyl structure.[69a]

Type A_5

$$\left[-\overset{|}{\underset{|}{C}}-X \right]^+ \longrightarrow -\overset{|}{\underset{|}{C}}{}^+ + \cdot X \quad (X = \text{halogen, OR, SR, NR}_2,\ R = H \text{ or alkyl}) \quad (3\text{-}21)$$

Cleavage of a C—X bond is more difficult than cleavage of a C—C bond if X is O, N, S, F, or Cl, and if it occurs, the positive charge preferably remains with the carbon atom, rather than with the heteroatom. Owing to the high electronegativity of these elements, cleavage of the carbon-oxygen bond in ethers always leads, for example, to an alkyl ion rather than an alkoxy ion:[5]

$$CH_3CH_2CH_2 \overset{|}{\underset{|}{|}} OCH_2CH_2CH_3$$

$$m/e\ 43 \quad \overset{|}{\underset{|}{}} \quad m/e\ 59$$

$$(50.3\%\ \Sigma_{15}) \quad (1.7\%\ \Sigma_{15})$$

This effect increases if substituents are attached to the carbon atom of the C—X grouping which increase the stability of a positive charge at that carbon atom, such as additional alkyl substituents. For this reason tertiary alcohols, e.g., 2-methyl-2-butanol (Fig. 3-3), give fragments due to the loss of OH, while primary alcohols preferentially eliminate H_2O (Fig. 3-13*a*).

Because of the low tendency of a C—X bond to cleave with retention of the positive charge at X, it is difficult to detect O—CH_3 or N—CH_3 groups in organic molecules, in contrast to C—CH_3 groups which in general give rise to $M - 15$ peaks of reasonable intensity.

[69a] J. M. S. Tait, T. W. Shannon, and A. G. Harrison, *J. Am. Chem. Soc.*, 84, 4 (1962).

Type B

$$\left[R-\underset{\underset{|X}{|}}{\overset{|}{C}}-R \right]^{+} \longrightarrow R\cdot \ + \ \overset{+}{\underset{\underset{|X}{C|}}{C}}-R \longleftrightarrow \underset{\underset{X^{+}}{\|}}{\overset{|}{C}}-R \qquad (3\text{-}22)$$

The free electron pair of a heteroatom stabilizes a positive charge on the adjacent carbon atom [Eq. (3-22)], and the various fragmentation processes involving the rupture of a bond between two carbon atoms, one of which bears a singly bonded heteroatom, are combined as Type *B*. Such a stabilization by resonance is much more effective than the inductive effect of an alkyl group, and the mass spectra of molecules containing such heteroatoms are much less monotonous than the spectra of hydrocarbons.

The participation of the free electron pair on oxygen in the $(CH_2-OH)^+$ fragment from methanol was first suggested by Cummings and Bleakney[12] on the basis of appearance-potential measurements on this ion (see Sec. 4-7C).

The mass spectra of alcohols,[26] esters,[36] mercaptans,[59] sulfides,[59] and amines [50,52] are characterized by intense peaks due to cleavage of the carbon-carbon bond next to the heteroatom. The effectiveness of this kind of stabilization increases from oxygen to sulfur to nitrogen, in that order, because of the decreasing tendency to donate electrons with increasing electronegativity of the heteroatom in question. Cleavage of the carbon-carbon bond in aminoethanol (5)

$$\underset{\substack{m/e\ 31 \\ (3.1\%\ \Sigma_{13})}}{\underset{\underset{OH}{|}}{\overset{+}{C}H_2} + \underset{\underset{NH_2}{|}}{\cdot CH_2}} \longleftarrow \underset{(5)}{\left[\underset{\underset{OH}{|}}{CH_2} - \underset{\underset{NH_2}{|}}{CH_2} \right]^{+}} \longrightarrow \underset{\substack{m/e\ 30 \\ (57.0\%\ \Sigma_{13})}}{\underset{\underset{OH}{|}}{CH_2\cdot} + \underset{\underset{NH_2}{|}}{\overset{+}{C}H_2}}$$

leads to two similar fragments, one of mass 30 and one of mass 31 (Fig. 3-11a). On the nitrogen-containing fragment the positive charge is stabilized more effectively than on the oxygen-containing fragment, and the peak at m/e 30 is therefore about ten times more intense than the peak at m/e 31. The oxygen can compete better with the more electronegative sulfur, and in thioethanol the fragment of mass 31 is more than half as intense as the fragment of mass 47 (Fig. 3-11b). Oxygen stabilizes the the positive charge much better than chlorine, as borne out by the spectrum of ethylene chlorohydrine (Fig. 3-11c).

These examples indicate the order N, S, O, Cl for decreasing effectiveness in the stabilization of a neighboring positive charge. This is not the order of electronegativity $(S < N < Cl < O)$, and it indicates that elements of the second row of the periodic table are somewhat less effective than their electronegativity would suggest. This fact may be associated with the lower tendency of those elements to engage in double bonds, the formation of which is implied in the resonance form of ions of Type B.

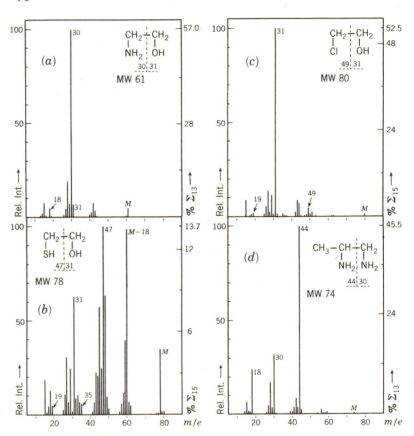

Fig. 3-11. Mass spectra of various simple, bifunctional molecules. (*a*) 2-Aminoethanol; (*b*) 2-thioethanol; (*c*) 2-chloroethanol; (*d*) 1,2-diaminopropane.

Stabilization of Type A obviously will add to stabilization of the positive charge according to Type B, which means that peaks due to cleavage of a carbon-carbon bond next to a heteroatom will be even more intense if the carbon atom to which the heteroatom is attached is a highly substituted one. This is borne out by the spectra of bifunctional molecules containing the same functional group, one of which is attached to a more highly substituted carbon atom, as for example, in 1,2-diaminopro-pane. Its spectrum exhibits a peak at m/e 44 which is three times as high as the peak at m/e 30 (Fig. 3-11d). The mass spectra of the polyamino alcohols used to deduce the amino acid sequence of the peptides from which they have been obtained are good examples for both the competition of N with O and for the influence of alkyl substitution and will be discussed in Sec. 7-2.

ˉAdditional stabilization due to alkyl groups may conceivably reverse the order in the previous paragraph and give rise to a more intense peak at m/e 59 compared with m/e 31 in 1-amino-2-methylpropanol-2:

$$CH_3-\underset{\underset{59\,\vert\,30}{OH\,\vert\,NH_2}}{\overset{\overset{CH_3}{|}}{C}}\!-\!\!-\!\!CH_2$$

This type of intramolecular competition of functional groups for the positive charge must be kept in mind if the functional groups and their position in the molecule are to be deduced from a mass spectrum. There may be occasion at which one such group strongly dominates the fragmentation pattern of a molecule, thus making it difficult to recognize the

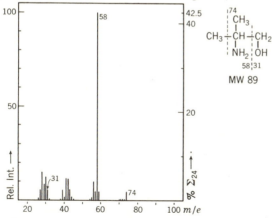

Fig. 3-12. Mass spectrum of 2-methyl-2-aminopropanol-1.

other one, which remains mainly on the uncharged fragment and thus is less easily detected in the mass spectrum. The extremely small peak at m/e 31 in the spectrum of 2-methyl-2-aminopropanol-1 represents such a situation (Fig. 3-12). The enhanced tendency for fragmentation of a highly branched molecule manifests itself in the virtual absence in Fig. 3-12 of a peak representing the molecular ion, in contrast to Fig. 3-11a.

It is of interest to note that the intensity ratios of the peaks at m/e 30 and m/e 31 in 3-aminopropanol-1 (H_2N—CH_2—CH_2—CH_2—OH) is about the same as in aminoethanol (Fig. 3-11a), indicating that there may be little difference in the stability of the radicals $\cdot CH_2OH$ and $\cdot CH_2CH_2OH$.

Competition with fragmentation of Type A_4 seems to be of importance in alcohols. The mass spectrum of β-phenylethanol (6) exhibits a ratio of 1:15 for the intensities of the peaks at m/e 31 and m/e 91 (the largest peak in the spectrum; admittedly, part of the ion of mass 91 originates from mass 92, formed in a rearrangement process of Type H). An amino group much more effectively stabilizes the positive charge on the nonaromatic fragment, as borne out by the spectrum of β-phenylethylamine (7), which shows a ratio of 10:1 for the peaks at m/e 30 and m/e 91, the former peak now being the most intense one of the spectrum.

$$\langle\text{C}_6\text{H}_5\rangle—CH_2\overset{|}{\underset{|}{}}CH_2OH \qquad \langle\text{C}_6\text{H}_5\rangle—CH_2\overset{|}{\underset{|}{}}CH_2NH_2$$

$$91 \mid 31 \qquad\qquad\qquad 91 \mid 30$$

$$(6) \qquad\qquad\qquad\qquad (7)$$

The much greater tendency of amines, compared with alcohols or ethers, to retain the positive charge on the fragments containing the heteroatom makes itself felt in the contribution to the spectrum of hydrocarbon fragments from the aliphatic chain. The spectrum of n-decanol (Fig. 3-13a) more closely resembles the spectrum of an unbranched hydrocarbon (Fig. 3-9a) with a few "alcohol peaks" superimposed, while in the spectrum of n-decylamine the "amine peaks" predominate (Fig. 3-13b). Mercaptans (Fig. 3-16) fall also in this respect between alcohols and amines.

Competition between Type-B and Type-C fragmentation appears to be considerable, at least for keto alcohols, since 2-hydroxy-3-butanone exhibits intense peaks both at m/e 43 and 45, the latter slightly higher:

$$CH_3—\underset{\underset{OH}{|}}{CH}\cdot\ +\ \overset{+}{C}—CH_3 \longleftarrow \left[CH_3—\underset{\underset{OH}{|}}{CH}—\underset{\underset{O}{\|}}{C}—CH_3\right]^+ \longrightarrow CH_3—\underset{\underset{OH}{|}}{CH}^+\ +\ \cdot\underset{\underset{O}{\|}}{C}—CH_3$$

$$m/e\ 43 \qquad\qquad\qquad\qquad\qquad\qquad\qquad m/e\ 45$$
$$(26.8\%\ \Sigma_{15}) \qquad\qquad\qquad\qquad\qquad\qquad (30.8\%\ \Sigma_{15})$$

Both an increase and decrease of the electron density on the heteroatom makes itself felt as increasing or decreasing effect on the stabilization of a positive charge at a carbon atom to which this heteroatom is attached. The inductive effect of alkyl substituents which leads to a higher electron density at the heteroatom is borne out by comparison of the mass spectra of a primary amine with its dimethyl derivative, for example, leucine ethyl ester and N,N-dimethylleucine ethyl ester (Fig. 3-14a and b). Most of the features of these spectra will be discussed in Sec. 7-1, and only the peaks at mass 86 and 114 are of interest at the moment. Both are due to the rupture of the C_1—C_2 bond, but the peak

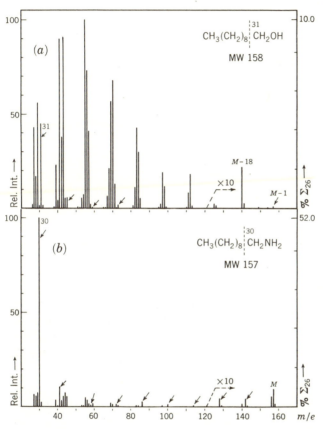

Fig. 3-13. Mass spectra of (a) n-decanol and (b) n-decylamine (arrows indicate ions of type $C_nH_{2n}OH^+$ and $C_nH_{2n}NH_2^+$, respectively).

at mass 114 in the dimethyl derivative is more intense, in terms of the sum of all peaks of the spectrum, than the fragment of mass 86 in leucine ester. A similar effect is noted if alcohols are compared with the corresponding ethers.

In addition to increasing the stability of Type-B ions, alkyl substituents on the heteroatom seem also to increase the stability of the molecular ions, since secondary and tertiary amines and ethers give more intense

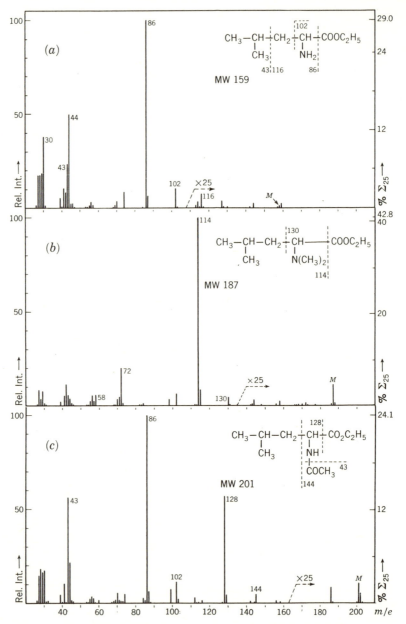

Fig. 3-14. Mass spectra of (a) leucine ethyl ester, (b) N,N-dimethylleucine ethyl ester, (c) N-acetylleucine ethyl ester.

peaks at the mass of the molecular weight than do primary amines and alcohols of comparable size and structure (see Table 3-1).

Electron-withdrawing groups decrease the electron density at the attached heteroatom, which in turn decreases its stabilizing effect on the positive charge on a neighboring carbon atom. The mass spectra of alkylacetamides [51] and alkylacetates [36] show this effect, for example, the spectrum of N-acetylleucine ethyl ester in Fig. 3-14c, which exhibits a relatively lower intensity of the peak at mass 128, as compared with mass 86 in leucine ester. One must keep in mind, however, that some of the ions of mass 128 formed originally may have decomposed further by elimination of a ketene molecule (Type E_1) to form the fragment of mass 86.

Further fragmentation of a Type-B ion is possible from either one of the two extreme resonance forms shown in Eq. (3-22). For example, an olefin molecule can be eliminated either from the carbonium-ion form (Type F) or from the "heteronium-ion" form (Type G). The double bond of the latter may also participate in a rearrangement of Type H. Such flexibilities are well known in chemical reactions, and the alkylation of carbonyl compounds may be cited as an example. Their anions are known to alkylate either on carbon or on oxygen, and the site of alkylation is frequently dependent also on rather subtle influences.

In the discussions following in this and later chapters, only the carbonium-ion form of Type-B ions will be written for the sake of convenience, but the resonance hybrid indicated in Eq. (3-22) should be understood.

The reason for discussing fragmentation of Type B in such detail, with illustrations of the effects governing the extent of stabilization of the positive charge on the resulting fragment, is mainly to demonstrate the influence of such stabilizing and destabilizing effects on the mass spectra of organic molecules, particularly important for polyfunctional compounds. A reasonably correct estimate of the stability of the positive ions formed upon fragmentation of a molecule of given structure is of extreme importance if one has to predict the major features of the mass spectrum of an organic molecule or to interpret a spectrum of an unknown compound in terms of its structure.

As a consequence of the effects discussed above for the fragmentation process of Type B, primary *alcohols* in general give a strong peak at mass 31 [Eq. (3-30)]. Secondary alcohols show a strong peak at mass $30 + R_1$ [Eq. (3-31)], while tertiary alcohols have a very intense peak at mass $29 + R_1 + R_2$ [Eq. (3-32)]. Methyl carbinols ($R_1 = CH_3$)

thus give a fragment of mass 45, ethyl carbinols one of mass 59, etc., and tertiary alcohols show very intense peaks at masses 59, 73, 87, etc. In all

$$\left[\begin{matrix} R-CH_2 \\ | \\ OH \end{matrix}\right]^+ \longrightarrow \begin{matrix} CH_2^+ \\ | \\ OH \end{matrix} \qquad (3\text{-}30)$$

$$m/e \ 31$$

$$\left[\begin{matrix} R-CH-R_1 \\ | \\ OH \end{matrix}\right]^+ \longrightarrow \begin{matrix} {}^+CH-R_1 \\ | \\ OH \end{matrix} \qquad (3\text{-}31)$$

$$m/e \ (30 + R_1)$$

$$\left[\begin{matrix} R_2 \\ | \\ R-C-R_1 \\ | \\ OH \end{matrix}\right]^+ \longrightarrow \begin{matrix} R_2 \\ | \\ {}^+C-R_2 \\ | \\ OH \end{matrix} \qquad (3\text{-}32)$$

$$m/e \ (29 + R_1 + R_2)$$

these cases, the larger alkyl groups are lost preferentially over the smaller alkyl groups.[26] Figures 3-13a, 3-20, and 3-3 provide examples of spectra of primary, secondary, and tertiary alcohols, respectively.

While this type of fragmentation is a very important one, the mass spectra of alcohols contain a number of peaks that do not arise via this simple mechanism. First, there is the possibility of further decomposition of the ion formed by fragmentation of Type B through elimination of an olefin molecule (Type F). This is possible if a chain of at least two carbon atoms, the second one bearing at least one hydrogen atom, is attached to the carbon atom bearing the positive charge. Such fragmentation yields alcohol-type ions with fewer carbon atoms than the primary species formed by cleavage of Type B and can lead to a misinterpretation of the placement of the hydroxyl group in the molecule. If, for example, the fragment of mass 59 eliminates a molecule of ethylene,

$$\begin{matrix} H \\ | \\ CH_2-CH_2-CH^+ \\ | \\ OH \end{matrix} \longrightarrow CH_2{=}CH_2 + \begin{matrix} CH_2^+ \\ | \\ OH \end{matrix}$$

$$m/e \ 59 \qquad\qquad\qquad m/e \ 31$$

an ion of mass 31 is produced, which was said to be characteristic for primary alcohols.

Obviously one therefore cannot make the statement that a fragment of mass 31 is indicative of a primary alcohol while its absence indicates the opposite. This is, however, true in a much more modified sense, namely, that a peak at mass 31 more intense than any one of its homologs (mass 45, 59, 73, etc.) makes the presence of a primary alcohol highly probable (but not exclusively so, as will be seen later on). A peak at mass 31, less intense than any one of its homologs containing at least two more carbon atoms, is a very good indication that one is dealing with a secondary or even tertiary alcohol and that the CH_2OH fragment arises from the Type-*B* fragment via one or two successive Type-*F* eliminations of olefins. Obviously, valuable conclusions as to the structures of the alkyl groups attached to the carbinol carbon atom can be drawn from such peaks if the mechanisms of these fragmentations and their structural prerequisites are considered.

A number of fragments, sometimes very intense ones, appearing in the mass spectra of alcohols are due to the elimination of H_2O via a rearrangement of Type E_1. This may occur in the molecular ion, giving rise to peaks which correspond to the mass of an olefin, but it is also possible that ions of Type *B* eliminate H_2O, which leads to fragments with masses 18 mass units below the alcohol fragment (e.g., m/e 55 in Fig. 3-3).

$$\left[R-CH_2-\underset{\underset{OH}{|}}{CH}-R_1 \right]^+ \longrightarrow \left[R-CH=CH-R_1 \right]^+ + H_2O$$

$$R-CH_2-\underset{\underset{OH}{|}}{CH}{}^+ \longrightarrow R-CH=CH^+ + H_2O$$

That such fragment ions arise by the sequence shown above is indicated by the presence of metastable peaks (Sec. 3-3) corresponding to the loss of H_2O from the Type-*B* ion. For reasons of simplicity the fragments are written with double bonds, although they are more likely to have a cyclic structure (see discussion of Type E_1, Sec. 3-2*B*).

A rather striking similarity between the olefin-type peaks in the mass spectrum of certain alcohols and the spectra of the corresponding olefins has been observed, e.g., 1-pentanol and 1-pentene.[26] This was taken as evidence of the formation of the corresponding olefin from the alcohol upon electron impact followed by fragmentation as an olefin. While this process may predominate in the case of primary alcohols, it is less probable for secondary and tertiary ones. The $C_nH_{2n} - 1$ peaks, particularly m/e 55 and 69, from 2- and 3-hexanol[26] differ appreciably in relative intensity from these peaks in any one of the n-hexenes [22] and in a fashion which suggests that these fragments arise from a Type-B ion (m/e 87 from 2-hexanol gives m/e 69; m/e 73 from 3-hexanol gives m/e 55).

It has been found [26] that elimination of water from both the molecular ion and fragment ions of alcohols occurs with particular ease in the case of primary alcohols while it plays a minor role in the mass spectra of tertiary alcohols (see, for example, m/e 140 in Fig. 3-13a versus m/e 70 in Fig. 3-3). This might be due also to the better stabilization of the fragments of Type B formed from tertiary alcohols in contrast to primary alcohols, in which the elimination of H_2O can therefore compete more successfully.

In mass spectra of some primary alcohols the peak at mass 31 is of comparatively low intensity. Many such instances have been pointed out during the general discussion above, namely, in molecules where two fragments of Type B can be formed from a polyfunctional molecule. A hydrocarbon fragment of Type A_1 can also dominate the spectrum of an unsubstituted aliphatic alcohol if a highly branched carbon atom is present in the molecule. The mass spectrum of neopentyl alcohol

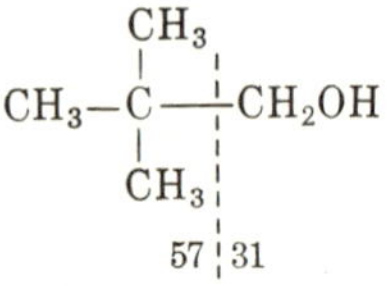

$$
\begin{array}{c}
CH_3 \\
| \\
CH_3-C-\!\!\!-CH_2OH \\
| \\
CH_3 \\
5731
\end{array}
$$

is a good example, since it shows a peak at mass 57 which is about five times as intense as the peak at mass 31.

The mass spectra of *aliphatic amines* [50] are in some respects similar to the spectra of alcohols. Primary amines, for example, exhibit an intense peak at mass 30, and the corresponding peaks are found at mass 44, 58, 72, etc., or at mass 58, 72, 86, etc., ($C_nH_{2n+2}N$), depending on whether the amino group is attached to a secondary or tertiary carbon atom, respectively [Eqs. (3-33) through (3-35)].

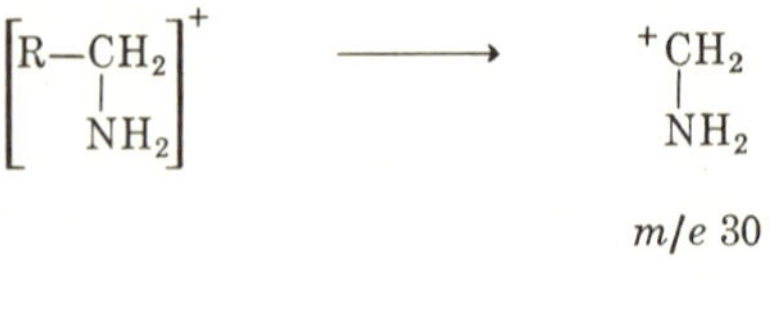

$$
\begin{bmatrix} R-CH_2 \\ | \\ NH_2 \end{bmatrix}^+ \longrightarrow \begin{array}{c} {}^+CH_2 \\ | \\ NH_2 \end{array} \tag{3-33}
$$

$$m/e\ 30$$

$$
\begin{bmatrix} R-CH-R_1 \\ | \\ NH_2 \end{bmatrix}^+ \longrightarrow \begin{array}{c} {}^+CH-R_1 \\ | \\ NH_2 \end{array} \tag{3-34}
$$

$$m/e\ 29 + R_1$$

$$\left[\begin{array}{c} R_2 \\ | \\ R-C-R_1 \\ | \\ NH_2 \end{array}\right]^+ \longrightarrow \begin{array}{c} R_2 \\ | \\ {}^+C-R_1 \\ | \\ NH_2 \end{array} \qquad (3\text{-}35)$$

$$m/e \ 28 + R_1 + R_2$$

The distinction between the two last classes must be made on a basis of the relative intensity of the peaks—they will be more intense for compounds bearing the amino group at a tertiary carbon atom [Eq. (3-35)] than for those bearing the amino group at a secondary one [Eq. (3-34)]—combined with a more detailed interpretation of the spectrum. Secondary fragmentation via Type F is significant also for amines and gives rise to ions representing lower homologs of the series ($C_nH_{2n+2}N$), which should not be confused with the primary fragment (Type B) used for the purpose of locating the amino group in the molecule. The elimination of ammonia, analogous to the elimination of water from alcohols, occurs, too, but to a smaller extent than in the oxygen analogs. The mass spectra of amino esters provide an abundance of examples of such fragmentations, some of which will be discussed in Sec. 7-1.

Secondary and tertiary amines also suffer fragmentation of Type B predominantly, frequently followed by rearrangement (Type G) if the structural requirements are fulfilled, e.g., m/e 30 in Fig. 3-14a.

In the mass spectra of ethers,[5] fragmentation of Type B, in part followed by olefin elimination (Type G), and of Type A_5 produces the most characteristic peaks in the spectra. The mass numbers (except of A_5) fall into the same homologous series as the oxygen-containing fragments of alcohols. It is sometimes difficult to tell from the mass spectra whether the compound is an ether or an alcohol. The elimination of water from the alcohol molecule upon electron impact and the presence of relatively intense olefin-type peaks (of masses corresponding to C_nH_{2n-1}) characterize the spectra of alcohols, while they are of much less significance in the mass spectra of ethers. Here again, additional alkyl substituents at the carbon atom bearing the heteroatom increase the tendency to form Type-B fragments, and this is particularly important in the mass spectra of cyclic ethers. If in tetrahydrofuran or tetrahydropyran derivatives an alkyl group is attached at C-2, loss of this alkyl group will lead to a very good carbonium ion:

This peak can be used to determine the number of carbon atoms in the ring (including the substituents not at C-2). It is more difficult to deduce the size of the substituent at C-2, since the substituent sometimes does not lead to a significant fragment, and it is often not easy to determine by difference, because the intensity of the molecular ions of such compounds is in general very low owing to the high tendency toward fragmentation just discussed.

Figure 3-15 shows the mass spectra of three isomeric cyclic C_{10} ethers containing a double bond in the side chain.[70] The intense peaks at mass 85 (Fig. 3-15a) and 99 (Fig. 3-15b) indicate the presence of five carbon atoms in and on the ether ring of (8), while there are six such carbon atoms present in (9). Figure 3-15c shows the strong influence of a double bond in certain positions: in structure (10), a compound isolated from Bulgarian rose oil, formation of the expected fragment of mass 99 is made much more difficult by the fact that it would involve cleavage of a carbon-carbon bond next to a double bond. Fragmentation is thus prevented, unless the double bond migrates in the molecular ion into another position prior to fragmentation, and many more molecular ions survive long enough to be fully accelerated, which leads to a much more intense peak at the mass of the molecular weight in comparison with their isomers. In this compound there remains the loss of a methyl group as the only simple mode of fragmentation that does not involve the cleaving of a bond next to a double bond or fragmentation of the ring system.

It should be noted that the fragmentation process (Type *B*) leading to the intense peaks at mass 85 and 99, respectively, in the two other isomers is enhanced by the fact that the neutral fragment is an allylic radical. Hydrogenation of compound (10) would lead to a molecule in which the loss of the alkyl group attached to C-2 is no longer hindered, and the compound would be expected to exhibit a very strong peak at mass 99.

The mass spectrum of an acid obtained on oxidative degradation of the oxide (10) did, in fact, exhibit a prominent peak of m/e 99, in agreement with structure (11), proposed for this compound: [70]

(11)

A carbonyl group is obviously much less effective than a carbon-carbon bond in preventing this fragmentation. The considerable difference be-

[70] C. F. Seidel, D. Felix, A. Eschenmoser, K. Biemann, E. Palluy, and M. Stoll, *Helv. Chim. Acta*, 44, 598 (1961).

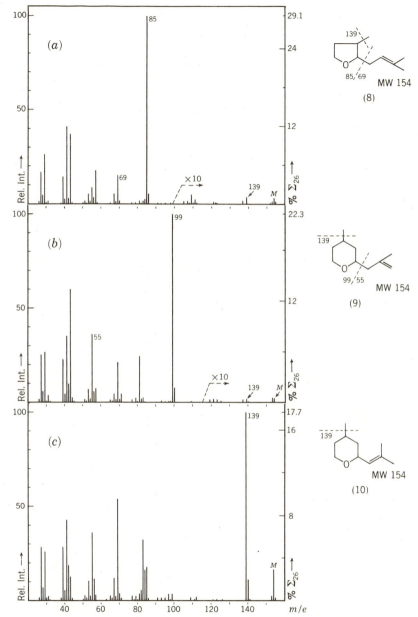

Fig. 3-15. Mass spectra of three isomeric monoterpenoid cyclic ethers.

tween the spectra of (9) and (10) is a further example for the statement made in the discussion of the fragmentation (Type A_2) of olefins: isomeric olefins exhibit very different spectra if there is a functional group present in the vicinity of the double bond, while the spectra become very similar if the double bond is further removed from the functional group or if no such group is present.

Mercaptans and *sulfides* exhibit spectra [59] which are somewhat analogous to the ones obtained with alcohols and ethers, with the exception that the sulfur atom is more effective in stabilizing the positive charge on a fragment than oxygen is (compare Figs. 3-11*b* and 3-16). It has been pointed out earlier (page 52) that the molecular ions of sulfur-contain-

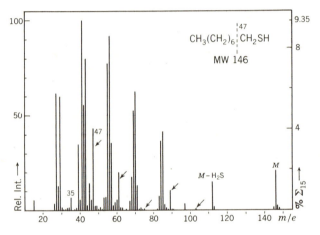

Fig. 3-16. Mass spectrum of octanethiol-1 (arrows indicate ions of type $C_nH_{2n}SH^+$).

ing molecules are of considerably higher intensity than the molecular ions of the oxygen or nitrogen analogs. The characteristic isotope ratio of sulfur provides a convenient means for the identification of such fragments.

The spectrum of octylmercaptan is presented in Fig. 3-16 as a typical example. The majority of the fragments are hydrocarbon ions; the $C_nH_{2n}SH$ ions are of moderate abundance, indicating that sulfur compounds range also in this respect between the oxygen analogs (Fig. 3-13*a*) and nitrogen compounds (Fig. 3-13*b*). The loss of H_2S (m/e 112 for octylmercaptan) gives rise to prominent peaks similar to loss of H_2O from alcohols. The periodicity of the $C_nH_{2n}SH$ peaks will be discussed in more detail on page 141.

The scale on which the spectrum is reproduced does not permit clearly seeing the peaks due to the presence of S^{34} (natural abundance 4.22 per cent), and one has to consult the original record for this purpose. The peak at m/e 148 can, however, be recognized even in the reproduction, and a comparison of this triplet (146 to 148) with the doublet at m/e 112 and 113 clearly shows that the former group is due to a sulfur-containing species, while the latter is not.

Acetals and *ketals* have up to three bonds which can undergo fragmentation of Type B. Particularly well stabilized is the fragment which arises by loss of an alkyl group from the potential carbonyl-carbon atom at which the positive charge is stabilized by any one of the two ether oxygens. Intense fragments of mass $C_nH_{2n+1}O$ and of mass $44 + C_mH_{2m+3}$ are formed; the latter is, for example, at mass 103 in diethyl acetals (Fig. 3-21). This ion may undergo fragmentation of Type G to mass 75. Owing to the presence of a number of bonds, the cleavage of which gives rise to very favorable positive ions, acetals and ketals exhibit peaks for molecular weight of extremely low intensity, and frequently the molecular weight of such compounds cannot be determined directly. Polycyclic acetals and ketals (Fig. 3-22) do exhibit small but recognizable peaks for the molecular weight, because of the increase in molecular-ion intensity due to the presence of ring systems, as discussed previously.

Type C. The stabilization of the positive charge on a carbon atom is also increased if a heteroatom is attached to it by a double bond (fragmentation of Type C). A number of examples are available of compounds in which the heteroatom is oxygen (ketones, esters, amides) but not of compounds containing the group C=N or C=S, mainly because of the instability of such substances. Cleavage of a carbon-carbon bond at the carbonyl group is the most favorable process of this type and leads to significant peaks in the mass spectra of ketones. Asymmetrical ketones will show two such peaks, since either alkyl substituent may be lost:

$$R-\overset{\underset{|\text{O}|}{\|}}{C}{}^{+} \longleftarrow \left[R-\overset{\underset{|\text{O}|}{\|}}{C}-R_1 \right]^{+} \longrightarrow {}^{+}\underset{|\text{O}|}{\overset{\|}{C}}-R_1$$

Obviously, peaks of this kind are very useful for the purpose of establishing the position of the carbonyl group in an aliphatic ketone. The same ion is formed from aldehydes, esters, and amides in which cases a C—H, C—O, or C—N bond, respectively, is broken. This process appears to occur more easily in esters than in amides. An aryl group attached to the carbonyl considerably enhances the stability of the acyl ion formed from aromatic ketones, aldehydes, esters, and amides.

An interesting example is the spectrum of phenyl acetone (12)

$$C_6H_5CH_2\cdot + CH_3CO^+ \ (m/e\ 43,\ 36.0\%\ of\ \Sigma_{25})$$

$$C_6H_5CH_2COCH_3 \longrightarrow CH_3CO\cdot\ + C_7H_7^+\ (m/e\ 91,\ 21.5\%\ of\ \Sigma_{25})$$

(12)

$$CH_3\cdot + C_6H_5CH_2CO^+\ (m/e\ 119,\ 0.1\%\ of\ \Sigma_{25})$$

illustrating the competition of a benzyl ion (or tropylium ion—see Type A_4 earlier in this section) versus an acyl ion. The ratio of the intensity at m/e 43 to the intensity at m/e 91 is about 1.8:1, indicating much better stabilization of the positive charge at the CH_3CO fragment. It must be pointed out, however, that the stabilization of the other fragment too is important, and the observed charge distribution is in part due to the undoubtedly greater stability of the benzyl radical compared with the acetyl radical. The lack of stabilization in a methyl radical may, in turn, be responsible for the low abundance of the peak at m/e 119.

The presence of the carbonyl group leads to the rearrangement of Type H if the structural requirements for that reaction are satisfied, and such rearrangement ions are prominent in the spectrum of carbonyl compounds.

Type D

(3-24)

In the above discussion three major fragmentation reactions have been discussed which are characterized by the fragmentation of a single bond, facilitated by the simultaneous formation of a well-stabilized positive ion. In contrast, fragmentation of Type D is characterized by the cleavage of two bonds of a cyclic system with formation of two rather stable, unsaturated fragments, without the necessity for rearranging a hydrogen atom from one part of the molecule to another. This fragmentation is therefore not a rearrangement process like all other decompositions of molecular ions during which more than one bond is broken simultaneously. The structural requirements for fragmentation of Type D,[71] which is the mass spectrometric equivalent of a "retro-Diels-Alder reaction," are (1) the presence of a cyclic olefin or a similar system and (2) the absence of other bonds which would cleave with particular ease via fragmentation processes of Type A_3, A_4, B, or C.

Limonene (13) exhibits a very strong peak at mass 68, which indi-

[71] K. Biemann, *Angew. Chem.*, **74**, 102 (1962); *Intern. Ed.*, **61**, 98 (1962).

cates a cleavage of this type into two isoprene molecules, one of which carries the positive charge:

(13)

It should be pointed out that this reaction is not a pyrolytic reversal of the formation of this molecule from isoprene, because the ratio of the intensities of mass 68 and 136 remains constant even if the sample is kept in the hot inlet system for a period of time.

The mass spectra of α- and β-ionone [(14) and (15)] (Fig. 17a and b) present an interesting example of the factors governing this decomposi-

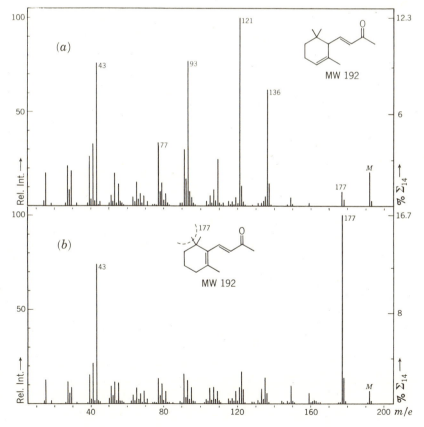

Fig. 3-17. Mass spectra of (a) α-ionone; (b) β-ionone.

tion, because the spectra are considerably different, although the two isomers differ only in the position of a double bond. In both molecules a quaternary carbon atom bearing two methyl groups is present, but in β-ionone (15) this carbon atom is also an allylic one, and loss of one of the geminal methyl groups leads to a tertiary allylic carbonium ion of high symmetry offering excellent stabilization for the positive charge.

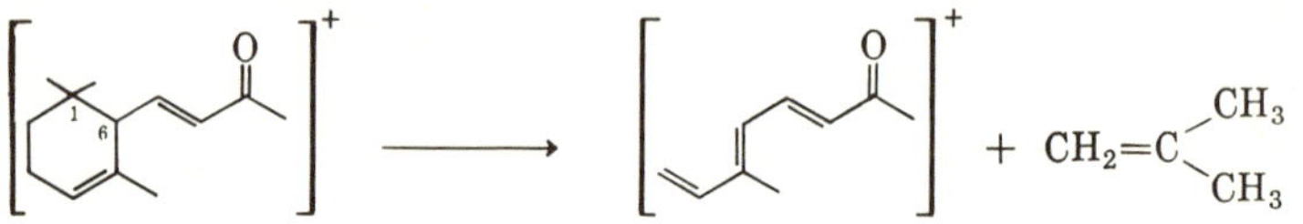

(14)   *m/e* 136

(15)   *m/e* 177

Loss of the same methyl group from α-ionone (14) merely gives rise to a tertiary carbonium ion, while cleavage of the allylic bond between C-1 and C-6 initiates fragmentation of Type *D*, leading to elimination of an isobutylene molecule and retention of the positive charge at the highly conjugated trienone fragment of mass 136.

The formation of a more substituted olefin (isobutylene) from α-ionone, while only ethylene would be formed if β-ionone underwent fragmentation of Type *D*, may be an additional factor governing the decomposition of these molecules upon electron impact. As in all other fragmentation reactions the two particles formed compete for the positive charge, and therefore the positive charge remains with the fragment on which it is more stabilized, i.e., on the more unsaturated one.

Metastable peaks at *m/e* 108.2 and 71.8 (calcd. 107.8 and 71.5) indicate further decomposition of the fragment of mass 136 from α-ionone [(14), Fig. 3-17a] in a two-step process to mass 93:

(14) ⟶   *m/e* 136   *m/e* 121   *m/e* 93

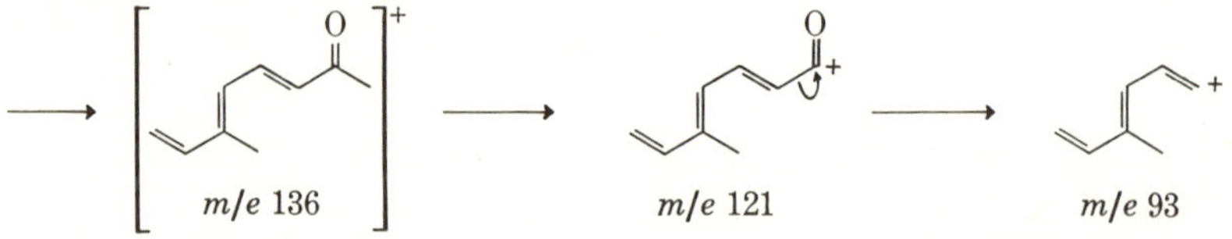

The last step is an interesting one because the driving force for the breaking of a bond attached to a carbon-carbon double bond seems to be the elimination of a neutral molecule, carbon monoxide. A certain similarity to this process exists with cleavage of Type A_2, in which an electron pair moves to a positively charged carbon atom, leaving a new carbonium ion behind but forming a neutral olefin molecule. In the process discussed above, an electron pair attached directly to the positively charged carbon atom moves, leading to the expulsion of a very stable one-carbon fragment, CO.

Another metastable peak points to loss of two hydrogens from the fragment of mass 93 to form mass 91, $(C_7H_7)^+$, most probably via a cyclization yielding possibly a tropylium ion:

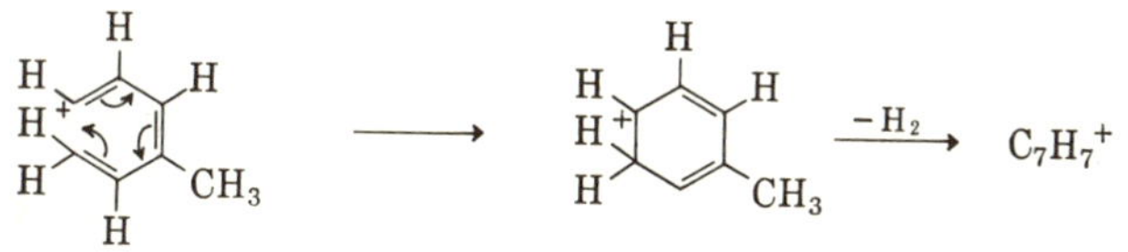

m/e 93

Thus most of the intense peaks in the spectrum of α-ionone seem to be triggered by the first step, namely, cleavage of Type D, leading to a spectrum entirely different from that of the β isomer.

The double bond responsible for the initiation of the retro-Diels-Alder cleavage does not have to be an alicyclic one but may in effect be an aromatic ring, for example, a tetralin system. The two isomers [22] 1-methyl-1,2,3,4-tetrahydronaphthalene (16) and 2-methyl-1,2,3,4-tetrahydronaphthalene (18)

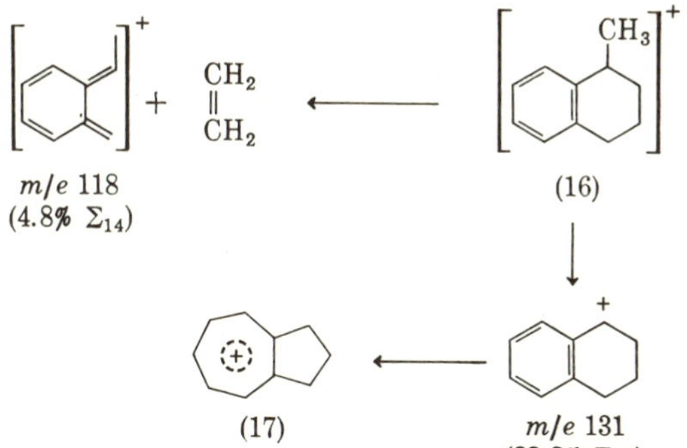

m/e 118
(4.8% Σ_{14})

(16)

(17)

m/e 131
(28.2% Σ_{14})

are another example of the decisive influence of the presence of an easily cleaved bond which suppresses fragmentation of Type D. The 1-methyl isomer (16) easily loses the methyl group under formation of a carbonium ion stabilized by the aromatic ring capable of rearranging to a tetrahydroazulenium ion (17) analogous to the process of Type A_4. The 2-methyl isomer (18), on the other hand, would give merely a secondary carbonium ion upon loss of the methyl group. Elimination of a propylene molecule

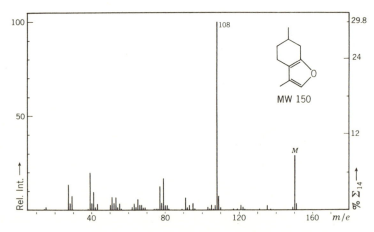

seems to be a more favorable process, as indicated by the differences in the mass spectra of the two compounds.

A similar fragmentation takes place in the decomposition of menthofurane (19) upon electron impact. The most intense peak (m/e 108) in

the mass spectrum of menthofurane (Fig. 3-18) is due to fragmentation of Type *D*, because no other facile cleavage of this molecule is possible.

A number of additional examples of this type will be discussed in Chaps. 8 and 9 in connection with some more complex problems. It ap-

Fig. 3-18. Mass spectrum of menthofurane.

pears that the double bond is not necessarily required for the decomposition in such fashion of a six-membered ring, which then decomposes into three particles:

$$\left[\vcenter{\hbox{⬡}} \right]^{+} \longrightarrow \left[\vcenter{\hbox{〓}} \right]^{+}$$

This process is not infrequently observed in complex polycyclic molecules such as some of the alkaloids discussed in Chap. 8. In those cases, the driving force seems to be due both to the formation of highly aromatic systems and to the release of steric strain.

B. Rearrangements

As is the case with fragmentation of Type *D*, simultaneous rupture of more than one bond is a frequently occurring process, provided the energy demand of such a fragmentation is balanced by the simultaneous formation of particles of low energy content, namely, neutral molecules. This is most frequently achieved in the course of a reaction in which as many new bonds are formed as have been broken, and in most cases this is accompanied by the migration of a hydrogen atom from one part of the molecule to another. Such rearrangements must therefore involve specific bonds and specific atoms in a molecule if the overall process is to be energetically favorable.

The formation of rearrangement peaks of high intensity thus requires a certain arrangement of the atoms in the molecule, which makes such peaks very useful for the interpretation of mass spectra. A deeper knowledge of the mechanism of these rearrangements is extremely important for this purpose. The specificity of such rearrangements is frequently overlooked or ignored by adding the notation "+H" or "−H" to any convenient fragment chopped off the molecule by a wiggled arrow. Notations of this kind might imply to the uninitiated reader either that a difference of plus or minus one mass number in a mass spectrum is insignificant or might often occur unexpectedly, a misleading and incorrect opinion.

The following discussion will show that certain fragments either never pick up a hydrogen atom or require the addition of a hydrogen atom from another part of the molecule for their formation. Some time ago the appearance of fragments of considerable intensity that indicated groups which were not present as such in the molecule led to the belief that mass spectra could not be used for the determination of the structure of an organic molecule. This was due particularly to the earlier work on the mass spectra of hydrocarbons, which do rearrange in a rather nonspecific manner, if at all. The examples presented in the following discussion show that heteroatoms present in a molecule play a very important role in rearrangement processes and lead to a high degree of specificity. It is of interest to note that in all these rearrangement processes a bond is broken the simple cleavage (without rearrangement) of which would lead to energetically unfavored fragments (destabilized positive ions or radicals) while simultaneous transfer of a hydrogen atom produces two daughter fragments one of which retains the positive charge and gives rise to a peak in the spectrum. Furthermore, molecules lacking bonds which are easily cleaved, particularly bonds prone to undergo fragmentation of Type *B*, appear to have a particular tendency for fragmentation with rearrangement if the structural requirements are met by the molecule.

Type E_1

$$\begin{bmatrix} \text{C}\!-\!\text{X} \\ | \\ \text{C}_n \\ | \\ \text{C}\!-\!\text{H} \end{bmatrix}^+ \longrightarrow \begin{bmatrix} \text{C} \\ \text{C}_n \, \| \\ \text{C} \end{bmatrix}^+ + \text{HX} \qquad (3\text{-}25)$$

A great variety of functional groups undergo elimination from the molecular ion or from a fragment with simultaneous abstraction of a hydrogen atom from the rest of the molecule (rearrangement of Type E_1). The positive charge remains in general at the carbon-containing fragment unless *X* contains an aromatic system. The abundance of these peaks, nominally corresponding to olefin ions or fragments thereof, is influenced by a number of factors. First, a low electron affinity of *X* permits rupture of bond *a*, giving a carbonium ion and the radical *X* [Eq. (3-36)].

$$\text{CH}_3\!-\!\text{CH}_2{}^+ + \text{X}\cdot \qquad (3\text{-}36)$$

$$\begin{bmatrix} \text{CH}_2^a\!-\!\text{X} \\ | \\ \text{CH}_2\!-\!\text{H} \end{bmatrix}^+$$

$$[\text{CH}_2\!=\!\text{CH}_2]^+ + \text{HX} \qquad (3\text{-}37)$$

Such is the case in alkyl iodides and alkyl bromides.[72,64a] The higher electron affinity of a chlorine atom suppresses this type of fragmentation, and the chlorine will be preferentially eliminated in combination with a hydrogen atom as HCl [Eq. (3-37)]. An extreme case of this type is the elimination of HCN from propionitrile,[22] the mass spectrum of which has its highest peak at mass 28 formed in this elimination of Type E_1 [Eq. (3-37), $X = \text{CN}$]. Owing to the considerable electron affinity of SH, NH_2, and OH

[72] J. Collin, *Bull. soc. roy. sci. Liège*, **25**, 426 (1956).

radicals, one should expect this reaction also to occur to a considerable extent in mercaptans, amines, and alcohols. Cleavage of the carbon-carbon bond to which the heteroatom is attached (fragmentation of Type *B*) competes here successfully with the elimination reaction, especially in the case of amines, as discussed above. For these reasons, elimination of Type E_1 is most pronounced for oxygen-containing molecules, particularly alcohols and esters, and for those nitriles which for lack of a γ hydrogen atom cannot undergo the otherwise much more favored rearrangement of Type *H*. The significance of the competition between fragmentation of Type *B* and elimination of Type E_1 makes itself felt in the much lower abundance of Type-E_1 ions from tertiary alcohols in comparison with primary alcohols, as previously mentioned (Sec. 3-2A).

In Eq. (3-36) the positive charge is shown at the olefin fragment, and in fact it is this species which retains the charge and thus appears in the spectrum if the fragmentation takes this simple path. The olefin fragment has a lower ionization potential than water, ammonia, or hydrogen sulfide, the positive ions of which are not so favorable. The positive charge is, however, much better stabilized on the protonated form of these molecules, and for this reason peaks at m/e 18 (NH_4^+), 19 (H_3O^+), 35 (H_3S^+), and 61 ($CH_3CO_2H_2^+$) are observed in the mass spectra of amines, alcohols, mercaptans, and acetates, respectively (see Fig. 3-11, for example).

The elimination of water from alcohols upon electron impact is usually depicted as a 1,2 elimination, and the mass spectrum [73] of ethanol-1-d_2 is cited as evidence because it eliminates H_2O rather than HDO. This observation, however, only precludes the possibility of 1,1 elimination, while the mass spectra of a number of more complex deuterated alcohols indicate that this process is definitely not 1,2 elimination if a longer alkyl chain is available in the molecule. The mass spectrum of 1,1,1,3,3-pentadeuterobutanol-2 does not exhibit a peak at $M - 19$ (corresponding to $M - 18$ in the nondeuterated compound), indicating that HDO is not eliminated in this case.[74] The presence in this spectrum of a strong peak $M - 18$ which is due, in large part at least, to the loss of a CD_3 group makes it difficult to detect the presence of an ion of the same mass ($M - 18$) arising by the loss of H_2O. This difficulty does not exist in the spectrum of 2,2,4,4-tetradeuterotetradecanol-3 (20), which loses H_2O ex-

[73] J. Momigny, *Bull. soc. roy. sci. Liège,* **24,** 111 (1955).
[74] W. H. McFadden, M. Lounsbury, and A. L. Wahrhaftig, *Can. J. Chem.,* **36,** 990 (1958).

clusively and to the same extent as does the nondeuterated molecule, thus precluding 1,2 elimination and formation of an olefin.[75] The ion formed through the loss of the elements of water must, therefore, be cyclic (21).

$$\left[\begin{array}{c} CH_3-CD_2-CH-CD_2-C_{10}H_{21} \\ | \\ OH \end{array}\right]^+ \longrightarrow [C_{14}H_{24}D_4]^+ + H_2O$$

(20)

$$\left[\begin{array}{c} CD_2-(CH_2)_n \\ | \quad \quad | \\ CH_3-CD_2-C \text{——} CH-(CH_2)_{8-n}CH_3 \\ | \\ H \end{array}\right]^+$$

(21)

The ring size of this ion and the structural specificity of the elimination cannot be determined on the basis of the data presently available. Participation of a γ-hydrogen and formation of a four-membered ring has been suggested for *n*-butanol,[74] but because of the lack of additional carbon atoms in the chain this is not a basis for generalization. Similarly, norborneol (82 and 83), with CD_2 next to the carbinol carbon, eliminates H_2O under formation of a tricyclic ion.[75]

The most important corollary of these findings is the fact that one should not conclude from the presence of a $M - 18$ peak that there is a hydrogen atom at the position α to the carbinol carbon in an alcohol.

Esters also show a considerable tendency for elimination of an acid molecule analogous to the elimination of water from alcohols. This is the reason for the similarity between the mass spectra of an alcohol and its acetate, and to differentiate between the two possibilities is sometimes difficult because both types of compounds have a tendency to give rather unstable molecular ions and therefore very small or negligible peaks for the molecular weight. The elimination of water and acetic acid, respectively, gives rise, of course, to a peak of the same mass in both molecules, and one has to rely on peaks due to the acyl moiety of the ester (mass 43, 60, and 61 for acetates) for a clear distinction between the two possibilities.

The mechanism of elimination of carboxylic acid may be as shown in Eq. (3-25) ($X = OCOR$), in which case, by analogy to alcohols, it should not be a 1,2 elimination. Another possibility, however, is open to carboxylates, namely, the participation of the carbonyl oxygen. If such is the case, abstraction of an α hydrogen atom is most likely:

[75] Unpublished experiments from the author's laboratory (by W. Vetter).

$$\left[\begin{array}{c} R_3 \overset{H}{\underset{C}{\vert}} \overset{H}{\diagdown} O \\ \overset{C}{\diagdown} \overset{C}{\diagup} \\ R_2 \overset{\vert}{\underset{H}{C}} O \diagdown R_1 \end{array} \right]^+ \longrightarrow [R_2-CH=CH-R_3]^+ \ + \ R_1COOH$$

The mass spectrum of the O-acetate of the deuterated tetradecanol-3 [(20), CH_3COO in place of HO] shows peaks at m/e 202 $(M - CH_3COOH)$ and m/e 201 $(M - CH_3COOD)$ in a ratio of 2:1, indicating that both mechanisms seem to operate.[75]

Such a mechanism is similar to the one discussed as rearrangement of Type H except that in the present case the positive charge is not retained on the acid moiety.

Esters can undergo an elimination of Type E_1 principally in two directions. One is loss of the acid moiety, just discussed. The other possibility is that the alcohol part is eliminated under formation of a ketene ion, particularly if there is no hydrogen atom in the alcoholic part of the molecule available for elimination as, for example, in benzyl esters, furfuryl esters, and phenyl esters. To illustrate, the mass spectrum of furfuryl acetate (22) is shown in Fig. 3-19a. The strong peak at mass 98 is due to the elimination of ketene from the acetyl group, while the peak at mass 81 is due to cleavage of the molecule (Type A_4) and is, of course, characteristic for all furfuryl derivatives not substituted further in the ring or in the α carbon atom. It should be noted that furfuryl formate does not exhibit an intense peak at mass 98, because the acid moiety cannot be eliminated in the form of a ketene in this molecule.

$$\left[\begin{array}{c} \overset{81}{\vert} \quad \overset{O}{\underset{\parallel}{}} \\ \boxed{}_{O}-CH_2-O-C-CH_3 \end{array} \right]^+ \longrightarrow \left[\boxed{}_{O}-CH_2-OH \right]^+ \ + \ O=C=CH_2$$

(22) m/e 98

Ethyl furoate, an isomer of furfuryl acetate, has an entirely different spectrum (Fig. 3-19b); this is in agreement with the fragmentation modes discussed elsewhere in this section: the fragment of mass 95 is formed via cleavage of Type C, while the peak at m/e 112 is due to elimination of ethylene (Type H) from the molecular ion.

In contrast to the elimination of a molecule of carboxylic acid from aliphatic esters containing at least two carbon atoms in the alcohol moiety, N-alkylamides [51] do not seem, comparatively, to eliminate the primary amide to any extent. The elimination of the acid moiety as ketene and

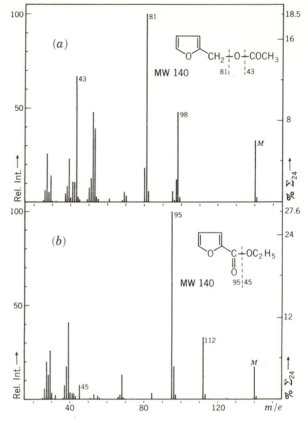

Fig. 3-19. Mass spectra of (a) furfuryl acetate and (b) ethyl furoate.

fragmentation of the resulting primary amine via Type B seems to be preferred:

$$[RCH_2NHCOCH_3]^+ \rightarrow CH_2{=}C{=}O + [RCH_2NH_2]^+ \rightarrow R\cdot + {}^+CH_2NH_2$$

The elimination of ketene is, of course, even more pronounced in the mass spectra of benzyl amides (23) and anilides (24).

CH₂NHCOR (23)

NHCOR (24)

Deuteration experiments have shown that in butyranilides, for example, it is in fact the hydrogen at the α carbon of the acid moiety which is eliminated in this reaction, by the fact that ordinary butyranilide (25), its 3,3-dideutero derivative, and its 4,4,4-trideutero derivative show a strong peak at mass 93 (C_6H_7N), while the 2,2-dideutero derivative has this peak at mass 94 (C_6H_6DN).[76] The elimination of ethyl ketene may involve a six-membered transition state and thus be of Type H rather than a 1,2 elimination:

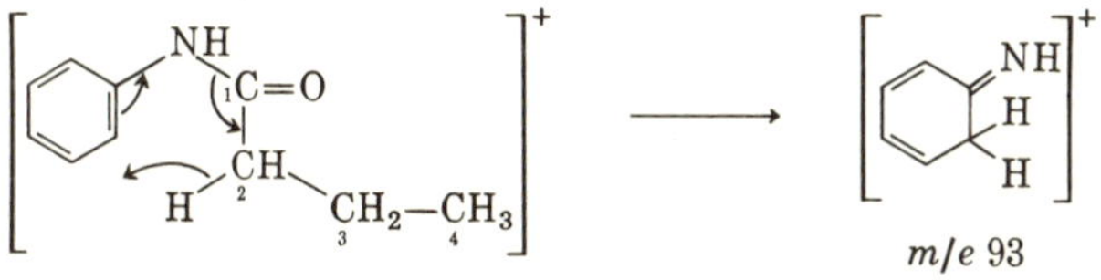

(25)

  The elimination of ketene from fragments still containing an acetyl group is rather common, and a few example of more complex molecules are discussed in other sections. The peaks at m/e 86 in Fig. 3-14c, at m/e 160 and 174 in Fig. 8-8d, at m/e 190 and 204 in Fig. 8-8e may be cited as examples.

  Type E_2

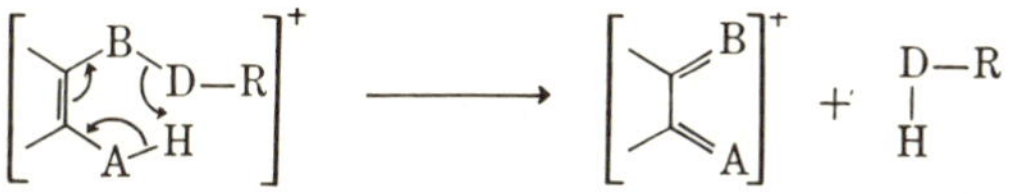

(3-26)

  A suitably substituted aromatic ring or *cis* double bond may bring the substituent and a hydrogen atom into close proximity so as to facilitate elimination. Obviously it will make itself felt in *cis* olefins and ortho-substituted aromatic molecules, and ions formed in such decompositions are useful in the characterization of such isomers. The elimination of methanol from the methyl ester of *cis*-crotonic acid (26) is much more pronounced than from the *trans* isomer, and the same holds true for the elimination of water from the free acids.

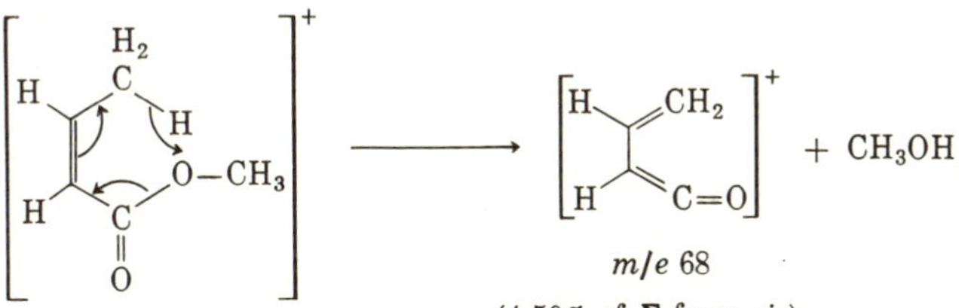

(26)

m/e 68

(4.50% of Σ from *cis*)
(0.96% of Σ from *trans*)

  The reason the *trans* isomer also undergoes this reaction is probably the relative ease of isomerization in the molecular ion.

  A greater variety of examples are available for the so-called "ortho effect" in the mass spectra of certain disubstituted benzene derivatives.

[76] T. E. Dickelman, unpublished master's thesis, M.I.T., 1962.

In this elimination of Type E_2 any one of the atoms A, B, or D [Eq. (3-26)] may be carbon, oxygen, nitrogen, or sulfur, and B may also be a carbonyl group. o-Methylbenzoic acid [45] (27), salicylic acid,[46] and anthranilic acid, their esters, and their amides give mass spectra with very strong peaks due to the fragment formed by elimination of H_2O, ROH, and NH_3, respectively; similarly, o-methylbenzyl alcohol [48] (28) and o-methylbenzylamine eliminate H_2O and NH_3, respectively. These peaks are almost but not entirely absent in the meta and para isomers, which therefore can easily be distinguished from the ortho isomer.

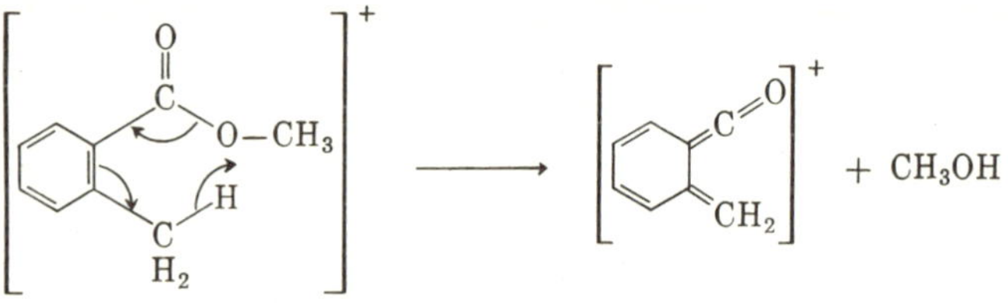

(27)

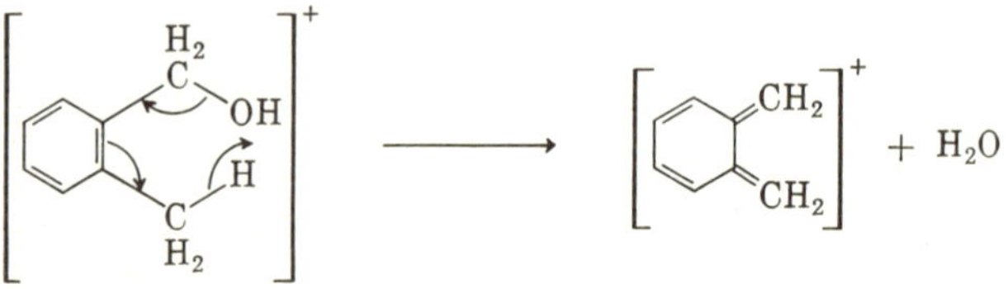

$+ CH_3OH$

(28)

$+ H_2O$

An interesting example is provided by the mass spectrum of o-xylyl-o-toluate (29),[77,78] a molecule which should be able to undergo this rearrangement in two directions:

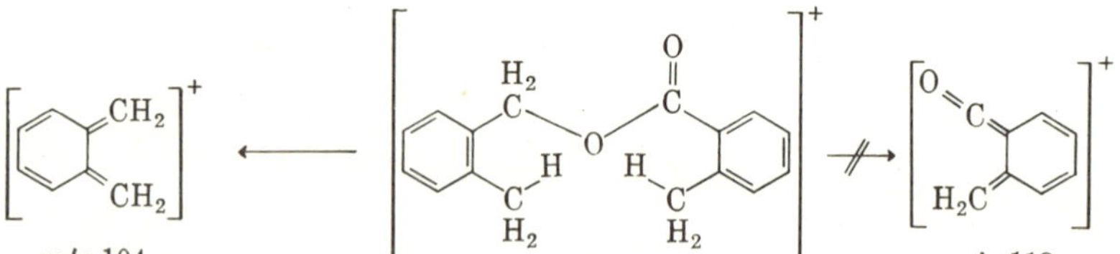

m/e 104

(30)

(29)

m/e 118

The fragment of mass 104 is almost as intense (27.66 per cent Σ_{73}) as the strongest peak in the spectrum (*m/e* 105, 30.2 per cent Σ_{73}, cleavage of the CH_2—O bond, Type A_5), but there is no peak at all at *m/e* 118, which indicates a much lower tendency of the o-substituted carboxylate to undergo the rearrangement of Type E_2.

Although these fragment ions are written here as monocyclic o-xylidene

[77] H. E. Lumpkin and D. E. Nicholson, *Anal. Chem.*, **32**, 74 (1960).
[78] T. Aczel and H. E. Lumpkin, *Anal. Chem.*, **34**, 33 (1962).

(30) or variations thereof, other structures have to be considered. Positive ions of benzcyclobutane (31), cyclooctatetraene (32), and styrene (33) have been suggested.[77] The first (30) would seem to be the most favorable one, since it still retains aromaticity and involves the least rearrangement of atoms.

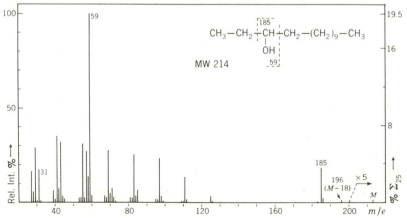

(31) (32) (33)

An eight-member ring (32) cannot easily be drawn for the fragments derived from acids and their derivatives, but this could be the reason, on the other hand, for the absence of the ion of mass 118 in the spectrum of (29).

Type F

$$-\overset{|}{\underset{|}{C}}-\overset{|}{\underset{\underset{X}{|}}{C}}-\overset{|}{\underset{|}{C}}^{+} \longrightarrow \hspace{0.3em} \diagdown C=C \diagup \hspace{0.3em} + \hspace{0.3em} \overset{|}{\underset{\underset{X}{|}}{C}}H^{+} \hspace{0.5em} (X=O,S,N,R,H) \hspace{2em} (3\text{-}27)$$

Frequently, peaks are found which appear to be formed from the molecular ion by cleavage of two bonds at the same carbon atom. Such a fragmentation would produce a number of energetically unfavorable fragments, whereas a two-step process, namely, fragmentation according to Types A or B followed by rearrangement of Type F, requires much less overall energy for the formation of such a fragment. The fragment of mass 31 from tetradecanol-3, undeuterated (20) (Fig. 3-20), or of mass 30 from leucine ethyl ester (34) (Fig. 3-14a) arises by such a decomposition.

Fig. 3-20. Mass spectrum of tetradecanol-3.

$$\left[\text{CH}_3-\text{CH}_2-\underset{\underset{\text{OH}}{|}}{\text{CH}}-\text{C}_{11}\text{H}_{23} \right]^+ \longrightarrow \overset{\overset{\text{H}}{|}}{\text{CH}_2}\overset{}{-}\text{CH}_2\overset{}{-}\underset{\underset{\text{OH}}{|}}{\text{CH}}{}^+ \longrightarrow \text{CH}_2\text{=CH}_2 + \underset{\underset{\text{OH}}{|}}{\text{CH}_2}{}^+$$

(20)   *m/e* 59   *m/e* 31

$$\left[(\text{CH}_3)_2\text{CH}-\text{CH}_2-\underset{\underset{\text{NH}_2}{|}}{\text{CH}}-\text{CO}_2\text{C}_2\text{H}_5 \right]^+ \longrightarrow (\text{CH}_3)_2\overset{\overset{\text{H}}{|}}{\text{C}}\overset{}{-}\text{CH}_2\overset{}{-}\underset{\underset{\text{NH}_2}{|}}{\text{CH}}{}^+ \longrightarrow (\text{CH}_3)_2\text{C=CH}_2$$

(34)   *m/e* 86 $+$

$$\underset{\underset{\text{NH}_2}{|}}{\text{CH}_2}{}^+$$

m/e 30

The ions formed in such a two-step process fall at the same mass number as do primary ions derived from molecules of isomeric structure having the hydroxyl or amino group at a terminal carbon atom, which might be misleading at first. As demonstrated in Figs. 3-20 and 3-14*a* the ions originating via Type-*B* fragmentation (*m/e* 59 and 86, respectively) and used for locating the functional group in the molecule are always much more abundant than the peaks due to their further decomposition via Type *F*.

Type G $-\overset{|}{\underset{|}{\text{C}}}-\overset{|}{\underset{|}{\text{C}}}-\overset{+}{\text{X}}\text{=C}\diagdown \longrightarrow \diagup\text{C=C}\diagdown + \text{H}\overset{+}{\text{X}}\text{=C}\diagdown$ $(\text{X}=\text{O,S,N})$ (3-28)

The resonance form of a Type-*B* ion can undergo olefin elimination if a chain of at least two carbon atoms with at least one hydrogen in the β position is attached to the heteroatom. Fragments formed by this mechanism are abundant in the mass spectra of ethers,[5] secondary and tertiary amines,[50] and dialkyl sulfides,[59] which lead to ions of high abundance at masses 31, 30, and 47, respectively, in the spectra of those compounds. The most abundant ion (mass 31) in the mass spectrum of diethyl ether is formed in this way:[5]

$$[\text{CH}_3-\text{CH}_2-\text{O}-\text{CH}_2-\text{CH}_3]^+ \longrightarrow \underset{\beta \quad \alpha}{\text{CH}_3-\text{CH}_2-\bar{\text{O}}-\text{CH}_2}{}^+$$

$$\updownarrow$$

$$\text{H}\bar{\text{O}}{}^+\text{=CH}_2 + \text{CH}_2\text{=CH}_2 \longleftarrow \overset{\overset{\text{H}}{|}}{\text{CH}_2}\overset{}{-}\text{CH}_2\overset{}{-}\bar{\text{O}}{}^+\text{=CH}_2$$

m/e 31

A substituent at the carbon atom retained in the fragment will, of course, increase its mass correspondingly. The mass spectrum (Fig. 3-21)

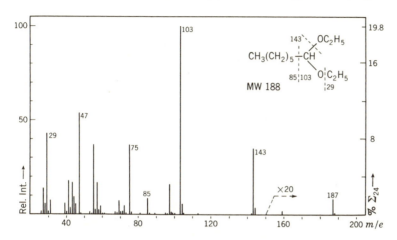

Fig. 3-21. Mass spectrum of heptanal diethyl acetal.

of the diethyl acetal of heptaldehyde (35) is a case in point. The details of the fragmentation are analogous to those of the previous one and are shown on page 129.

$$C_6H_{13}-\overset{+}{C}H \underset{OC_2H_5}{\diagdown} \quad \longleftarrow \quad \left[C_6H_{13}-CH \overset{OC_2H_5}{\underset{OC_2H_5}{\diagup}} \right]^+ \quad \longrightarrow \quad \overset{+}{C}H \overset{OC_2H_5}{\underset{OC_2H_5}{\diagup}}$$

m/e 143 (35) *m/e* 103

$$\overset{+}{C}H \overset{OH}{\underset{OH}{\diagup}} \quad \longleftarrow \quad \overset{+}{C}H \overset{OC_2H_5}{\underset{OH}{\diagup}}$$

m/e 47 *m/e* 75

An example of a much more complex molecule, the fragmentation of which involves such a rearrangement, is the tricyclic acetal (36),[79] the mass spectrum of which (Fig. 3-22) has the strongest peak at mass 123. The loss of the cyclooctyl group from the acetal carbon atom corresponds to Type B, the resonance form of which undergoes intramolecular hydrogen migration (Type G), which in the case of a cyclic ion does not result in fragmentation. It takes place in the last step, which constitutes merely

[79] A. C. Cope and P. E. Burton, *J. Am. Chem. Soc.*, **82**, 5439 (1960).

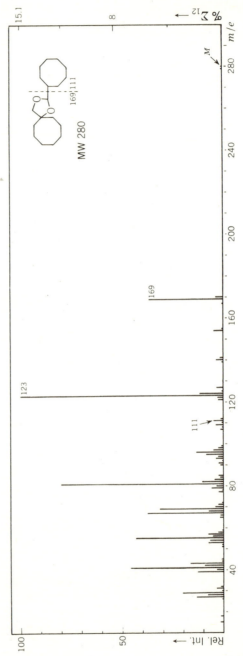

Fig. 3-22. Mass spectrum of a complex cyclic acetal (36).

an electron shift, resulting in elimination of a molecule formic acid and formation of the allylic cation of mass 123:

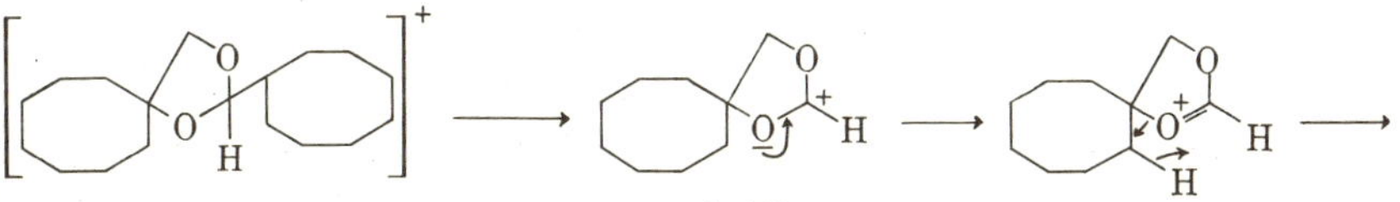

(36)   *m/e* 169

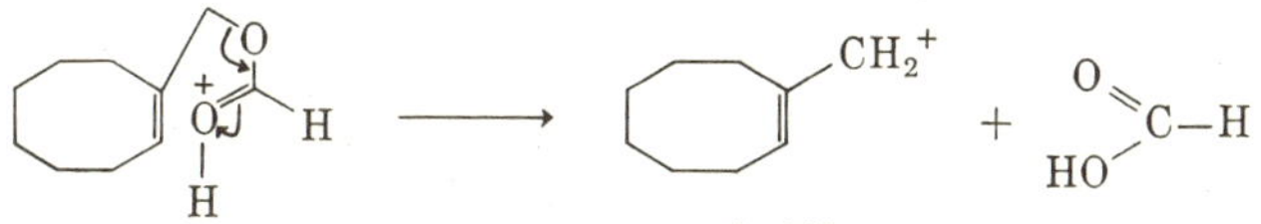

m/e 123

These examples point out again that the most intense peaks in a spectrum do not necessarily arise by cleavage of only one bond but may involve the rupture of many bonds, if the process is accompanied by the concerted formation of new bonds and elimination of neutral molecules and if not more than one radical is produced (see Sec. 3-2C). Earlier it was stated that acetals and ketals exhibit only very small peaks, or sometimes none, for the molecular weight, and this is borne out by Fig. 3-21. For compound (36) the intensity is somewhat higher because of the polycyclic nature of the molecule. Essentially the same fragmentation is found for the ketal (37), which exhibits intense peaks at mass 183 and 123, involving elimination of acetic acid in the last step.

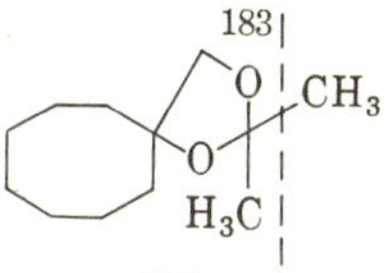

(37)

Type H

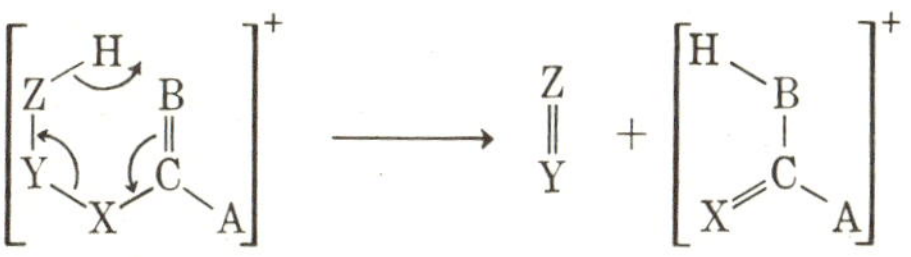

(3-29)

One of the most general rearrangements involves the migration of a hydrogen atom to a double bond. The mechanism involving a six-membered cyclic transition state for the elimination of an olefin molecule from alkyl ketones and esters containing an alkyl group of at least three carbon atoms was first proposed by McLafferty: [13,80]

[80] F. W. McLafferty, *Anal. Chem.*, **31**, 82 (1959).

$$\left[\begin{array}{c} \\ \end{array}\right]^{+} \longrightarrow \begin{array}{c} -C \\ \parallel \\ -C \\ \end{array} + \left[\begin{array}{c} H\diagdown O \\ \diagup C \\ H_2C \diagup \diagdown R \end{array}\right]^{+}$$

In this decomposition the positive charge remains with the oxygen-containing fragment unless an additional substituent is present in the side chain which can aid in the stabilization of the positive charge on the olefin fragment. This is the case, for example, if a double bond is already present in the side chain of the ester or ketone.[81]

The structural requirements for this rearrangement include a side chain of at least three consecutive atoms, the last one bearing a hydrogen atom, because it is specifically this hydrogen which migrates to the carbonyl oxygen as indicated by the fact that a fully substituted γ carbon prevents this rearrangement and by a number of deuteration experiments. The mass spectra of three specifically deuterated ethyl butyrates (38, 39, 40) (Fig. 3-23) clearly show that the proposed mechanism is correct and

$CH_3CH_2CD_2CO_2C_2H_5$ $CH_3CD_2CH_2CO_2C_2H_5$ $CD_3CH_2CH_2CO_2C_2H_5$
(38)   (39)   (40)

that it is in fact exclusively the γ hydrogen which migrates to oxygen when C_β and C_γ are eliminated as an olefin molecule.[76] Both α hydrogens are retained. Essentially the same results have been obtained by Stenhagen et al.[82,83] using esters of longer aliphatic acids. Their experiments show, in addition, that hydrogen atoms farther removed from the ester group are definitely not involved, a conclusion which could not be reached on the basis of the mass spectra of esters of butyric acid alone.

Measurements of the appearance potential[84] (Sec. 4-7) of the rearrangement ion are also in agreement with the formation of the positively charged enol form as shown above rather than the carbonyl structure:

$$\begin{array}{c} O \\ \parallel \\ C \\ H_3C \diagup \diagdown R \end{array}$$

[81] S. Meyerson, ASTM E-14 Conference on Mass Spectrometry, Atlantic City, N.J., June, 1960.

[82] E. Stenhagen, *Z. Anal. Chem.*, 181, 462 (1961).

[83] Ng. Dinh-Nguyen, R. Ryhage, S. Ställberg-Stenhagen, and E. Stenhagen, *Arkiv Kemi*, 18, 393 (1961).

[84] A. G. Sharkey and W. M. Hickam, ASTM E-14 Conference on Mass Spectrometry, New York, May, 1957.

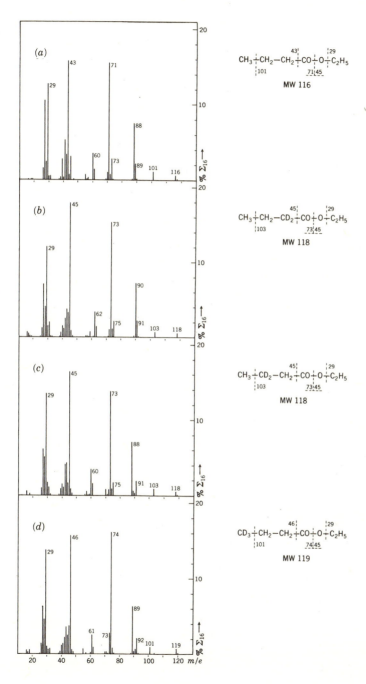

Fig. 3-23. Mass spectra of (a) ethyl butyrate and (b, c, d) various deuterated derivatives.

Fragmentation of Type H is not limited only to ketones and esters but is exhibited also by acids,[80] aldehydes,[30] olefins,[25] alkylbenzenes,[24] phenyl ethanols,[85] alkyl heterocycles,[56,57] aryl ethers,[80] amides,[51] and nitriles,[53a] indicating that the three atoms in the side chain [X, Y, Z in Eq. (3-29)] need not be carbon but may be any combination of C, N, or O and that the double bond need not necessarily be part of a carbonyl group but may be an olefinic double bond or an aromatic system.

Similar experiments with deuterated propylbenzenes[86] demonstrate that the same mechanism is operative in the formation of the fragment of mass 92 from certain alkylbenzenes where the C=B bond [Eq. (3-29)] is not carbonyl as above but the benzene ring:

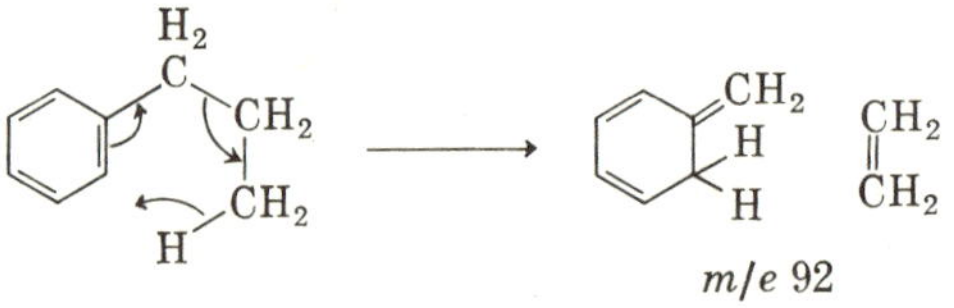

m/e 92

The rearrangement of Type H seems to be most pronounced in the mass spectra of compounds in which the positive charge at the α atom is energetically unfavorable, as is the case, for example, in molecules in which the double bond is present in the form of a carbonyl group. A positive charge next to a carbonyl-carbon atom is destabilized by the polarization of the carbonyl bond. Fragmentation of the α,β bond would create two positive centers next to each other:

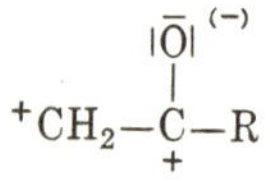

Rearrangement of the γ hydrogen to the oxygen atom of the carbonyl group is, therefore, a kind of escape mechanism. For this reason the rearrangement of Type H is most pronounced in the mass spectra of aldehydes, ketones, acids and their derivatives, and nitriles. The mass spectra of ethyl butyrate (Fig. 3-23) and of methyl stearate (Fig. 6-1) are examples. Olefins[25] and alkyl benzenes[24] exhibit simple cleavage of the α,β carbon bond (Types A_3 and A_4) but also to a certain extent the rearrangement of Type H. In alkyl heterocycles the degree of stabilization of ions of Type A_4 varies considerably among isomers; its effect on the extent of the rearrangement of Type H is discussed in Sec. 3-2D.

If the extent of stabilization of a carbonium ion α to the carbonyl group in esters is increased considerably, simple cleavage of the α,β bond

[85] J. A. Gilpin, *J. Chem. Phys.*, **28**, 521 (1958).
[86] J. D. McCollum and S. Meyerson, *J. Am. Chem. Soc.*, **81**, 4116 (1959).

becomes more pronounced, and the rearrangement of Type H may be completely suppressed. Introduction of an amino group in the α position

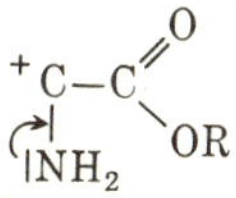

$$\overset{+}{C}-C\overset{O}{\underset{OR}{\diagup\diagdown}}$$
$$\underset{\overset{|}{\lvert}NH_2}{}$$

leads to such stabilization, and the mass spectra of α-amino esters [52] do not, in general, exhibit a rearrangement peak (at m/e 103 for R $=$ C$_2$H$_5$) of this type even if the structural requirements for their arrangement—a three-atom chain with a γ hydrogen—are fulfilled by the molecule. A strongly electron-donating group is necessary to overcome the destabilizing effect of the carbonyl carbon, and only a fully available free electron pair at nitrogen is capable of doing so; substitution of the α carbon atom by oxygen or two alkyl groups is not sufficient, and in such molecules the rearrangement of Type H still occurs. Even N-acetyl [75] or N-formyl-α-amino esters [53] undergo rearrangement (m/e 145 in Fig. 3-14c) rather than simple cleavage of the C$_\alpha$—C$_\beta$ bond, because of the electron-withdrawing effect of the amide carbonyl.

The importance of peaks due to the rearrangement of Type H is considerably reduced if elsewhere in the molecule a functional group is present that enables the molecular ion to undergo cleavage of Type B or C. The mass spectra of esters of aliphatic acids substituted with carbonyl, hydroxy, methoxy, epoxy,[43] and amino groups [52] exhibit this rearrangement, which gives rise to the strongest peak in the spectra of unsubstituted esters of butyric acid and its higher homologs, to a much smaller extent (see Secs. 6-1 and 7-1).

The striking influence which the nature of atoms B and X [Eq. (3-29)] exerts upon the extent of the rearrangement of Type H is illustrated by the mass spectra of some substituted benzenes.[80] No simple cleavage of the C—O bond is observed in the mass spectrum of phenetole (41),

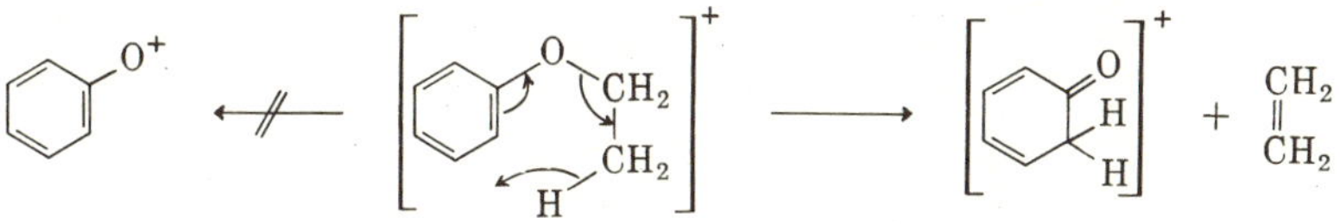

m/e 93   (41) m/e 94

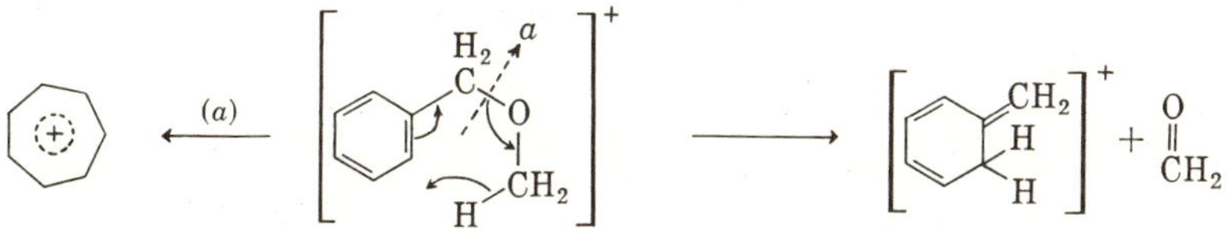

m/e 91   (42) m/e 92

$$\left[\underset{CH_3}{\overset{NH}{\bigcirc}}\overset{CH_2}{}\right]^+ \longrightarrow \overset{NH}{\bigcirc}CH_2^+$$

(43) m/e 106

and this bond is broken exclusively via rearrangement of Type H, giving rise to a peak at m/e 94. The fragment of mass 93 formed by rupture of the C—O bond without rearrangement of a hydrogen atom would have a positive charge at the oxygen atom, an ion much less favorable than the one obtained on cleavage of the same bond in benzylmethyl ether (42), the spectrum of which indicates both simple cleavage (mass 91) and rearrangement to mass 92. β-Phenyl ethanol ($C_6H_5CH_2CH_2OH$) also exhibits both simple cleavage of the O—C bond and rearrangement to give the fragment of mass 92. In contrast to phenetole, N-ethylaniline (43) does not undergo rearrangement and exhibits instead a very intense peak due to rupture of the C—C bond. The resulting carbonium ion is much better stabilized by the free electron pair of the nitrogen compared with the stabilization due to oxygen in phenetole. Oxygen is much less effective, as has been pointed out in the discussion of Type B.

The various degrees of competition between fragmentation of Types B and H in this system are borne out by comparison of the aryl ether (44a), the sulfide (44b), and the amine (44c). In this series the extent of simple cleavage increases while the rearrangement decreases:

$$\underset{H_3C}{\bigcirc}\overset{\oplus}{X}CH_2 \longleftarrow \left[\underset{H_3C}{\bigcirc}\overset{X}{\underset{H}{\overset{CH_2}{\underset{CH_2}{}}}}\right]^+ \longrightarrow \left[\underset{H_3C}{\bigcirc}\overset{X}{\underset{H}{\overset{H}{}}}\right]^+$$

0.14% Σ_{27} (X=O)	(44a) X=O	24.2% Σ_{27} (X=O)
11.3% Σ_{27} (X=S)	(44b) X=S	6.3% Σ_{27} (X=S)
36.6% Σ_{27} (X=NH)	(44c) X=NH	0.4% Σ_{27} (X=NH)

Esters of alcohols other than methanol can undergo the rearrangement of Type H in another direction too, namely, one involving the alkoxy group:

$$\left[\underset{R_1}{\overset{H}{\underset{C}{\overset{O}{}}}}\overset{CHR_3}{\underset{O}{\overset{CHR_2}{}}}\right]^+ \longrightarrow \underset{R_1}{\overset{OH}{\underset{C}{}}}\overset{}{\underset{O}{}} + \left[\overset{CHR_3}{\underset{CHR_2}{}}\right]^+$$

(45)   (46)   (47)

If the charge is retained as shown on the olefinic fragment (47) a peak at $[M - (R_1 + 45)]^+$ is found, as mentioned earlier (page 111). The positive charge seems to be stabilized on the acid fragment (46) only if it abstracts another hydrogen and forms the protonated form of (46) $[(RCO_2H_2)^+]$, a rather stable ion.[80] The reason for this difference in charge retention between the two otherwise very similar processes seems to be the fact that in the former the enol form of an ester (48) is produced but the carbonyl structure (49) of an acid in the latter and the positive charge is better stabilized on (48) than on (49):

(48)   (49)

For the formation of a fragment of mass $(RCO_2H_2)^+$—for example, m/e 61 in esters of acetic acid—two hydrogens have to be abstracted from the alcohol moiety. From the mass spectra of *sec*-butyl acetates [(45), $R_1 = R_2 = R_3 = CH_3$] monodeuterated on C-2 and C-3 of the *sec*-butyl group (in two separate samples) McLafferty[87] has concluded that C-1, C-3, and C-4 supply 80 per cent of the rearranged hydrogens of which C-3 supplies 15 per cent. It is, however, difficult to generalize from these findings because of the limited choice of different hydrogens (with respect to distance from the oxygen atoms) in this molecule. In addition, the presence of a CHD group makes it difficult to draw such quantitative conclusions regarding the fate of the hydrogen atoms on that carbon atom, because the probability of removal of H versus D is certainly not equal.

The cyclic rearrangement of Type H is also encountered in the decomposition of fragment ions involving the double bond of the resonance form of Type-B fragments.[52] The peak at m/e 44 in the spectrum of leucine ethyl ester (34) (Fig. 3-14a) is thought to be due to such a decomposition of the fragment of mass 86, which eliminates propylene:

m/e 84 m/e 44

Aspartic ester yields the same ion in a multistep process:

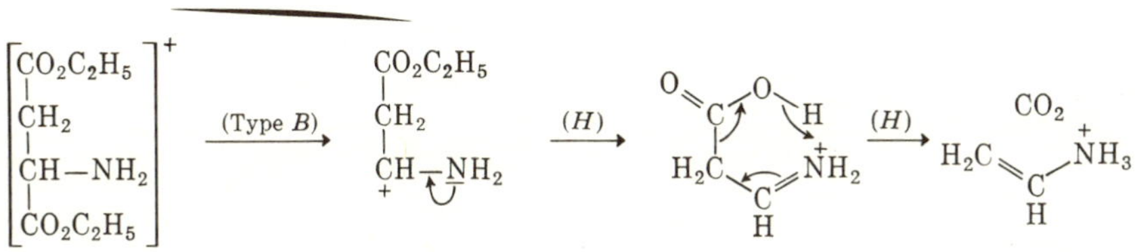

m/e 44

[87] F. W. McLafferty and M. C. Hamming, *Chem. & Ind. London*, 1958, 1366.

Unless there is present a substituent which considerably stabilizes a positive charge at the α carbon (see page 123), the rearrangement of Type H gives rise to a rather intense peak. Its mass indicates whether, and by which groups, the molecule is substituted at the carbon next to the carbonyl group. The methyl ester of n-butyric acid or of any homologous acid exhibits an intense peak at m/e 74; the ethyl ester, at 88; propyl ester, at 102; etc. The methyl ester of an acid bearing a methyl group at the α carbon will exhibit this rearrangement peak at m/e 88, and if the substituent is an ethyl group, the peak will be found at mass 102. Usually the alcohol moiety of the ester is known, and no confusion with an unsubstituted propyl ester will occur. If the nature of the alcohol moiety of the ester is unknown, it can be deduced from other features of the spectrum, for example, from Type-C fragments.

The following two examples of structure determinations illustrate the information derivable from the rearrangement of Type H. The macrocyclic antibiotic lagosine, upon reductive degradation, yielded an aliphatic acid which was converted to the methyl ester and purified by gas chromatography.[88] The mass spectrum [82] of the major fraction indicated a mol. wt 312 and showed strong peaks at mass 158 and mass 228 but no intense peak at mass 74. The even mass numbers of the two fragment peaks indicated that they were produced via a rearrangement, since fragmentation by the simple cleavage of a bond can lead only to particles of odd mass numbers in a molecule that does not contain nitrogen.

Both mass 158 and mass 228 are homologs of the ester rearrangement peak of mass 74 containing six and eleven more carbon atoms, respectively, than the rearrangement peak expected (mass 74) for the methyl ester of an aliphatic acid unsubstituted at the α carbon atom. The fragments found in the mass spectrum of the methyl ester of the degradation acid of lagosine indicated the presence of a hexylundecylacetic acid [(50), $R_1 = C_9H_{19}$, $R_2 = C_4H_9$], the ester of which, upon electron impact, loses either a C_6 olefin or a C_{11} olefin by rearrangement.

m/e 158 ($R = C_6H_{13}$)
m/e 228 ($R = C_{11}H_{23}$)

(50)

[88] M. L. Dhar, V. Thaller, M. C. Whiting, R. Ryhage, S. Ställberg-Stenhagen, and E. Stenhagen, *Proc. Chem. Soc.*, **1959**, 154.

Chemical evidence had already indicated that the alkyl groups are not branched, and this was proved to be correct by synthesis of methyl α-n-hexyltridecanoate [(50), $R_1 = n\text{-}C_9H_{19}$, $R_2 = n\text{-}C_4H_9$]; its mass spectrum proved it to be identical with the natural material.

On degradation of another natural product, ryanodine, a mixture of compounds was obtained, one of which was a γ-lactone, as indicated by its IR spectrum.[89] The mass spectrum (Fig. 3-24) shows that it has a

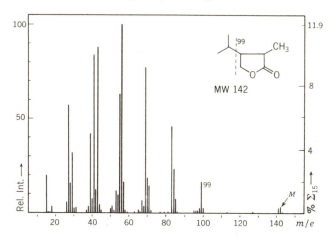

Fig. 3-24. Mass spectrum of a lactone obtained on degradation of ryanodine.

mol. wt 142 and therefore contains four carbon atoms in addition to the five-membered ring. The relatively intense molecular-ion peak suggests that there is no alkyl substituent at C-4, since such a substituent would be lost very easily for reasons discussed previously (cleavage of Type *B*).

The four carbon atoms must be present in the form of a methyl, ethyl, propyl, or butyl group, the loss of which would give rise to peaks at mass 127, 113, 99, or 85. Of these only mass 99 is an intense peak, indicating that a C_3 fragment is lost preferentially. It has to be attached to C-3, because C-4 has already been eliminated because the ratio of the intensity of $(M - 43): M$ is 4.55 in this compound, for example, while the analogous ratio of $(M - 71): M$ is $\approx 1,000$ in the mass spectrum of the γ-lactone (51):

$$n\text{-}C_5H_{11}$$

(51)

[89] D. R. Rabin, J. A. Finlay, T. P. Forrest, F. Fried, M. Götz, Z. Valenta, and K. Wiesner, *Tetrahedron Letters*, no. 15, p. 31, 1960.

Attachment of the propyl group at C-2 as in (52) is ruled out, because loss of 43 mass units would create a particle of mass 99 with a positive charge α to the carbonyl-carbon atom, and one would rather expect a rearrangement of Type *H*, producing a fragment of mass 100 via elimination of propylene:

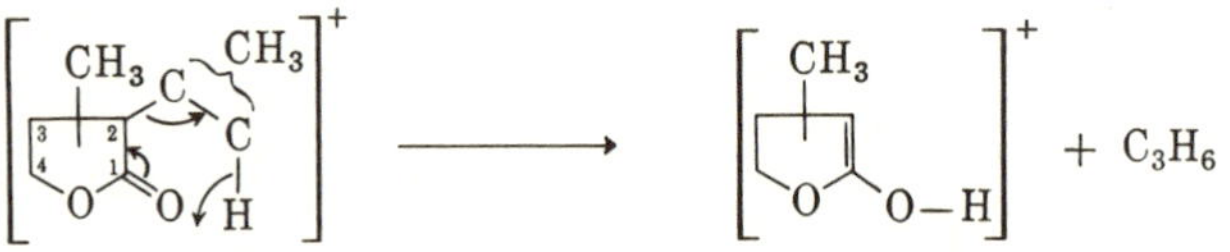

(52)   *m/e* 100

The C_3 fragment must, therefore, be at C-3. The methyl group, which could not be attached to C-4 for reasons already discussed, is best placed at C-2 in accordance with the fact that there is no considerable peak at *m/e* 127 ($M - 15$). An $M - 15$ peak would also be expected if the methyl group were attached to C-3, which then would be a quaternary carbon atom, and loss of either substituent would be expected. Structure (53) is therefore the only possible one for this γ-lactone. A distinction between *n*-propyl and isopropyl for the C_3 fragment cannot be made unambiguously from the mass spectrum, although the rather intense peak at mass 43 would give support to isopropyl over *n*-propyl. This was indicated much more conclusively from the NMR spectrum of the compound, which showed the presence of three methyl groups.[89]

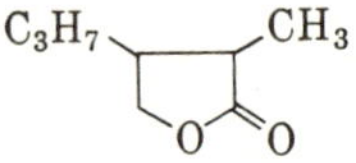

(53)

The example above illustrates very nicely the effective combination of these physical methods. Both the IR spectrum and the NMR spectrum were able to provide just the information which was not obtainable from the mass spectrum, and vice versa. The chemical correlation [89] of the structure of the lactone led to a much more ambiguous result, one which did not permit distinguishing between the 2-methyl-3-isopropyl and 3-methyl-2-isopropyl structure.

One important structural requirement for these rearrangement processes needs to be pointed out: not only must there be a hydrogen atom four atoms away from the one to which it is to become attached, but these four atoms have to be arranged in such a way that the hydrogen to be shifted comes within bond distance of the atom to which it is to be attached. Rearrangement processes therefore show much more stereospecificity than do the cleavage processes of Types *A* through *D*. This factor gives rise to considerable differences in certain pairs of isomers and will be discussed in Sec. 3-2*D*.

C. General Factors Influencing Fragmentation

Multistep Fragmentation. In Secs. 3-2*A* and *B* it was repeatedly mentioned that even quite abundant fragments may be formed in a process involving more than one discrete step, each of which is supported by the appearance of a peak corresponding to fragments which did not decompose further and often also by a metastable peak (Sec. 3-3).

The fragmentation processes which can follow one another are, however, restricted to certain types if the overall process is to be energetically favorable. Usually there is only one cleavage involved, leading to simple cleavage of a single bond (Type *A*, *B*, or *C*), while in the fragmentations preceding and/or following, a new bond is formed for each one broken. The total number of unsatisfied valences (onium ions or radicals, one of each) is thus the same as in a simple fragmentation (Type *A*, *B*, or *C*), and only neutral molecules are formed in addition.

One such example, the formation of the fragment of mass 47 from heptanal diethyl acetal (35), was discussed in connection with Fig. 3-21. The first step involves the rupture of a C—C bond next to oxygen (Type *B*), which is followed by two consecutive eliminations of ethylene (Type *G*):

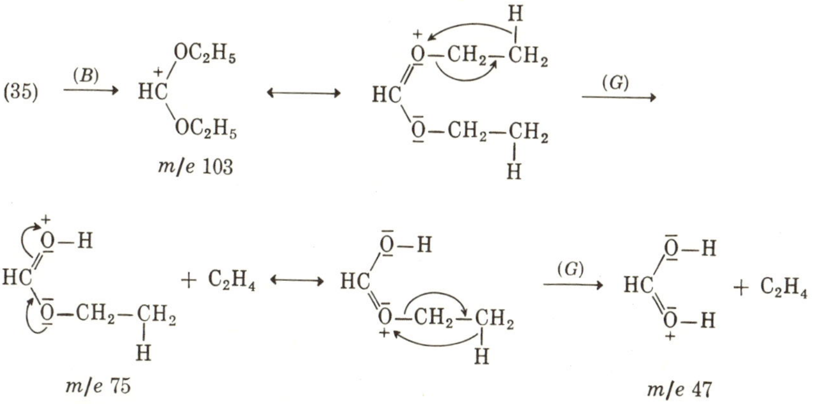

It should be noted that both the development of a positive charge toward which the hydrogen atom moves and the transfer of the positive charge by resonance from one atom to another are essential parts of such processes.

Another multistep process was mentioned in connection with the mass spectrum of α-ionone (Fig. 3-17a), which illustrates a sequence of fragmentations of Types D and A_1 and a variant of A_2. The latter (A_2) is the only one in group A producing, aside from the carbonium ion, a neutral molecule rather than a radical.

Rearrangement of Type H may also follow a simple cleavage, and examples have been discussed earlier. The double bond present in the resonance form of Type-B ions [Eq. (3-22)] seems to be particularly prone to undergo this rearrangement, as it has a fully developed positive charge to which the γ hydrogen is transferred (see, for example, the formation of m/e 44 from leucine ester, page 125).

Consecutive Type-H rearrangements occur only if the newly formed double bond in the product ion may participate as such in the next step. A few examples will best illustrate these limitations.

If there are attached to atom X [Eq. (3-29)] two side chains fulfilling the structural requirements for that rearrangement, only one will be eliminated as an olefin molecule while the second one can then undergo fragmentation of Type A_3. The mass spectrum of 2-(4-heptyl)pyridine (54) (Fig. 3-25a) shows that this compound first eliminates propylene.[56]

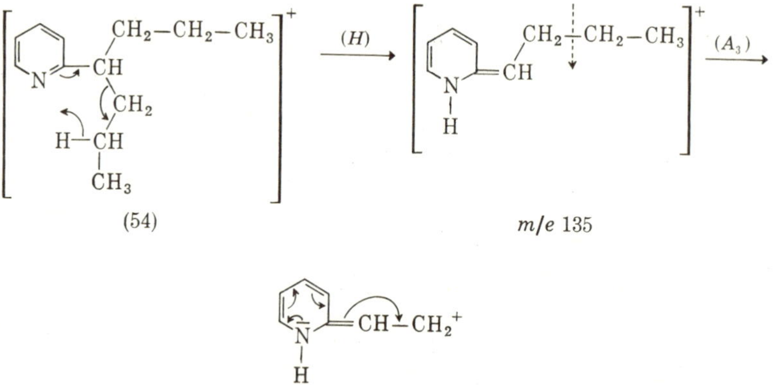

$$\left[\text{structure} \right]^+ \xrightarrow{(H)} \left[\text{structure} \right]^+ \xrightarrow{(A_3)}$$

(54) m/e 135

m/e 106

The arrangement of the double bonds in the pyridine ring has now changed, and the remaining C_3 side chain cannot be eliminated via Type H, as would be the case for the isomeric 2-n-butylpyridine.

Compounds appropriately disubstituted at a carbon atom alpha to carbonyl behave in a similar fashion. Methyl α-n-hexyltridecanoate (50) may eliminate one alkyl group (see page 126), but the fragments of m/e 228 or 158 thus formed seem to undergo only cleavage of the C_β—C_γ bond to give the well-stabilized ion of mass 87, the third largest peak in the spectrum.[82]

$$(50) \xrightarrow{H} [\text{R}-\text{CH}_2-\text{CH}_2-\text{CH}=\text{C(OH)OCH}_3]^+ \xrightarrow{A_3} \overset{+}{\text{CH}}_2-\text{C}=\text{C} \begin{smallmatrix} \text{O}-\text{H} \\ \\ \text{OCH}_3 \end{smallmatrix}$$

m/e 158 (R=C_4H_9) m/e 87
m/e 228 (R=C_9H_{19})

The methyl ester fragment of m/e 74, the expected product of two consecutive Type-H rearrangements, is only a minor peak. The same situation prevails for related compounds, e.g., aldehydes, and the virtual

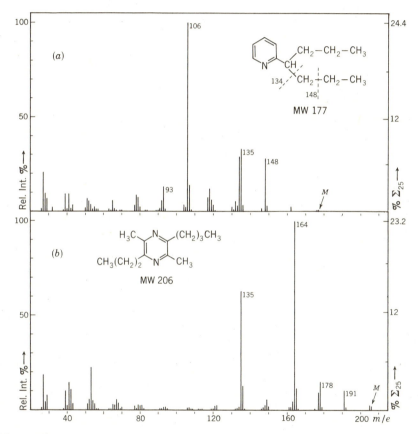

Fig. 3-25. Mass spectra of (*a*) 2-(4-heptyl)pyridine and (*b*) 2,4-dimethyl-3-*n*-propyl-6-*n*-butylpyrazine.

absence of a peak at m/e 44 in the spectrum of 2-ethylbutanal [30] is a case in point.

Alkyl side chains, even if attached to different positions of an aromatic system, do not seem to be lost as two olefin molecules; this is borne out by the spectrum of 2,4-dimethyl-3-n-propyl-6-n-butylpyrazine (55) (Fig. 3-25b),[57] which eliminates the butyl chain as propylene, followed by loss of two carbon atoms as C_2H_5 from the propyl group:

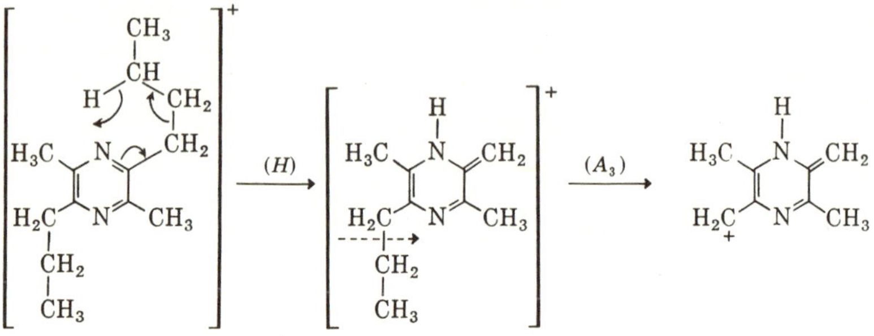

| (55) | m/e 164 | m/e 135 |

The only small peak at m/e 178 indicates that the elimination of ethylene followed by C_3H_7 is much less favored, in agreement with the general observation that large substituents are lost preferentially.

Only if certain structural requirements are met by the molecule—namely, suitable groups attached to both atom X and atom A in Eq. (3-29) —may a double rearrangement of Type H involving the newly formed double bond occur. The peak at m/e 58 in ketones lacking a $COCH_3$ group, such as 4-nonanone,[32] would arise in this fashion:

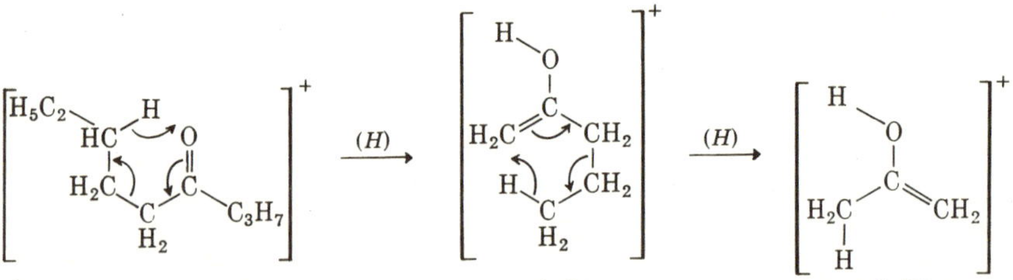

| m/e 86 | m/e 58 |

Esters of long chain acids ($>C_3$) with ethanol or its higher homologs give rise to peaks at m/e 60 and 61 due to such a double rearrangement, in part involving the abstraction of additional hydrogen from the alcohol moiety discussed on page 125. The spectrum of ethyl butyrate (Fig. 3-23a), the simplest compound that can undergo this process, may serve as an example. The variation in mass of these fragments upon incorporation of deuterium into the acid moiety is in perfect agreement with the proposed mechanism.[76]

The frequently observed cleavage (via Type F or G) of a Type-B ion has been discussed on a number of occasions in Sec. 3-2A.

Careful consideration of the possibility of a multistep fragmentation, which frequently leads to peaks that could also be due to a primary fragment from a molecule of different structure (e.g., a peak at m/e 58 is usually thought to indicate the presence of a methyl ketone with a γ hydrogen and a peak at m/e 31 thought to be due to a primary alcohol), is important for the correct interpretation of a complex mass spectrum. In later sections, particularly in Chap. 8, examples of even more involved fragmentation processes will be discussed. The basic principle stated at the outset of this section, the formation of a new bond for each one broken except one, has to be always kept in mind in the formulation of such mechanisms or in their use as an explanation for the occurrence of certain intense peaks.

Factors Decreasing Fragmentation. On page 75 a number of factors apparently governing the extent of fragmentation processes have been suggested, and the foregoing discussions have emphasized those effects which lead to an increase of the probability of fragmentation. Factors decreasing this probability have been mentioned intermittently and will be summarized in the paragraphs that follow.

In analogy to the reasoning presented on page 76, there are mainly three factors which may suppress a particular mode of fragmentation: first, the localization of the positive charge at a certain atom, particularly one of high ionization potential, rather than its distribution over a larger area by resonance or inductive effects; secondly, formation of a neutral fragment (radical) of high energy content; and, finally, as in the cases just mentioned, a particular spatial arrangement of the atoms in the molecule may preclude a rearrangement process. One of the most important examples of the first group, namely, a highly localized positive charge, is one next to a carbonyl-carbon atom, as pointed out earlier. Simple rupture of a carbon-carbon bond, one carbon atom removed from a carbonyl group, is a very unfavorable process, as borne out by the mass spectrum of diisopropylketone,[32] which exhibits only an extremely small peak due to the loss of 15 mass units although the compound has four methyl groups attached to highly substituted carbon atoms.

$$(CH_3)_2CH-\overset{\overset{\displaystyle O}{\displaystyle \|}}{C}-CH(CH_3)_2 \quad ----\rightarrow \quad (CH_3)_2CH-\overset{\overset{\displaystyle O}{\displaystyle \|}}{C}-\overset{+}{C}H-CH_3$$

$$(0.12\% \ \Sigma_{27})$$

The hydrocarbon analog 2,4-dimethylpentane[22] loses one of the methyl groups much more easily:

$$(CH_3)_2CHCH_2CH(CH_3)_2 \quad \longrightarrow \quad (CH_3)_2CHCH_2\overset{+}{C}HCH_3 \qquad 4.36\% \ \Sigma_{12}$$

A similar effect is found in nitrogen-containing six-membered hetero-cyclic compounds,[56,57] in which a positive charge at a carbon atom attached to the α position of the ring (with respect to the nitrogen) is much less stabilized than the positive charge at a carbon atom in the β position.

The mass spectra (Fig. 3-26) of 2-ethylpyridine (56) and 3-ethylpyridine (57) show very marked differences, particularly in the intensity of the peak at mass 92 ($M - 15$), which is the most intense peak in (57) but virtually absent in the mass spectrum of (56).

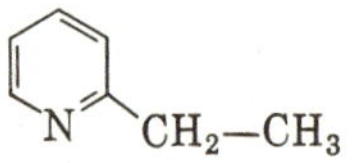

(56)

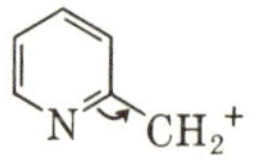

$N-CH_2-CH_3$

m/e 92

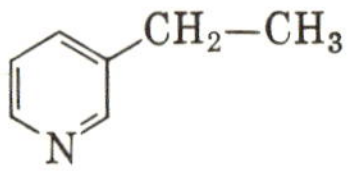

$N-CH_2^+$

(57)

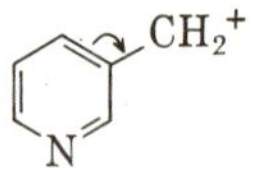

CH_2-CH_3

m/e 92

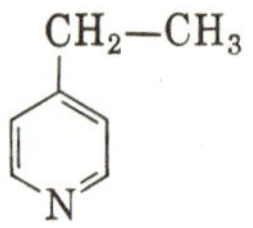

CH_2^+

(58)

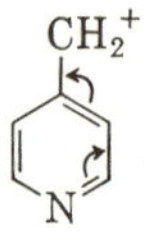

CH_2-CH_3

m/e 92

CH_2^+

In one of the resonance forms of the fragment of mass 92 from the 2-ethyl isomer, the positive charge would be localized at a nitrogen atom with only six electrons, an energetically unfavorable configuration. While one of the resonance forms of the analogous ion from 4-ethylpyridine (58) would be of the same type, its contribution does not seem to be too important, because the $M - 15$ fragment is present to a certain extent in the mass spectrum of this isomer, which occupies in this respect a position between 2- and 3-ethylpyridine. This effect is, of course, peculiar neither to pyridines nor to the ethyl derivatives, and further examples of such situations will be given in later discussions.

The stability of a carbonium ion is also very much decreased if the three remaining bonds cannot attain a planar configuration, and the great strain in bridgehead carbonium ions in small bicyclic ring systems is well known. It makes itself felt also in the fragmentation of molecules upon electron impact, but it is much more difficult to predict, because one has to keep in mind that simultaneous opening of a bond at the bridgehead via a rearrangement process may make it possible to obtain

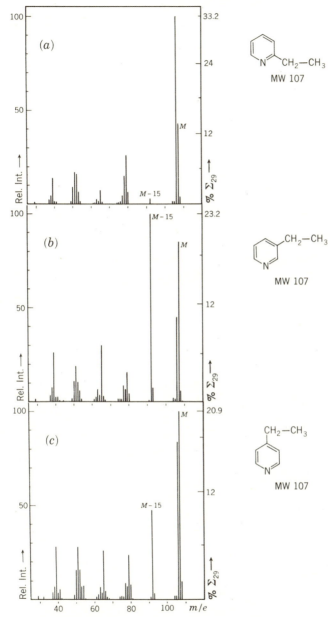

Fig. 3-26. Mass spectra of isomeric ethylpyridines.

135

a fragment which, at a first glance, would seem to contain a strained carbonium ion. The increase in energy required to produce a bridgehead ion is indicated by the higher appearance potential (10.66 ev) of the C_7H_{11} ion from 1-bromobicyclo (2,2,1) heptane (59) compared with the appearance potential (9.98 ev) of the C_8H_{13} ion from 1-bromobicyclo-(2,2,2)octane(60) and the *tert*-butyl ion appearance potential (9.6 ev) from *tert*-butyl bromide (61).[90]

(59)    (60) 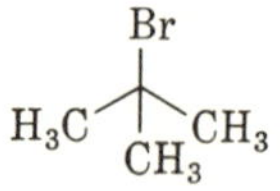   (61)

For similar reasons one would expect that a bridgehead heteroatom is not able to participate in the resonance forms which make fragmentation of Type *B* so important, because it would require the formation of a double bond on a bridgehead. The fragment of mass 136, which gives the most intense peak in the spectrum of quinine, must arise from the quinuclidine moiety of the molecule, as indicated in structure (62).

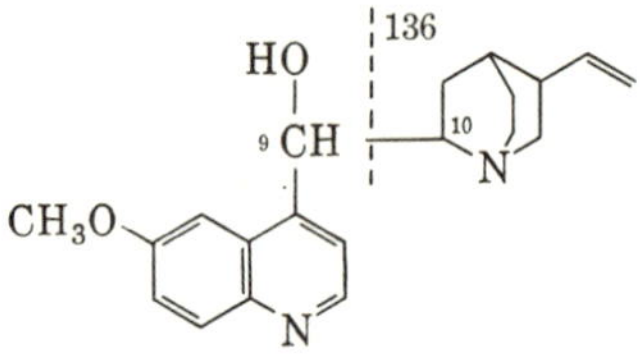

(62)

The bond broken in this process is admittedly the only carbon-carbon bond which is not part of a ring or attached to a double bond or aromatic system, but one would expect the positive charge to be retained at C-9 if it did not receive additional stabilization at C-10. There is also a possibility that in this case the structure of the ion of mass 136 is not as shown but is a monocyclic isomer, formed on rearrangement of the molecular ion.

The influence of the electron-donating or electron-withdrawing power of substituents on an aromatic ring on the stability of a positive charge elsewhere in the molecule is transmitted by resonance effects. On a large number of compounds of the type

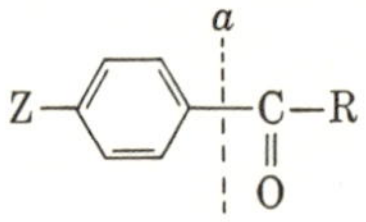

[90] J. L. Franklin and F. H. Field, *J. Chem. Phys.*, **21**, 550 (1953).

it was shown [15] that the extent of fragmentation at bond a follows Hammett's σ constant for the substituent Z.

Similarly, the ionization potential of substituted benzyl radicals [91] was found to decrease in the order m-CN, m-NO$_2$, p-CN, m-F, p-Cl, p-F, p-i-Pr, p-CH$_3$O (e.g., 8.58 ev for m-CN and 6.82 ev for p-CH$_3$O). A very satisfactory plot versus the σ^+ constant of these groups is obtained.

The influence of the energy content of the neutral fragment, a halogen atom or CN, is best illustrated by the comparison of some benzyl derivatives (Table 3-5), in which the intensity of the C$_7$H$_7$ fragment of mass 91 versus the intensity of the molecular ion decreases remarkably in the series X = I, Br, Cl. A C—CN bond seems also to be cleaved only with great difficulty, since the mass spectrum of benzyl cyanide exhibits only a very small peak at m/e 91 but shows a considerable one at m/e 90, indicating that the loss of HCN is preferred, probably involving the abstraction of a ring hydrogen.

Table 3-5. Fragmentation of Benzyl Derivatives C$_6$H$_5$CH$_2$X

X	Abundance of ion in % Σ_{25}	
	C$_7$H$_7^+$	M$^+$
I	52.9	1.11
Br	48.1	5.05
Cl	43.2	11.0
CN	1.68	27.9

Unusual Fragments. Sometimes one encounters mass spectra exhibiting a strong peak which cannot be reconciled with the structure of the compound, at least not at a first glance. This occurs, however, only if there is absent in the molecule a grouping which is able to undergo decomposition via one of the more favored fragmentation mechanisms of Types *A* through *H* discussed earlier. Such a molecule will have to fragment in some manner and this leads to fragmentation which seems at first unexpected. Most frequently the molecular ion will rearrange to another structure in which there are bonds capable of an energetically more favorable cleavage. Obviously, molecules lacking aliphatic chains

[91] A. G. Harrison, P. Kebarle, and F. P. Lossing, *J. Am. Chem. Soc.*, **83**, 777 (1961).

and functional groups in the structural environments outlined earlier in this section will belong to the group of polycyclic and/or aromatic hydrocarbons and small highly unsaturated molecules. To mention only a few examples, there is butadiene (63), the strongest peak of which is due to the loss of a methyl group, obviously not present in the molecule. This fragment must be the result of an extensive rearrangement of the molecular ion, since the methyl group is lost as CH_2D, CHD_2, and CD_3 (in a ratio of about 1:3:1) from 1,1,4,4,-tetradeuterobutadiene.

Similar unexpected loss of a methyl group is observed in the mass spectra of polycyclic hydrocarbons like norbornene (64) and the tricyclic molecule (65).[92] The mass spectra of both isomers (mol. wt 94) exhibit intense peaks at m/e 93, 91, and 79. Consideration of their structures shows that no simple fragment can be obtained by cleavage of only one bond or by a specific rearrangement process.

$$CH_2=CH-CH=CH_2$$

(63)   (65)

Although it is possible on paper to formulate the conversion of those hydrocarbons to dihydrotoluene

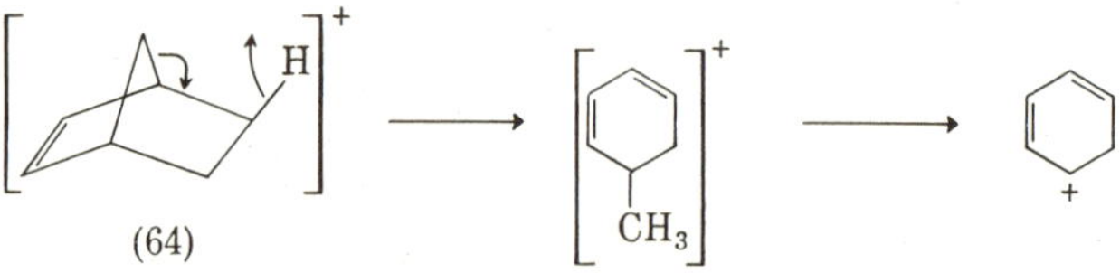

(64)

it is doubtful that the processes formulated above, for example, would survive a deuteration experiment. Considerable random rearrangement of the hydrogens (or even carbons) in the molecular ion is to be expected. It is interesting to note the intense peak at mass 91 in the spectrum of compound (65), which seems to arise by the loss of first one and then two hydrogens from the molecular ion and the formation of the tropylium ion (C_7H_7).

Examples of nonhydrocarbons exhibiting rather anomalous mass spectra are benzylbenzoate (66), which besides giving the expected fragment of mass 105 (cleavage of Type C) also loses the elements of water to give a fragment at mass 194 and the elements of carbon dioxide and hydrogen to yield the fragment of mass 167.

[92] W. R. Moore, H. R. Ward, and R. F. Merritt, *J. Am. Chem. Soc.*, **83**, 2019 (1961).

$$[C_{14}H_{10}O]^+ + H_2O$$
$$m/e \ 194$$

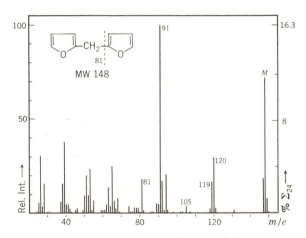

$$[C_{13}H_{11}]^+ + HCO_2$$

(66) $m/e \ 167$

In this last fragmentation the two aromatic rings must become attached to one another. The elemental composition of these ions has been verified by accurate mass measurement, using a double-focusing mass spectrometer (Sec. 4-6).

Fig. 3-27. Mass spectrum of difurylmethane.

The mass spectrum of difurylmethane (Fig. 3-27) is very interesting inasmuch as it looks a good deal more like a benzenoid molecule on the basis of the fragments at mass 91, 105, 119, 147, resembling a benzyl group (mass 91) with two carbonyl groups (28 mass units each) attached. Only the peak at mass 81 provides a hint of a furane derivative. Cleavage of both rings accompanied by extensive rearrangement of the central hydrogen atoms and elimination of the oxygens in the form of carbon monoxide are necessary to give rise to such a mass spectrum.

The elimination of carbon monoxide seems to be an energetically quite favorable process, and its elimination may even be accompanied by a rejoining of the atoms to which it was attached. A number of interesting examples of this type have been published by Beynon,[93] and high-resolution mass spectra have shown that it is indeed carbon monoxide

[93] J. H. Beynon, G. R. Lester, and A. E. Williams, *J. Phys. Chem.*, **63**, 1861 (1959).

that is eliminated. One of the more striking examples is the spectrum of benzalacetophenone (67)

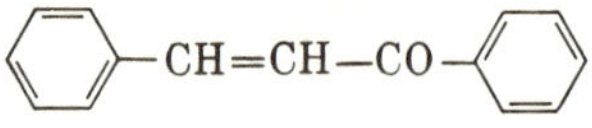

$$\langle\!\!\bigcirc\!\!\rangle\text{—CH=CH—CO—}\langle\!\!\bigcirc\!\!\rangle$$

(67)

which eliminates hydrogen and carbon monoxide while retaining all other atoms in one fragment. Both groups originally attached to the carbonyl group become linked during this fragmentation.

A rather unexpected fragmentation has been observed for β-naphthyl methyl ether (68) which gives a peak at $M - 43$ as the most abundant fragment.[93a] There is also present a small peak at $M - 15$, and a metastable peak indicates the sequence $M^+ \rightarrow (M - 15)^+ \rightarrow (M - 43)^+$. The driving forces for the elimination of carbon monoxide in the second step seem to be threefold: (1) the unfavorable positive charge localized on an oxygen atom with only six electrons, (2) the expulsion of a neutral molecule (CO), and (3) the formation of the very stable indenyl ion:

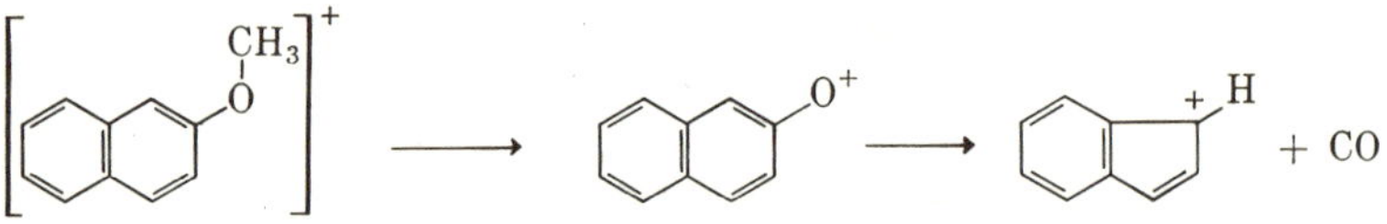

$$\left[\bigcirc\!\!\bigcirc\!\!-\overset{CH_3}{\underset{}{O}}\right]^+ \longrightarrow \bigcirc\!\!\bigcirc\!\!-O^+ \longrightarrow \bigcirc\!\!\overset{+}{\bigcirc}\!\!\overset{H}{} + CO$$

(68)

This unexpected behavior (loss of 15 and 43 mass units, respectively, usually associated with the presence of a CH_3CO group) is again due to the absence of any other easily cleaved bond in the entire molecule. Cleavage of the weakest bond available (CH_3—O) produces a highly unfavorable species which immediately decomposes further.

Although these cases appear to cast some doubt upon the reliability of mass spectra for structure determinations, it is clearly pointed out by all these examples that such unexpected fragmentation processes occur only if the molecule does not contain a group or an arrangement of atoms which could lead to fragmentation of the molecular ion into well-stabilized fragments without prior rearrangement. Major misinterpretations will be prevented if this fact is kept in mind, particularly wherever the conclusions drawn in the course of the interpretation of the mass spectrum seem to contradict each other, as, for example, a typical furyl peak (m/e 81) in an otherwise benzyl-type spectrum.

[93a] B. Willhalm, private communication.

Cyclic Stabilization. In the discussion of the fragmentation processes of Types A through C, the effect of the free electron pair of a double bond or heteroatom upon a positive charge on the *neighboring* carbon atom was pointed out. While this is the major effect giving rise to by far the strongest peaks of this type in a given spectrum, there is also the possibility that such stabilization takes place through space leading to a cyclic ion. A plot of the intensity of the homologous peaks versus the number of carbon atoms attached to the heteroatom indicates the existence of such an effect. Figure 3-28 summarizes the intensity of these peaks for alcohols, amines, nitriles, chlorides, and mercaptans.

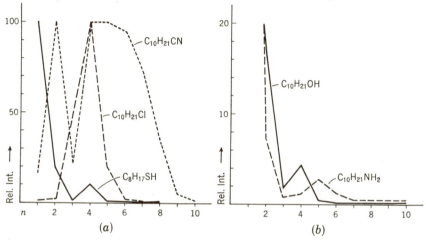

Fig. 3-28. Intensity of homologous ions X-$(CH_2)_n$ (in terms of the most intense one $= 100$) in the spectrum (a) of n-decylchloride ($X = Cl$) (*from Ref. 64a*), n-octylmercaptan ($X = SH$), and n-decylcyanide ($X = CN$) and (b) of n-decanol ($X = OH$), n-decylamine ($X = NH_2$).

It is evident from the curves that the probability of fragmentation of a carbon-carbon bond along the chain is neither constant nor does it decrease smoothly. After the high intensity at the fragment retaining one carbon atom (cleavage of Types B and C) there is a considerable peak at $n = 2$, which would correspond to a three-membered ring; nitriles are a notable exception for reasons discussed on page 122. The intensities of the homologous peaks become smaller with increasing carbon numbers but exhibit a maximum peak at $n = 4$ for alcohols, nitriles, chlorides, and mercaptans, which indicates particular stability of five-membered cyclic ions, and $n = 5$ for amines. Beyond this point the intensities of such peaks are again much lower.

This effect is most striking for n-alkyl halides, which exhibit a very intense peak for $C_4H_8X^+$, suggesting high stability of a five-membered cyclic ion.[64a] Aliphatic nitriles, on the other hand, seem to form ions with $n = 5$ or 6, indicating that a larger ring is required for the approach of the terminal carbonium ion to the negative side of the nitrile group.[53a]

This phenomenon could lead to misinterpretations of a mass spectrum if the increased intensity were erroneously attributed to another factor such as a substituent aiding the rupture of a certain carbon-carbon bond in the molecule. An example is the spectrum of β-amino butyric acid ethyl ester,[52] which exhibits a peak at mass 102 generally indicative of the presence of an ethyl ester of an α-amino acid (Sec. 7-1). The loss of 29 mass units (C_2H_5) is in this case due to cleavage of the carbon-oxygen bond in the alcohol moiety of the molecule, which never occurs in α-amino esters. The resulting fragment from ethyl β-aminobutyrate may form a cyclic ion (69) in which the free electron pair of the nitrogen atom stabilizes the positive charge on oxygen. A similar five-membered cyclic ion (70)

$$
\begin{array}{cc}
\text{CH}_3\text{—CH—CH}_2 & \text{H}_2\text{C——CH}_2 \\
\mid \quad\quad \mid & \mid \quad\quad \mid \\
\text{H}_2\text{N}_{+}\diagdown\text{O}\diagup\text{C=O} & \text{H}_2\text{N}_{+}\diagdown\text{C}\diagup\text{CH}_2 \\
& \quad\quad \| \\
& \quad\quad \text{O} \\
(69) & (70)
\end{array}
$$

seems to be involved in the formation of the fragment of mass 86 in the spectrum of ethyl γ-aminobutyrate formed by loss of the ethoxy group, another process which does not occur in the spectrum of α-amino esters.

In the mass spectra of esters having a long chain which may be either part of the acid moiety [36] or due to the alcohol part,[37] a number of peaks of considerable intensity have been noted which must be due to a cyclic product. For example, the cleavage of the C-4,C-5 bond in esters of long-chain alcohols with simultaneous rearrangement of a hydrogen gives rise to a fragment of mass $101 + R_2$ ($R_2 =$ the alkyl group of the ester moiety). This fragment may be formed in the following way:

$$
[R_1(CH_2)_6\text{—OCOR}_2]^+ \;=\;
\left[
\begin{array}{c}
\text{H}_2 \\
\text{C} \\
\text{H}_2\text{C}\diagup\quad\diagdown\text{CH}_2 \\
\mid \quad\quad\quad \mid \\
\text{CH}_2 \quad\; \text{O} \\
\text{H}_2\text{C}\diagdown\quad\diagup\text{C} \\
\mid \quad\quad \|\quad \diagdown\text{R}_2 \\
\text{R}_1\text{—CH}\quad \text{O} \\
\diagdown\text{H}
\end{array}
\right]^+ \longrightarrow
$$

$$\left[\begin{array}{c} \underset{\underset{H_2C}{|}}{\overset{H_2}{C}} \\ H_2C \overset{}{\diagup} \overset{}{\diagdown} CH_2 \\ H_2C \diagdown \underset{C}{\diagup} O \\ HO \diagup C \diagdown R_2 \end{array} \right]^{+} + R_1-CH=CH_2$$

An analogous mechanism has recently been proposed for the formation of the fragment of mass 97, which gives rise to the most intense peak in the spectra of dodecano- and hexadecanonitrile.[53a]

A particular steric arrangement present in a molecule sometimes brings a given carbon atom in the vicinity of a region of high electron density present in the molecule; in this case the positive charge at the carbon atom may be much better stabilized than expected if only the covalently bonded neighboring atoms are considered. One of the more striking examples of this kind is the preferred loss of a methyl group from the indole alkaloid ibogamine (71) and its derivatives (Sec. 8-2A), a fragmentation leading to a primary carbonium ion, the more stable resonance form of which is the quaternary ammonium ion (72)

(71)   (72)

with a four-membered ring.[94] In this particular molecule C-20 is held rigidly in the vicinity of the tertiary nitrogen because of the interlocked isoquinuclidine ring system. Epi-ibogamine,[94a] the isomer in which the ethyl group is *trans* to the nitrogen, does not show this preferred loss of a methyl group, as is to be expected on the basis of the argument just advanced.

A reaction involving a point apparently far removed from a functional group seems to take place in cyclic ketones, which have a tendency to eliminate the elements of water upon electron impact. Surprisingly, this occurs in cyclohexanone to an appreciable extent ($M - 18$ is 0.76 per cent Σ), becomes negligible in cyclooctanone, and is again more pronounced in larger rings. This elimination does not appear to involve the enol form of the ketone, because cyclohexadecanone (exaltone), for example, eliminates H_2O even after all hydrogen atoms alpha to the carbonyl group have been replaced by deuterium.[95]

Similarly, the elimination of 18 mass units (H_2O) from straight-chain

[94] K. Biemann and M. Friedmann-Spiteller, *J. Am. Chem. Soc.*, 83, 4805 (1961).
[94a] N. Neuss and M. Gorman, *Tetrahedron Letters*, no. 6, p. 206, 1961.
[95] Unpublished experiments from the author's laboratory.

aldehydes with six or more carbon atoms [30] or from formic esters of long-chain alcohols [37] is most probably due to a cyclization, possibly to the following ion:

$$
\begin{array}{c}
R \\
\searrow C \\
\quad \parallel \quad (CH_2)_n \\
\diagup C \diagdown \\
H \qquad X
\end{array}
\qquad
\begin{array}{l}
X = CH_2 \text{ or } O \\
n \leqslant 3
\end{array}
$$

D. Isomers

Optical Isomers. The mass spectra of optical antipodes, and also of the corresponding racemic compounds, are identical, because both in the D form and in the L form all bond energies and all fragments that can be formed are identical. No difference is found in their mass spectra, in contrast to most other physical constants, which differ for the optically active compound versus its racemate, because at the very low sample pressures employed there is no interaction between the D form and the L form in the racemate, which therefore behaves merely as a 1:1 mixture of the D and L compound. It is for this reason that the mass spectrum is particularly suited for the comparison of a natural compound which is optically active and a racemic sample which has been synthesized.

Diastereomers. If two asymmetric centers are present in the molecule, one may find slight differences on comparison of the mass spectra of the two possible diastereomeric racemates (or the corresponding optically active forms). For certain aliphatic molecules, such as *meso-* and $(-)$3,4-dimethyladipic acid dimethyl ester (73) and the methyl esters of 2L,9L- and 2L,9D-dimethyltetracosanoic acid (74), this difference is reported to be insignificant.[41] The mass spectra of threonine and allothreonine ethyl ester (75) are also very similar, while the intensity differences found in the mass spectra of threo- and erythro-β-hydroxyaspartic acid diethyl ester (76) are sufficient to permit the identification of either isomer if the mass spectrum of an authentic sample is available.[75] The presence of polar groups of appreciable size seems to increase the differences in the spectra.

$$
\begin{array}{cc}
CH_3OCOCH_2CH-CHCH_2COOCH_3 & CH_3(CH_2)_{14}CH(CH_2)_6CHCOOCH_3 \\
\qquad\qquad | \quad | & \qquad\qquad | \qquad\quad | \\
\qquad\qquad CH_3 \ CH_3 & \qquad\qquad CH_3 \qquad CH_3 \\
(73) & (74)
\end{array}
$$

$$
\begin{array}{cc}
CH_3CH-CHCOOC_2H_5 & C_2H_5OCOCH-CHCO_2C_2H_5 \\
\quad | \quad\ | & \qquad\qquad | \quad\ | \\
\quad OH \ NH_2 & \qquad\qquad OH \ NH_2 \\
(75) & (76)
\end{array}
$$

The similarity of the mass spectra of aliphatic diastereomers is due to a large extent to the ease of rotation along the bonds attached to the asymmetric centers, facilitated by the relatively high temperature (250°) in the ion source and the large amount of energy imparted to the molecule upon electron impact.

The differences between such diastereomers become much more significant in alicyclic compounds where it is possible in certain cases to deduce the stereochemistry of the molecule from the mass spectrum. It has been found on a number of pairs of epimeric polycyclic alcohols that the isomer which represents the more crowded molecule exhibits a molecular-ion peak of lower intensity if compared with the less crowded isomer.[96] For borneol (77) the intensity of this peak is 0.17 per cent Σ_{20}, while it is only 0.14 per cent Σ_{20} for isoborneol (78).

(77)   (78)

While this seems to be very little in absolute terms, it has to be kept in mind that even the relatively small peaks can be measured with high accuracy and that the difference between those two values is about 30 per cent of the lower one.

A few other pairs of epimeric alcohols are listed in Table 3-6, and it can be seen that this rule holds in all these cases. In addition, the $M - 18$ peak, which is due to the loss of the elements of water from the molecular ion, is always larger in the more crowded molecule, and it would seem that this might be the path of fragmentation most sensitive to the stereochemistry of the molecule.

These findings are best explained by the assumption that the strain relief experienced by the molecular ion upon fragmentation provides a greater driving force in the more crowded molecular ion than in the less crowded one. The two other steps in the overall reaction,

$$M \rightarrow M^+ \rightarrow F^+$$

namely, the ionization of the molecule and the driving force due to the energetics of the fragments, must be the same in both epimers, first because, as was pointed out earlier (Sec. 2-10), the ionization cross section of isomers is the same and, second, because the stability of the fragments produced must be the same since the fragments themselves are identical in both cases, as evidenced by the otherwise great similarity of

[96] K. Biemann and J. Seibl, *J. Am. Chem. Soc.*, **81**, 3149 (1959).

the mass spectra. If the spectra are not very similar in respects other than the intensity differences discussed here, one has to assume that either the two compounds are not merely epimeric alcohols but differ in another structural aspect or that the stereochemical differences give rise to a

Table 3-6. Abundance of Selected Fragments from Epimeric Alcohols and Acetates, Per Cent Σ

Secondary alcohols	$M+$	$(M-18)+$
Borneol (77)	0.17	1.47
Isoborneol (78)	0.14	2.41
exo-cis-Bicyclo[3.3.0]octan-2-ol	1.44	3.53
endo-cis-Bicyclo[3.3.0]octan-2-ol	0.36	4.02
Epiandrosterone	4.58	0.53
Androsterone	3.53	0.66
cis-cis-2-Decalol	0.08	8.22
cis-trans-2-Decalol	0.02	10.62
Tertiary alcohols	$M+$	$(M-18)+$
Patchouli alcohol [*]	3.46	0.70
Epipatchouli alcohol [*]	0.045	4.52
Epimaaliol [†] (79)	0.48	2.74
Maaliol [†] (80)	0.09	3.03
Secondary acetates	$M+$	$(M-60)+$
Borneol acetate	0.31	5.08
Isoborneol acetate	0.04	5.94
Epiandrosterone acetate	1.07	4.56
Androsterone acetate	0.29	5.98

[*] G. Büchi, R. E. Erickson, and N. Wakabayashi, *J. Am. Chem. Soc.*, **83**, 927 (1961).

[†] G. Büchi, M. Schach Von Wittenau, and D. M. White, *J. Am. Chem. Soc.*, **81**, 1968 (1959).

different fragmentation path (see page 148). In either case, the structure of the two isomers will be reflected more in the mass and intensity of these fragment peaks than in the result of a comparison of the intensity of the molecular ions discussed here.

The assumption that the steric requirements of the hydroxyl group are responsible for the faster decomposition of the molecular ion of the more crowded species is further corroborated by the finding that the corresponding acetates exhibit an even more pronounced difference in the intensities of the molecular ions (see Table 3-6). Conversion of the alcohol to its acetate may thus be used to corroborate the assignment made on the basis of the mass spectra of the alcohols.

In the case of tertiary alcohols such as epimaaliol (79) and maaliol (80)

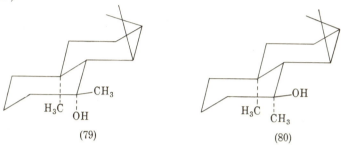

(79)   (80)

it seems to be the isomer with the hydroxyl group in the less crowded position (80) which gives the less intense molecular ion, and this is due to the fact that now the methyl group necessarily gives rise to the more significant nonbonded interactions.

Both isomers have to be available in order to make such an assignment, since the relative differences are rather small and it is impossible to predict even the approximate intensities of the molecular ion of such a compound. If the difference in intensity is not too small, it may suffice if one of the two epimers is available only as a mixture of both isomers. The mass spectrum would still indicate whether the intensity of the molecular-ion peak in the spectrum of the unavailable isomer is higher or lower than in the spectrum of the other one.

It is obvious that the M^+ intensity of these compounds should not be too low if this technique is to give reliable results, and this is one of its limitations. Molecules such as (81),[97]

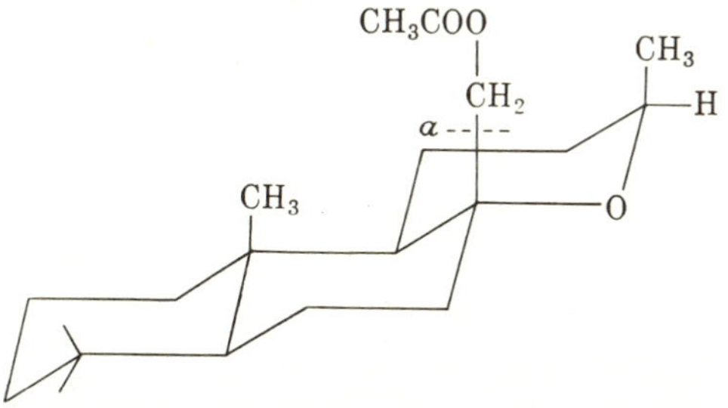

CH₃COO
|
CH₂

CH₃ —H

CH₃

O

(81)

[97] Spectrum determined with a sample kindly provided by K. Schaffner.

which contain bonds (e.g., at *a*) that are very easily broken, frequently do not fulfill this requirement, and it is therefore not possible to deduce their stereochemistry in this manner. Secondly, if the nonbonded interactions within the molecule are only slight, the differences between the spectra of the two isomers will also be negligible. While borneol and isoborneol are well suited for this technique *exo-* and *endo*-norborneol [(82) and (83) respectively],

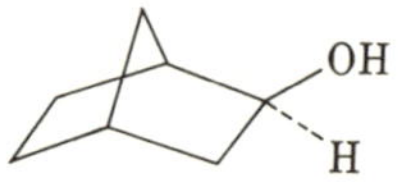

(82) 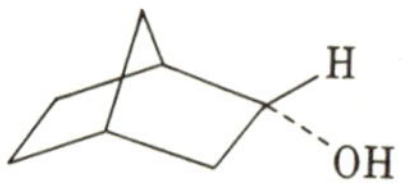   (83)

which lack the space-demanding methyl groups, give inconclusive results.

It seems that this technique is best applicable to rigid polycyclic molecules, such as derivatives of *trans*-decalin or steroids.

Occasionally one finds a pair of epimers giving rather different mass spectra. This is the case if the steric arrangement of the atoms in one of the isomers facilitates a rearrangement process which is made more difficult in the other isomer. An example is provided by the two isomeric bicyclic ketones (84) and (85) (Fig. 3-29):[98]

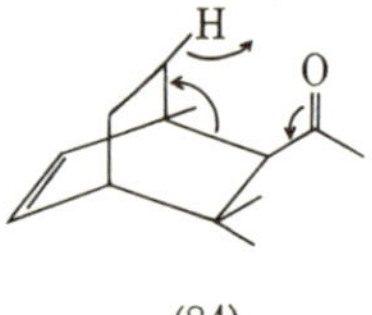

(84) 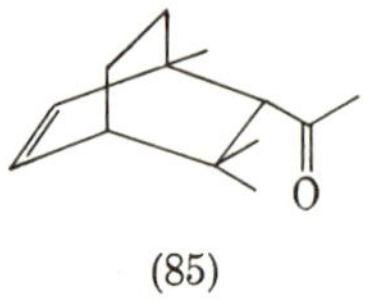   (85)

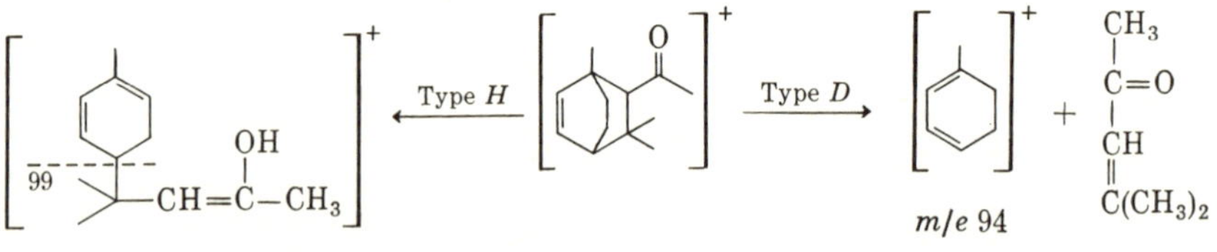

In both molecules the fragmentation of Type *D* can operate, leading to the most intense peak in both spectra at m/e 94, but only in (84) is the carbonyl group held near a hydrogen atom which can be abstracted during a rearrangement of Type *H*.

While this rearrangement still does not lead to any fragments, cleavage of one additional bond gives rise to the ion of mass 99, in which the

[98] Spectrum determined with samples kindly provided by G. Büchi and C. W. Perry.

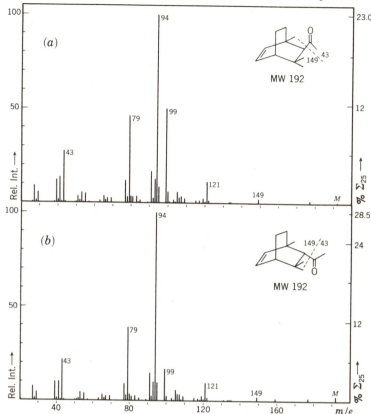

Fig. 3-29. Mass spectra of the isomeric. bicyclic methyl ketones (a) 84 and (b) 85.

positive charge is at a tertiary carbon atom and, in addition, is stabilized by the free electron pair on oxygen through the double bond:

$$H_3C\diagdown \overset{+}{\underset{H_3C\diagup}{C}}\diagup CH=C\diagdown \overset{\overset{\displaystyle \frown}{O}-H}{CH_3}$$

m/e 99

The ion of mass 99 is not entirely absent in the mass spectrum of isomer (85), because the same rearrangement can take place involving a hydrogen atom of the bridgehead methyl group. This requires, however, a more strained transition state, which makes the fragmentation less favorable.

The peak at *m/e* 79 seems to be due to loss of the methyl group from the fragment of mass 94, possibly after rearrangement of the double bonds to form the isomeric ion postulated as the first step in the decomposition of norbornene (64). Stepwise loss of first CH_3CO and then C_2H_4 [Type *D* (solid arrows) or Type A_2 (broken arrows)] leads to the fragment of mass 121:

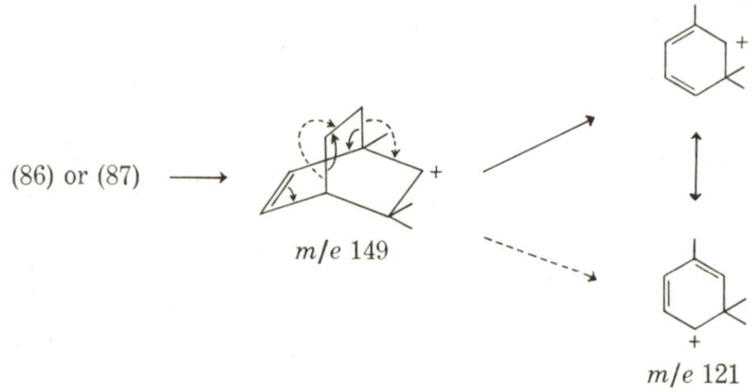

(86) or (87) $\longrightarrow$

m/e 149

m/e 121

Most of the processes discussed above, with the exception of the Type *H* rearrangement, can operate equally well in both isomers. The spectra shown in Fig. 3-29 are thus very similar, differing markedly, however, in the abundance of mass 94. The lower intensity of the molecular-ion peak in Fig. 3-29*b* reflects both the greater steric strain in this ion and the availability of an additional favorable mode of fragmentation.

A related example is the diester (86) and its isomer (87),

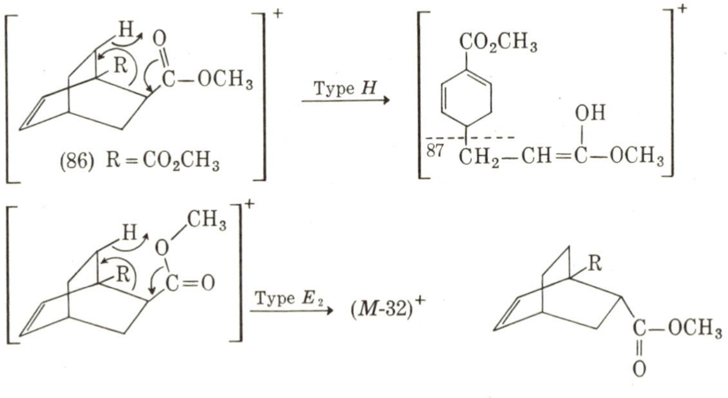

(86) R = CO_2CH_3

$\xrightarrow{\text{Type } H}$

CO_2CH_3

OH

87 $CH_2-CH=C-OCH_3$

$\xrightarrow{\text{Type } E_2}$ $(M\text{-}32)^+$

(86) R = CO_2CH_3

(87) R = CO_2CH_3

R

$C-OCH_3$

O

in which the peaks at mass 87 amount to 3.07 and 0.54 per cent Σ_{24}, respectively.[99] It is of interest to note that there is also a considerable difference between the $M-32$ peaks, which are 8.45 and 1.56 per cent Σ_{24}, respectively. This difference is nicely explained on the basis of the stereochemistry of these compounds, because elimination of methanol (by a variation of Type E_2) is facilitated in isomer (86).

[99] Spectrum determined with a sample kindly provided by F. D. Greene.

These few examples illustrate that it is possible, with certain limitations imposed by the nature of the compounds, to deduce the stereochemistry of a molecule from its mass spectrum. It is evident that in all but extreme cases the spectra of both isomers are required. Consideration of all possible interactions on hand of molecular models is imperative to evaluate the steric differences between both isomers correctly.

Cis and Trans Olefins. It was mentioned in the discussion of Type A_3 (Sec. 3-2A) that a double bond may migrate within the molecular ion and lead in effect to isomerization of the double bond. Even more facile is the isomerization of a *cis* double bond to a *trans* double bond, which merely requires rotation around the σ bond remaining in the molecular ion:

$$
\begin{array}{cc}
\text{H} & \text{H} \\
| & | \\
\text{R}-\overset{+}{\text{C}}\!-\!\!-\!\overset{\cdot}{\text{C}}-\text{R}'
\end{array}
$$

If the double bond is far removed from other functional groups, the mass spectra of the two isomers are virtually identical (e.g., methyl oleate versus elaidate).[42] Pronounced differences are found if the double bond comes close to the ester group.

Positional Isomers—Polyalkyl-substituted Aromatic Compounds. It has been already pointed out that the isomeric xylenes have virtually identical spectra because they all form the same methyltropylium ion.[69] Similarly, the mass spectra of the isomeric methylethylbenzenes shown in Fig. 3-30 fail to exhibit appreciable differences. It is somewhat easier to distinguish between similar isomers in heterocyclic compounds, as borne out by the mass spectra of 3-ethyl-4-methylpyridine and 3-ethyl-5-methylpyridine, which differ, for example, considerably in the $M/(M\text{-}1)$ ratio (Fig. 3-31). Even more pronounced is the difference if the ethyl group is attached to the 2 or 4 position as in 2-ethyl-6-methylpyridine, for reasons discussed on page 134.

Examples of isomers of more complex molecules differing only in the position of a substituent in the aromatic ring are discussed in Chap. 8.

In summary it can be said that the ease with which such isomers can be distinguished on the basis of their mass spectra varies considerably, and polyalkylbenzenes present the most difficulty.

Other Positional Isomers. Compounds differing in substitution at bonds which do undergo fragmentation upon electron impact give rise to very different mass spectra, as has been clearly shown in Sec. 3-2A. If the difference in substitution is such as to give rise to fragments of different mass produced in the major fragmentation processes, no particular diffi-

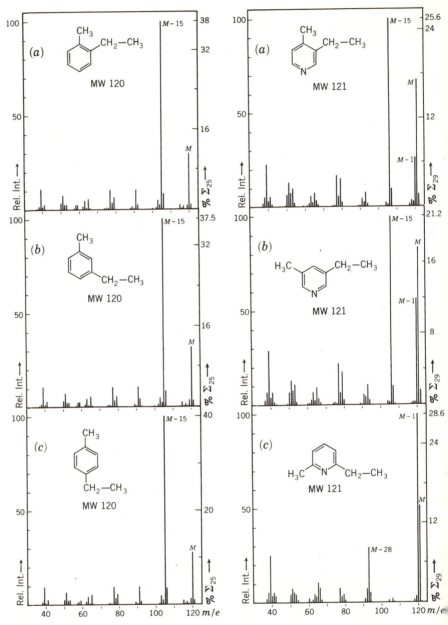

Fig. 3-30. Mass spectra of isomeric methyl-ethylbenzenes. (a) 1,2 isomer; (b) 1,3 isomer; (c) 1,4 isomer.

Fig. 3-31. Mass spectra of isomeric pyridines. (a) 3-Ethyl-4-methylpyridine; (b) 3-ethyl-5-methylpyridine; (c) 2-ethyl-6-methylpyridine.

culty will be encountered in interpretating the spectrum correctly without having any authentic samples available. If, however, the fragments of the possible isomers have the same mass, interpretations will be more difficult, and frequently an authentic sample of either isomer is required. Of the three amino alcohols

$$
\begin{array}{ccc}
\mathrm{CH_2-CH-CH_3} & \mathrm{CH_2-CH_2-CH_2} & \mathrm{CH_2-CH_2} \\
\mid \quad \mid & \mid \qquad \mid & \mid \quad \mid \\
\mathrm{OH} \quad \mathrm{NH_2} & \mathrm{OH} \qquad \mathrm{NH_2} & \mathrm{OH} \quad \mathrm{NHCH_3} \\
(88) & (89) & (90)
\end{array}
$$

(88) and (89) will produce very different mass spectra, while (88) and (90) are much more alike.

3-3. METASTABLE PEAKS

In this chapter the fragmentation processes have been discussed mainly on the basis of the positively charged fragments formed, the particles giving rise to the peaks in the mass spectrum, while the nature of the uncharged fragment not recorded in the spectrum was deduced from the mass difference between the molecular ion, or primary fragment ion, and the ion under consideration. This approach is based on the assumption that the decomposition is a one-step process, but as has been pointed out earlier, multistep fragmentation is rather common. For this reason it would be important also to determine the mass of the neutral fragment, which is not possible with a mass spectrometer of conventional design.

In many cases the so-called "metastable peaks" permit calculation of the mass of the neutral fragment formed in a given decomposition process. The term "metastable peak" is somewhat misleading, because it is, of course, not the peak in the spectrum which is unstable and would disappear. Rather is it the primary ion which is considered metastable and may decompose into other fragments before it is deflected into the collector.

When a molecule becomes ionized upon electron impact, the positively charged molecular ion will, under the influence of the potential gradient in the ion source, begin to travel toward the accelerating region, owing to the slightly more positive repeller plates (Fig. 1-3). If the rate of decomposition of this molecular ion into fragments is very fast, all such ions will decompose before reaching the first accelerating plate, and only the fragments will be accelerated and deflected. The spectrum will consist only of fragment peaks, with no peak for the molecular ion, a situation which is common for branched alcohols, for example, for reasons discussed earlier. If on the other hand, the molecular ion is a very stable one with little chance to decompose, as in the case of aromatic hydrocarbons, for example, virtually all molecular ions originally formed will be accelerated as such, and the mass spectrum will exhibit a very strong peak for the molecular ion. Molecular ions which decompose at an intermediate rate will, in part, pass intact through the accelerating region and, in part, decompose earlier. In such a case, we will find intense peaks both for the molecular weight and for the fragments.

Obviously there will be some primary ions which happen to decompose into fragments while traversing the accelerating region. They will be accelerated first as mass m_1. At the point of decomposition, part of the achieved kinetic energy will be carried off by the neutral fragment, while mass m_2 will continue to be accelerated and deflected as such, and as a result the particle will be recorded neither as m_1 nor as m_2 but will give rise to a broad peak of low intensity with a maximum at mass m^* (Fig. 3-32). It turns out that in magnetic-deflection mass spectrometers, either of the sector or semicircular type, the resulting ion is collected only when the decomposition has taken place in the vicinity of exit slit d (Fig. 1-3), and all others get lost. Mass m^*, at which such ions are recorded, can be simply related to the mass of the original ion m_1 and the mass of the product ion m_2 by the following equation: [100]

$$m^* = \frac{(m_2)^2}{m_1} \qquad (3\text{-}38)$$

As it takes about 10^{-6} sec for the ion to reach the accelerating region and about 10^{-4} sec for it to become fully accelerated, metastable peaks will be found for such ions, the half-life time of which lies within this range. Owing to the nature, just discussed, of the whole phenomenon, there always must be a number of ions of mass m_1 surviving long enough to be collected at that mass, but many ions of mass m_2 must also be present, because otherwise it would be impossible to have a considerable number of primary ions decomposing just while traversing the accelerating region. In other words, a metastable peak may be expected only if there are peaks of considerable intensity for both the primary ion and for the daughter ion.

If a metastable peak with a maximum at mass m^* is present in the spectrum which can be related by Eq. (3-38) to the masses of two other intense peaks, m_1 and m_2, it can be assumed with reasonable certainty

[100] J. A. Hipple and E. U. Condon, *Phys. Rev.*, **68**, 54 (1945).

that the fragment of mass m_2 arises in a one-step decomposition from the species of mass m_1. It has to be kept in mind that there might be more than one possible combination of two peaks giving the same value for the metastable peak, but frequently the others will be ruled out because certain mass differences could not possibly correspond to a neutral fragment that could be eliminated in one step, e.g., mass 22. The absence of a metastable peak, on the other hand, does not exclude the formation in one step of one ion from another, because the collection efficiency might be low for various reasons.

Consideration of metastable peaks is important not only for studies concerned with the mechanism of fragmentation of ions formed in the mass spectrometer but also has considerable value in the interpretation of mass spectra. From the occurrence of the metastable peak relating two peaks of the spectrum, it follows that those two peaks must be derived from one and the same substance and cannot be due to two different compounds present as a mixture. It also follows that the smaller fragment of the two which are found to be related to each other by a single fragmentation step must necessarily be composed entirely of atoms present in the larger fragment from which it arose. Such considerations are extremely valuable if the structure of the molecule is to be reconstructed from the fragments.

While in the discussion of the origin of metastable peaks the decomposition of a molecular ion into a primary fragment was used as an example, it is clear that the same argument applies to the decomposition of a primary fragment into a secondary one.

The intensity of metastable peaks is always rather low,[101] mostly below 1 per cent, and in rare cases, up to 3 per cent of the most intense peak of the spectrum.

Although the original mass spectra do contain a considerable number of metastable peaks, these are not indicated in the illustrations used throughout his book, because they could hardly be seen in most instances if drawn to scale. The mass at which they appear will be discussed in the text whenever necessary. To illustrate their appearance on the record, which is strikingly different from the peaks ordinarily encountered in mass spectra, part of the mass spectrum of deacetylaspidospermine [(17c), Chap. 8] is shown in Fig. 3-32.

It should be pointed out that the maximum of the metastable peak is generally found at a mass slightly higher (about 0.1 to 0.4 mass unit)

[101] E. G. Bloom, F. L. Mohler, C. E. Wise, and E. J. Wells, *J. Research Natl. Bur. Standards*, **43**, 65 (1949).

than the value based on Eq. (3-38), at least in mass spectrometers of the semicircular type. With these instruments, in particular, metastable peaks are very broad and could never be mistaken for a normal peak in the mass spectrum, or vice versa; but if it should become necessary definitely

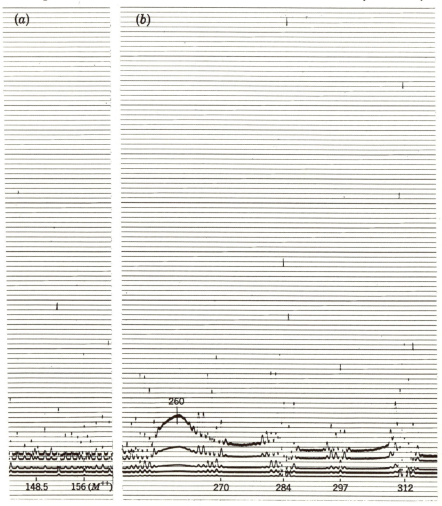

Fig. 3-32. Typical appearance (*a*) of peaks due to doubly charged ions and (*b*) of a metastable peak in the spectrum of deacetylaspidospermine [(17*c*), Chap. 8]. Part (*a*) was determined at a lower intensity than (*b*).

to identify a metastable peak as such, the variation of its intensity with change of the repeller potential may be employed. Decrease of this potential leads to a longer time spent by the ions in the ion source; this will affect the number of ions which decompose at the exit slit and which are responsible for the metastable peaks. This relationship has, in fact, been used to determine the half-life time of a number of ions.[102]

The previous discussion was concerned with the behavior of ions in a mass spectrometer employing semicircular or sector deflection. In the cycloidal instrument (Sec. 1-2G), the metastable peak is found at apparent masses higher than either m_1 and m_2, and m^* is dependent on the injection voltage. If this is 60 volts the metastable peak for the loss of methyl from methylcyclopentane (mass 84), for example, is found at m/e 92.[102a]

In the time-of-flight mass spectrometer the two species, m_2 and the natural species m_0 formed on decomposition of m_1 during its flight, both retain the original velocity and arrive at the collector at the same time; they are therefore not resolved. The charged particles may be deflected off the electron multiplier or forced to take a bent (and therefore longer) path, which results in the appearance of the neutral species as a "ghost" (a less well resolved shadow of the actual peaks).

3-4. MULTIPLY CHARGED IONS

The majority of the ions formed in the mass spectrometer under the conditions generally employed when one is dealing with organic compounds bear a single positive charge. Such ions are collected and recorded in the mass spectrum at a mass-to-charge ratio (m/e) equal to their mass, since $e = 1$. It is possible, however, to obtain multiply charged ions if in the initial ionization process two electrons are removed from the molecule, which then decomposes into neutral fragments and doubly charged fragments:

$$AB + e^- \rightarrow AB^{++} + 3e^-$$
$$AB^{++} \rightarrow A^{++} + B \cdot$$

although the decomposition of a singly charged ion into a doubly charged fragment plus a negative ion

$$AB^+ \rightarrow A^{++} + B^-$$

cannot be ruled out.

The particle bearing two positive charges will be collected and recorded at the mass-to-charge ratio which corresponds to half its weight. The doubly charged molecular ion of pyridine (C_5H_5N, mol. wt 79) will appear in the spectrum at mass 39.5. Doubly charged ions can be identi-

[102] J. A. Hipple, *Phys. Rev.*, **71**, 594 (1947).
[102a] L. G. Hall, private communication.

fied easily if the mass of the ion is an odd value, because division by 2 results not in an integral number, as is necessarily the case for singly charged ions, but in half mass numbers instead (see Fig. 3-32). The doubly charged molecular ions of compounds containing an odd number of nitrogens are, therefore, easy to recognize. This is not the case for other molecules, the doubly charged molecular ions of which cannot easily be distinguished from a singly charged fragment ion which happens to have half the mass of the molecule.

The best indication that a peak at integral mass is due to a doubly charged species of even mass is the presence of a small peak $\frac{1}{2}$ mass unit higher owing to the doubly charged C^{13}-isotope peak of the fragment. From its intensity, it is possible to calculate the peak height at integral mass, indicating whether the peak is due entirely to the doubly charged species or is of mixed origin.

If such a distinction were of particular importance, substitution of one hydrogen atom in the molecule by deuterium would lead to a molecule of odd-number molecular weight, and its doubly charged ion would then fall exactly between integral mass numbers. The mass of a fragment, singly charged, would increase for one full mass unit if the original hydrogen atom, which was replaced by deuterium, were contained in this fragment.

The appearance potentials of doubly charged ions are much higher than those of singly charged ones (Fig. 3-1), because the removal of two electrons from the molecule requires, of course, much more energy than if only one electron has to be removed. Mass spectra determined with electrons of less energy than about 30 ev do not contain multiply charged ions, a fact which may be used for the differentiation between singly and doubly charged species.

The removal of two electrons from a molecule is facilitated by the presence of a high π-electron density and by the absence of bonds which can undergo fragmentation with great ease. It is for this reason that saturated aliphatic hydrocarbons have a very slight tendency to yield doubly charged ions, while their abundance increases in the series monoolefins, polyolefins, aromatic molecules, and heterocyclic molecules. The absolute intensity of doubly charged ions is, of course, much lower than for singly charged particles, in general of the order of about 1 per cent of the most intense singly charged peak. The mass spectra of heteroaromatic molecules, particularly of polycyclic ones, exhibit doubly charged molecular ions the intensity of which may be 20 to 30 per cent of their singly charged counterparts (see some of the figures in Chap. 8).

For fragment ions no direct relationship between the intensity of the singly and doubly charged species should be expected, since the mechanism of decomposition of the molecular ion to this particular fragment ion may be very different for the singly charged compared with doubly charged species. Not infrequently one finds a rather intense doubly charged ion, while the peak at twice its mass is quite small. Beynon[7] describes an interesting example, namely, the spectrum of maleic anhydride (91), which exhibits a very small peak due to the loss of one oxygen atom from the molecule, while the corresponding doubly charged species (92) is about seven times as intense.

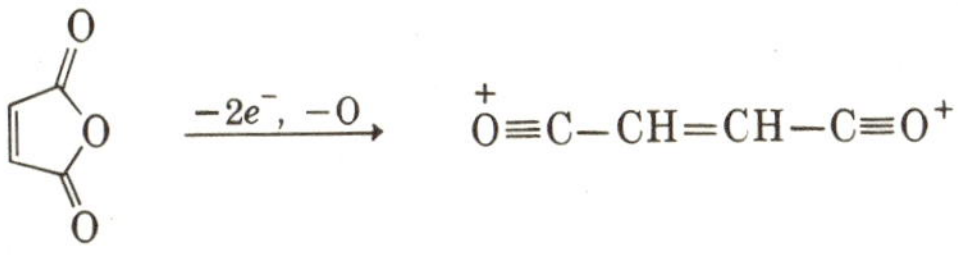

$$\underset{(91)}{\text{[structure]}} \quad \xrightarrow{-2e^-, \, -O} \quad \underset{(92)}{\overset{+}{O}\equiv C-CH=CH-C\equiv O^+}$$

Stabilization of the two positive charges, one on each oxygen atom, is proposed as an explanation.

The importance of doubly charged peaks in the interpretation of mass spectra lies in the above-mentioned relationship between their abundance and molecular type to which the compound belongs. If a considerable number of peaks at half mass numbers—therefore due to doubly charged ions—are present in the mass spectrum, this can be taken as an indication that the compound is highly unsaturated or aromatic. With some experience it is thus possible to deduce from the abundance of such peaks whether the compound is saturated, olefinic, or aromatic. One has to be somewhat careful, however, because strongly electron-withdrawing substituents (such as NO_2) present in aromatic compounds decrease the tendency for formation of multiply charged ions. Furthermore, one should keep in mind that the UV spectrum of the compound may be a much better indication for the degree and type of unsaturation of the compound.

3-5. NEGATIVE IONS

During the previous discussions we have been concerned only with the production and the recording of positively charged ions formed from organic molecules upon electron impact. While the positive ions are of almost exclusive interest for our purposes here, a brief consideration of the formation and significance of negative ions [103] is in order.

[103] H. S. W. Massey, "Negative Ions," Cambridge University Press, New York, 1950.

Negative ions may be formed principally in three ways: [104]

1. By ion-pair formation

$$XY + e^- \to X^+ + Y^- + e^-$$

2. By resonance attachment

$$XY + e^- \to XY^-$$

3. By resonance attachment with dissociation

$$XY + e^- \to X \cdot + Y^-$$

The probability of the first process, ion-pair formation, increases with increasing electron energy above the ionization threshold, giving rise to an ionization efficiency curve which resembles the curve for positive ions (Fig. 3-1) in shape. Process (2), resonance attachment, is, however, confined to a very narrow energy range, because the energy of the electron has to be high enough to lead to resonance capture of the electron, but not much higher, because otherwise too much kinetic energy is transferred to the molecule, which then may either undergo dissociation or form positive ions by the loss of one of its electrons. This process is discussed in Chap. 2. The ionization efficiency curve for negative ions [105] therefore exhibits a narrow first maximum at low electron energy due to the resonance attachment process and a broad second maximum due to dissociation and ion-pair formation.

Spectra of negative ions may be obtained principally in the same way as positive ions with a normal mass spectrometer after reversal of the potentials. The major difficulty lies in the extremely low yield of negative ions compared with positive ions, generally a factor of 10^3 lower. The study of negative ions is therefore hampered by the difficulty of obtaining spectra of reasonable intensity and the necessity of using high sample concentration in the ion source, requiring relatively large amounts of material which must have considerable vapor pressure. While the design of special ion sources permitting the use of an extremely intense electron beam combined with a high sample concentration in the ionization region gives reasonable ion currents,[106] the technique is not very useful in investigations of the kinds of problems we are concerned with here, namely,

[104] R. M. Reese, V. H. Dibeler, and F. L. Mohler, *J. Research Natl. Bur. Standards*, **57**, 367 (1956).

[105] J. Marriott and J. D. Craggs, "Applied Mass Spectrometry," Institute of Petroleum, London, 1954.

[106] M. Von Ardenne, *Z. angew. Phys.*, **11**, 121 (1959).

the identification, estimation, or determination of structure of organic molecules.

The proponents of negative-ion mass spectrometry frequently point to the fact that negative-ion spectra mainly consist of a peak due to the molecular ion and do not show fragmentation of the molecule.[107] Both these characteristics are said to be of particular advantage for the identification or characterization of organic molecules. While the determination of the molecular weight in such problems is of course very important, it may be deduced also from the usual (positive-ion) mass spectra. Furthermore, the few published negative-ion spectra of organic molecules other [108] than aromatic [107] or halogen-containing [109] compounds frequently show no peak for the molecular weight but fragments and also species of higher mass due to attachment of oxygen, hydroxyl, or other atoms or groups. The absence of fragmentation is of course an enormous disadvantage rather than an advantage if any insight into the structure of the molecule is to be gained. Any attempt to argue for the opposite indicates a considerable lack of understanding of the present state of positive-ion mass spectrometry of organic molecules.

The only area in which negative-ion spectroscopy has certain advantages is the investigation of polyhalogenated molecules, particularly fluorocarbons. Such substances have a higher tendency to form negative ions and give, in contrast to their completely absent positive molecular ion, a negative molecular ion which is of considerable intensity compared with the negative fragment ions. For problems concerning highly fluorinated compounds, the combination of positive- and negative-ion spectra has been shown to be very useful.[109]

[107] M. Von Ardenne, K. Steinfelder, and R. Tümmler, *Angew. Chem.*, **73**, 136 (1961).

[108] M. Von Ardenne and R. Tümmler, *Naturwissenschaften*, **45**, 414 (1958).

[109] J. Von Hoene and W. M. Hickam, *J. Chem. Phys.*, **32**, 876 (1960).

4. Additional Techniques

4-1. IDENTITY OF TWO COMPOUNDS

The complexity of mass spectra provides an almost ideal technique for proving the identity of two compounds. Not only do mass spectra contain a very large number of peaks, but also the intensity of these peaks is highly reproducible for both large and very small peaks, all of which may be measured with the same degree of accuracy. Comparison of mass spectra is, therefore, one of the most conclusive methods for proof of identity whenever the substances are suitable for mass spectrometry. A further advantage is the fact that very little material is required for such comparisons, of importance when the material to be compared is scarce. Also, the spectra of optically active substances and their racemates are identical, since in the gas phase there is, of course, no interaction between the D and L forms. This is particularly useful in the comparison of synthetic materials with a natural product, because it eliminates the necessity for resolution of the former.

The extreme sensitivity of the mass spectrometer may, however, turn into a disadvantage in such problems, because impurities present to only a small extent may suffice to change the spectrum to a degree that one can no longer consider it superimposable on the spectrum of the pure, authentic material. However, it may still be possible, in such a case, to subtract the spectrum of the pure sample from the contaminated one and show that the remaining spectrum is completely accounted for by a known substance, for example, a trace of solvent. The situation becomes even more complex if the two samples are contaminated with different materials. This may occur when the two substances are of different origin, for example, a synthetic compound containing a trace of starting material

162

which is to be compared with one obtained from natural materials, possibly containing a trace of a related compound. Careful and sometimes tedious purification of both samples will be necessary before a conclusive comparison can be made. It may be possible in such instances to deduce the nature of the impurities, determine their mass spectra on pure samples, and subtract these from the spectra which are to be compared.

Compounds of very low volatility sometimes have to be introduced into the inlet system at relatively high temperatures, with a resulting slight thermal decomposition, the products of which may give rise to spurious peaks. Since these decompositions are not easily reproduced, the mass spectra of two identical and pure compounds may show certain differences, particularly in the low mass range. If such is the case, it frequently suffices to compare the mass spectra in the region of higher masses if this region still represents the major part of the spectrum. Certain alkaloids, for example, are frequently of low volatility but have the most characteristic peaks at higher mass range (Chap. 8). Traces of degradation products may then be neglected.

If two mass spectra can be said to be identical in every respect (with the exception of the few cases just discussed), the two compounds are proved to be identical. This statement is correct in general, but a few points have to be kept in mind. Optical antipodes and also their racemates give identical spectra, as was indicated above. Certain stereoisomers, particularly aliphatic ones and cyclic stereoisomers which do not differ very much in the nonbonded interaction between groups (see Sec. 3-2D), give very similar or almost identical mass spectra. Conclusive proof by mass spectrometry of the identity of such substances is rather difficult, or sometimes impossible. Structural isomers, on the other hand, exhibit very different mass spectra, as would be expected on the basis of the discussion presented in Chap. 3. The only exceptions noted there were polysubstituted alkylbenzenes, differing in the point of substitution at the nucleus but not in the structure of the substituents (Sec. 3-2D). The great similarity of the mass spectra of the isomeric xylenes are a good example; the meta and para isomers are virtually indistinguishable. The mass spectra of positional isomers of heterocyclic compounds differ considerably, and the substances can be easily differentiated.

4-2. MIXTURES

Frequently one will be faced with the problem of interpreting the mass spectrum of a mixture which has been run on purpose, or unintentionally because it was thought to be a pure compound. It is of course important to recognize the presence of a mixture and to differentiate between the peaks belonging to the different components. Three types of mixtures will be most commonly encountered.

First, mixtures of isomers are most difficult to detect and to interpret, since the components will have the same molecular weight and their fragments will be of the same general type. If the substances present are structural isomers, one will reach a point in the interpretation when it becomes obvious that certain intense fragments are not compatible with only one structure. Such is the case, for example, if two fragments are

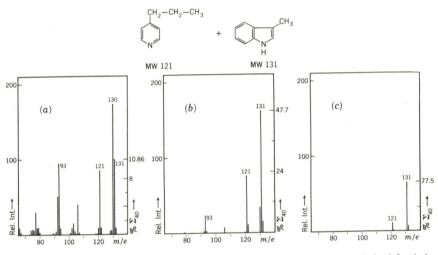

Fig. 4-1. Mass spectra of a mixture of 4-*n*-propylpyridine and 3-methylindole (*a*) with 70-volt electrons, (*b*) with 12-volt electrons (uncorrected), and (*c*) with 9-volt electrons. For all three ordinates, *m/e* 131 in (*a*) = 100.

found to contain different parts of the molecule while the sum of their masses exceeds the molecular weight. Unfortunately this often cannot be decided with certainty, and mixtures of isomers for which the mass spectra of the pure components are not available are difficult to interpret. Fractionation of the mixture, at least partially, is then required.

The second group of mixtures generally encountered, but somewhat easier to recognize, are those of homologs of a given class of compounds. Such mixtures are recognized by the presence of a considerable peak 14 mass units below the one thought to be due to the molecular weight, because the loss of 14 mass units (CH_2) is highly improbable. A strong peak 28 mass units below the molecular weight must not necessarily be a lower homolog of two carbon atoms less but may be a fragment formed by elimination of ethylene from the molecule via a rearrangement of Type *H*.

The third group of mixtures is composed of compounds of quite different type such as, for example, the product of a reaction taking more than one path. Such mixtures can, in general, be recognized by the appearance of peaks with mass differences which cannot possibly be due to an easily eliminated fragment. A molecular ion cannot easily lose less than 15 mass units but more than 3 mass units, for example, in a decomposition reaction which would be energetically so favorable as to lead to an intense fragment. A strong peak, obviously the molecular weight at mass 131, followed by another peak at mass 121 (Fig. 4-1*a*) thus indicates the presence of a mixture, like a methyl indole (C_9H_9N) and a pyridine substituted with alkyl groups totaling three carbon atoms ($C_8H_{11}N$), since the loss of 10 mass units from a molecule is impossible. It has to be kept in mind that there is always a possibility that neither one of the two peaks is the molecular weight and that both are fragments.

A. Characteristics of Mixtures

A number of techniques may be used to recognize the presence of a mixture and to deduce at least the major features of the mass spectra of the individual components. The extent of fragmentation of the molecules decreases with decreasing energy of the bombarding electrons, as discussed in Chap. 2, and it is thus possible to determine whether there is only one molecular species present and if not, what the molecular weights of the individual components of the mixture are. For this technique to be successful, it is of course necessary that these components exhibit a considerable peak for the molecular weight; otherwise the intensity of the spectrum obtained at 70 volts would merely be decreased. Compounds giving rise to certain very characteristic and intense peaks for particular fragments without appreciable intensity of the molecular ion may still be recognized in mixtures if the spectrum is determined with low-energy electrons and if there is reason to assume that the sample is composed of compounds of that type. A good example for such situations is the considerable amount of information obtained from the mass spectra determined with low-energy electrons of even complex mixtures of amino acid esters, as discussed in Chap. 7. The more general situation in which the molecular-weight peaks are used is illustrated in Fig. 4-1 exhibiting a mass spectrum of a mixture run at 70 ev and near the ionization potential. The presence of two different molecular species of mass 121 and mass 131 is clearly shown. It should be noted that the intensity of the spectrum determined with low-energy electrons is, of course, much smaller; but since the background and contributions of impurities are decreased to a considerable extent at the same time, the remaining small peaks of the compound become very significant. Increasing the ionizing current counterbalances, in part, the effect of the intensity of reduced electron energy.

Earlier in this section it was pointed out that a peak 28, 42, etc., mass units below the molecular weight does not have to be due to a lower homolog containing two, three, etc., carbon atoms less but may be due to a rearrangement peak of Type *H*. This can also be checked using a spectrum determined at low electron energy, because the appearance potential of such a fragment will be higher than the appearance potential of a lower homolog, which should be about the same as the compound with a few carbon atoms more. If the peak in question is such a rearrangement peak, its intensity will decrease more if the spectrum is scanned at lower and lower electron energy as compared with the intensity of the molecular-weight peak. If it is, however, really a lower homolog, the two peaks will become less and less intense at about the same rate. The peak at m/e 93 in Fig. 4-1a is therefore due to the loss of 28 mass units from the C_3 pyridine and not to the molecular ion of a picoline.

If a metastable peak is found, the mass of which indicates that two peaks are the initial ion and the fragment ion, respectively, of a one-step decomposition, then this is a very good indication that the two come from the same compound and are not due to dfferent components of a mixture, even though their masses would differ for an amount which could be the mass difference of two related molecules.

If a given spectrum is recognized to be due to a mixture, it becomes necessary to determine which peaks correspond to which components. If their nature is radically different, it is sometimes possible to recognize such a relationship from a single spectrum. For example, if one deals with one compound that contains a chlorine atom and a second component that does not, all fragments exhibiting the characteristic isotope ratio of chlorine must be due, of course, to the first and not to the second substance.

B. Fractionation

More frequently the situation is not such a fortunate one, and it is then necessary to fractionate the mixture in some way and to repeat the mass spectrum in which certain peaks will now have a considerably lower intensity than before. In that case they are due to the component lost preferentially in this fractionation process, while the peaks which are relatively enhanced belong to the compound which has been enriched. If one is able to find a single peak in each one of the two groups which is due to only one component while the other component does not contribute to its intensity, then it is possible to calculate the pure mass spectra of each one of the components in a two-component mixture.[1] Frequently a more qualitative consideration of the differences between the two spectra will enable one to identify the more intense and characteristic peaks of each component. The more complex the mixture is, the more difficult is this process, of course. The fractionation may be done either externally, before the sample is introduced into the mass spectrometer, or internally, i.e., while the sample of the mixture is still in the inlet system of the mass spectrometer.

The techniques available for external fractionation, such as the various types of chromatography and distillation, will be discussed in the section dealing with the pretreatment of the sample (Sec. 4-5). Here we will discuss only one technique which is in fact a more modified way of introducing the sample into the mass spectrometer, namely, fractionated distillation or sublimation into the inlet system. The sample in amounts sufficient for five to ten spectra is placed in the distillation tube discussed earlier (Fig. 2-7), the tube connected to the inlet system and evacuated while the bulb of the tube is cooled, if necessary. After evacuation, the temperature of the tube is raised slowly to permit the most volatile component to vaporize into the inlet system. When a sufficient sample pressure has been attained, the valve between reservoir and tube is closed and the mass spectrum scanned. After the pumping off of the sample, the process is repeated while slightly raising the temperature of the introduction tube.

In this manner a series of mass spectra is obtained, the first of which will be due predominantly to the most volatile component while the last one is due to the least volatile. The spectra of the pure components can be obtained if the difference in boiling point is a considerable one for the different components, but even for mixtures of homologs this technique provides sufficient fractionation to indicate clearly the qualitative and at least semiquantitative composition of the sample.

This technique may be illustrated by a case in which a presumably pure sample of a fatty acid turned out to be a mixture of homologs. On degradation, pithecolobine,[2] the elemental composition of which was

[1] S. Meyerson, *Anal. Chem.*, **31**, 174 (1959).
[2] D. E. Orr and K. Wiesner, *Chem. & Ind. London*, **1959**, 672.

for some time in doubt, yielded a fatty acid assumed to be possibly a branched C_{13} acid. Since the mass spectrum (Fig. 4-2a) of the sample showed peaks at mass 200, 214, and 228 but otherwise was consistent with the general appearance of normal fatty acids (Fig. 6-2), the presence of a mixture of homologs was suspected.

Fractionated introduction in the fashion described above gave a series of mass spectra; some of them are shown in Fig. 4-2b–d It can be seen that in the earlier fractions the peak at mass 200 is much stronger than the ones at 214 and 228, which become more and more prominent in the later fractions, with 228 the most persistent one. The peak at m/e 185 corresponds to loss of 15, 29, and 43 mass units from mass 200, 214,

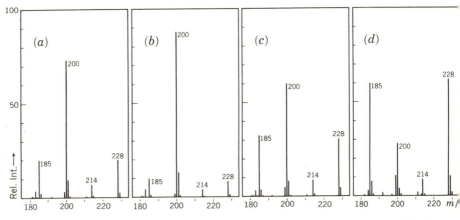

Fig. 4-2. Mass spectra of a mixture of lauric, tridecanoic, and myristic acid (mol.wt 200, 214, and 228, respectively) (a) introduced as such into the inlet system and (b)–(d) fractionated by slowly raising the temperature of the sample. Intensities in terms of the sum of mass 200, 214, and 228.

and 228, respectively. Since all the other peaks at lower mass numbers were consistent with the spectra of unbranched acids, it was assumed that there was present a mixture of lauric acid, tridecanoic acid, and myristic acid, which was then confirmed by determination of the spectra of authentic samples of those three acids. Furthermore, it was also possible to estimate the concentration to be about 75 per cent, 7 per cent, and 18 per cent, respectively. These findings, besides the implications regarding the structure of pithecolobine, at the same time explained the difficulties in the determination of the empirical formula of this compound which, in fact, was a difficult-to-separate mixture of homologs.

Another example of fractionated introduction of a mixture into the mass spectrometer will be discussed later (Sec. 7-1C) in connection with the determination of N^{15} in amino acids, for which it is of advantage to simplify the originally present very complex mixture in order to avoid certain interferences by some of the components.

It is, however, also possible to fractionate the mixture once it has been completely introduced into the inlet system. The equivalent of fractionated introduction is, of course, fractionated pumping out of the sample, which can be achieved if the vapor pressure of the components differs considerably. If one is dealing with a mixture of a compound of high molecular weight and some remaining solvent, the spectra obtained before and after quickly opening the pump valves of the inlet system will exhibit peaks for the solvent, which are very much decreased in intensity in the second run while the less volatile material will still give rise to peaks of considerable intensity. An extreme example is the background remaining after running a substance which is just on the border line of the volatility requirements.

A variation of this technique, partial recondensation of the sample, can be used if the sample has been introduced from the distillation tube (Fig. 2-7) or as a solid from a simple glass tube (Fig. 2-6). The mass spectrum of the entire sample is determined first. The valve to the sample tube is then opened and the tube cooled to room temperature or below, if necessary. The component of lower vapor pressure will recondense in the tube more efficiently than the component of higher vapor pressure, and a redetermination of the spectrum will then show more pronounced peaks for the more volatile component.

Finally, one may make use of the fact that a compound of lower molecular weight diffuses from the reservoir, through the leak, into the ion source faster than a compound of higher molecular weight, since the rate of effusion through a molecular leak is inversely proportional to the square root of the molecular weight (see Sec. 4-4). If the mass spectrum is redetermined after the sample has been in the inlet system for a considerable time ($\frac{1}{2}$ to 1 hr), the component of lower molecular weight is depleted more than the other, and the two mass spectra will exhibit these differences, which can then be interpreted in the same way as if any other fractionation technique had been used. This effect can be enhanced if the reservoir is made smaller by closing off part of the total volume of the inlet system (see Chap. 2).

It is obvious that the interpretation of mass spectra is much simpler for pure compounds than for mixtures. A careful separation before the spectra are obtained will always save considerable time and effort. In this discussion it has been shown, however, that valuable information can frequently be obtained with mixtures too, at least to an extent which makes it possible to arrive at a working hypothesis or to decide on a particular chemical or physical method for the separation of the mixture into the individual components.

4-3. FREQUENTLY ENCOUNTERED ARTIFACTS

The incidental co-isolation of some foreign material may sometimes result in spurious peaks in the spectrum and lead to confusion. Because of the small sample used for mass spectrometry such contamination, of no consequence in other experiments, may be serious. Some of these arti- facts occur more frequently and warrant a brief discussion.

Dioctylphthalate ("Octoil") is commonly used in the oil diffusion pump of the inlet system and may stream back into the reservoir. In that case its spectrum (Fig. 4-3) appears superimposed on the one of the

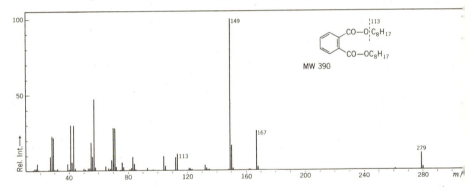

Fig. 4-3. Mass spectrum of "octoil" (dioctylphthalate).

sample. The presence of a peak at m/e 149 is always reason for sus- picion. This peak is accompanied by others at m/e 167 and m/e 279 (23 per cent and 10 per cent of the intensity of the 149 peak).

Loss of the alkyl chains, involving a Type H rearrangement with re- tention of an additional hydrogen (page 119), leads to the ion of m/e 279, which is followed by elimination of the other alkyl chain (Type H), producing an ion of m/e 167 and the further loss of H_2O to m/e 149:

$$m/e\ 279$$

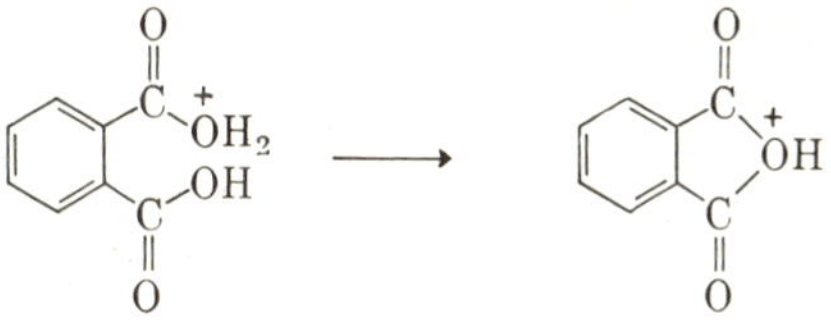

m/e 167 $\longrightarrow$ m/e 149

This fragmentation sequence is supported by metastable peaks at m/e 133.2 and 100.5 (calcd. 132.9 and 100.0). An intense peak at m/e 149 is thus characteristic for dialkylphthalates other than the dimethyl ester.[3,4] Dibutylphthalate, a plasticizer, is another occasionally encountered impurity giving rise to such a peak.

The wide use of *silicone compounds* both as lubricants and as stationary phase in gas chromatographs results in the frequent occurrence of silicones in samples prepared on a small scale (thus increasing the relative proportion of stopcock grease to reaction product) or collected from a "leaking" silicone column. Fortunately the characteristic isotope ratios of silicon (Table 3-2) make it easy to recognize its presence. A spectrum of silicone oil is shown in Fig. 4-4. Characteristic triplets of peaks at m/e 133 to 135, 207 to 209, 281 to 283, 355 to 357, and 429 to 431 are due to the species:[5]

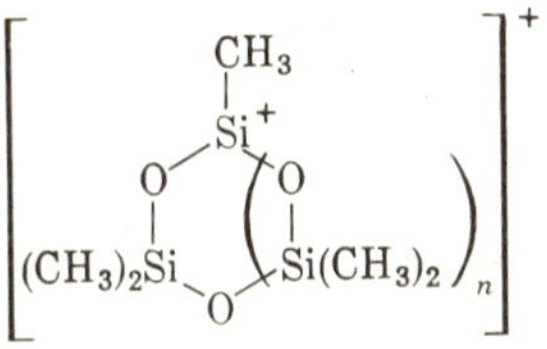

$A: n = 0, 1, 2, 3, 4, \cdots$

Two other series of peaks (B and C), also differing by 74 mass units from peak to peak, seem to be due to the following ions:

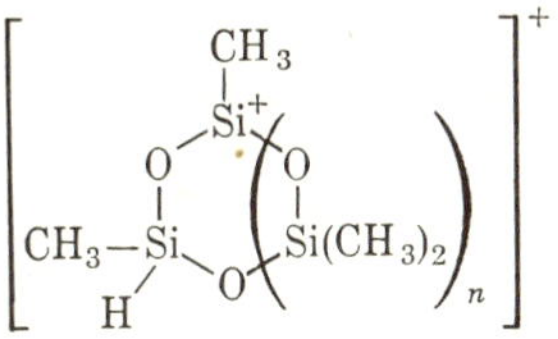

$B: n = 0, 1, 2, 3, 4, \cdots$

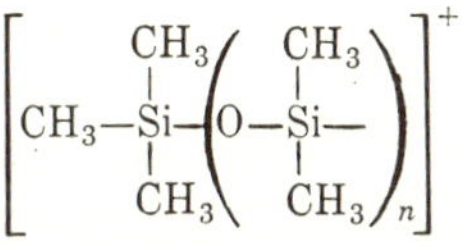

$C: n = 0, 1, 2, 3, \cdots$

[3] F. W. McLafferty and R. S. Gohlke, *Anal. Chem.*, **31**, 2076 (1959).
[4] E. M. Emery, *Anal. Chem.*, **32**, 1495 (1960).
[5] F. W. McLafferty, *Appl. Spectroscopy*, **11**, 148 (1957).

As a common plasticizer *tributylphosphate* is, for example, eluted by organic solvents or steam from plastic tubing. One of the characteristics of its spectrum (Fig. 4-5) is a peak at m/e 99 and the virtual absence of a peak at m/e 100. The fragment of mass 99 is due to $H_4PO_4^+$, arising

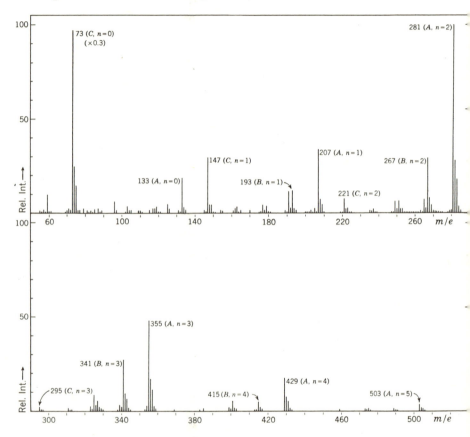

Fig. 4-4. Mass spectrum of the more volatile component of silicone grease.

from a rearrangement characteristic of trialkylphosphates.[6] The very low intensity of the isotope peak at m/e 100 is due to the low abundance of O^{17} and D; phosphorus is monoisotopic.

The major peaks in the spectrum are due to consecutive elimination of alkyl groups as olefins (Type H), the first one involving the additional retention of a hydrogen, similar to the decomposition of dialkylphthalates discussed earlier.

[6] A. Quayle, in J. D. Waldron (ed.), "Advances in Mass Spectrometry," p. 365, Pergamon Press, London, 1959.

Contamination with *hydrocarbon grease* leads to a spectrum exhibiting a peak at each mass number with decreasing intensity up to very high masses is an indication of the presence of high-molecular-weight hydrocarbons of different degrees of saturation. At higher masses these peaks show a definite grouping effect, namely, maximum height at intervals of 14 mass units, resulting in the spectrum's having a wavy appearance.

It is advisable to determine the spectra of the "leakage" of all the different types of gas-chromatography columns used in the laboratory.

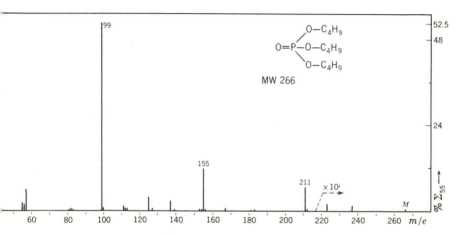

Fig. 4-5. Mass spectrum of tri-*n*-butylphosphate. (*From Ref. 6.*)

This helps in becoming familiar with prominent peaks due to such artifacts and prevents serious misinterpretations of mass spectra of gas-chromatographic fractions.

4-4. RATE OF EFFUSION

In Chap. 2 it was mentioned that the sample streams from the reservoir through a tiny hole into the ion source. If this leak is small enough, it will give rise to molecular flow for which Graham's law holds:

$$k_1 m_1^{1/2} = k_2 m_2^{1/2}$$

The rate of effusion (k_1, k_2) is inversely proportional to the square root of the mass (m_1, m_2). If all the requirements for molecular flow are fulfilled, e.g., that the diameter of the leak is at least ten times smaller than the mean free path of the particles, it is possible to determine the molecular weight of a compound by measuring the intensity of any one peak of the spectrum over a period of time. Since the peak height is proportional to the sample pressure in the ion source, which in turn is proportional to the pressure in the reservoir, the decay of the latter by effusion through the leak can be measured by monitoring the intensity of any peak. This technique has been suggested for determining the molecular weight by measuring the rate of decay (k_1) of a standard of mass m_1 and the rate (k_2) of the unknown m_2.[7] Reasonable values have been obtained for small molecules, such as acetone and the components of air, but the deviations from the calculated value were appreciable at higher molecular weight (e.g., $+$ 5 per cent for tetrachloroethane). This was shown [8] to be due to too large a leak, and much better results (up to mass 200) were obtained with a leak the diameter of which was less than one-tenth of the mean free path of even these large molecules.

Unfortunately, it is in the range of higher molecular weight that an auxiliary method for determining the molecular weight would be needed. Aside from the short mean free path, in these cases there are the problems of adsorption on the walls of both inlet system and ion source, back-streaming from the exhaust system, fluctuation in pumping speed, and sometimes slow decomposition of the compound. These factors introduce errors of such magnitude as to eliminate this technique for determining the molecular weight in most of the cases where it would be of practical importance. Exceptions may be substances of relatively low molecular weight not exhibiting a peak for the molecular ion. If this method is to be applied to any polar and/or relatively large molecule, a substance of similar type and size should be used as a standard—internal, if possible.

The relationship between rate of effusion and molecular weight may be used more reliably for differentiating between a pure compound and a mixture. A logarithm plot of the intensity of a number of selected peaks from spectra recorded in certain intervals versus time has to result in a set of parallel lines. Two such groups of lines are obtained for a two-component mixture if each one of the peaks selected originates from only one of the two compounds present, unless they are isomers.

The difference in effusion rate of 4-n-propylpyridine (mol. wt 121) and 3-methylindole (mol. wt 131) is reflected in the difference in the slopes of the broken lines and full lines in Fig. 4-6. These should be straight but are actually slightly curved owing, as discussed in the previous paragraph, to the nonideal conditions of the experiment. Frequently, some of the peaks will fall on lines of intermediate slope if both com-

[7] M. Eden, B. E. Burr, and A. W. Pratt, *Anal. Chem.*, **23**, 1735 (1951).

[8] P. D. Zemany, *J. Appl. Phys.*, **23**, 924 (1952).

pounds contribute to that peak. Both 4-*n*-propylpyridine and 3-methylindole exhibit a peak at m/e 77 which is more pronounced in the latter compound. The rate of decrease of this peak is thus more like m/e 131 and 103 than m/e 121, 106, and 93.

Although it often might not be possible to calculate the correct molecular weights for the reasons outlined earlier, such measurements indicate

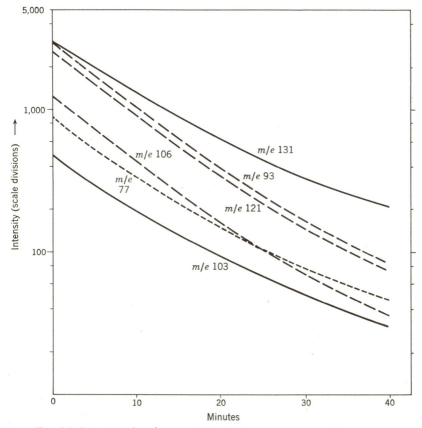

Fig. 4-6. Intensity of peaks versus time in the mass spectrum of a mixture.

which peaks originate from which component and thus aid in the interpretation. Because of the slow depletion of the sample from the large reservoir commonly employed, only part of it (e.g., the valve block) is used in such an experiment to decrease its duration. Care has to be taken not to confuse peaks due to a product formed by thermal decomposition with those due to a component of high molecular weight; the peaks of the former may appear to decay more slowly than the ones due to the undecomposed molecules, because the degradation products are continuously replenished while the original substance decays both by effusion and decomposition. Such is the case for the peak at m/e 84 in glutamic acid ethyl ester formed on electron impact both from the original molecule and from a product of thermal cyclization. The fragment of mass 84 is a very abundant one in the spectrum of the cyclization product (ethyl 2-pyrrolidone-5-carboxylate), and the corresponding peak therefore does not seem to decrease as fast as others. The reactions involved are discussed in more detail on page 267.

Finally, it should be pointed out that such leaking by molecular flow discriminates also against the species containing the lighter isotopes, leading to the accumulation of the heavier species in the reservoir. This effect must be considered in measuring the concentration of heavy isotopes (see Chap. 5).

4-5. CHEMICAL PRETREATMENT

A simple chemical reaction carried out on the compound to be investigated frequently makes it possible either to extend the area of applicability of mass spectrometry or to increase the amount of information obtainable from a spectrum. The choice of the most suitable reaction or derivative may become the decisive factor in the solution of a particular problem, and it is in these situations that a combination of the knowledge of organic reactions and of the resulting changes in the spectra becomes so important.

Chemical conversion may be required for one of the following reasons:

1. To increase the volatility of the substance
2. To degrade the substance to smaller molecules more suitable for mass spectrometry
3. To obtain additional information useful in the interpretation of the spectra
4. To obtain a derivative giving a more pronounced peak for the molecular ion

The reactions to be used should fulfill all or most of the following criteria:

1. They should be simple to carry out one-step reactions, or if involving more steps, they should not require the isolation and purification of intermediates.

2. They should proceed with high yield and without side reactions to give a pure product that does not require extensive purification.
3. They should be applicable to less than a milligram of material.
4. The group, if any, introduced into the molecule by the reaction should not increase the molecular weight beyond the convenient range; this is an important consideration in the case of polyfunctional substances.
5. The groups should not give rise to additional modes of cleavage of the molecule, unless the fragments thus formed are of value in the interpretation.

Since these reactions are used mainly on a very small scale, many of the considerations so important in synthetic organic chemistry may be disregarded. For example, expensive reagents may be used, even in large excess; an inert atmosphere is easily achieved by producing the reaction in a sealed ampoule filled with nitrogen; the reaction mixture may be worked up by gas chromatography after removal of part of the solvent; the product may be solvent-extracted, the solution transferred, after drying, to the distillation tube (Fig. 2-7), and the spectrum of the solute obtained by the technique discussed in Sec. 2-5A.

A. Derivatives of Increased Volatility

The presence of polar groups—such as hydroxyl, carboxyl, amido, sulfonic acid groups, cations and anions either in the form of zwitterions or actual salts—decreases the volatility of the substance and increases its tendency to become adsorbed on the inner surface of inlet system or ion source. Some of these groups make it even impossible to vaporize the sample into the mass spectrometer, and conversion of these groups into others not exhibiting this effect will be necessary (see, however, Sec. 7-3).

The order in which the groups are listed above roughly expresses the degree of polarity: While even quite large molecules containing only one hydroxyl group are sufficiently volatile to give good spectra, a small molecule containing both an acidic and a basic group, such as an amino acid, will not have sufficient vapor pressure, and the same will be true for small molecules with many hydroxyl groups, e.g., glucose. One will therefore quite easily acquire some experience in judging when chemical conversion to a more volatile derivative will be necessary.

A number of chemical reactions will be mentioned briefly which fulfill the requirements stated above and which have been used or may prove useful for the conversion of a compound to a more volatile derivative.

Most of these reactions and the experimental procedures are too well known to warrant detailed descriptions, and references will be given only to papers dealing with the application of less familiar reactions to a mass spectrometric problem. If necessary advanced texts in organic chemistry and the standard works of organic experimentation should be consulted, such as Wagner and Zook's "Synthetic Organic Chemistry," Weygand's "Preparative Organic Chemistry," Theilheimer's "Synthetic Methods of Organic Chemistry," Foerst's "Newer Methods of Organic Chemistry," Houben-Weyl's "Methoden der organischen Chemie," Adam's "Organic Reactions." Books dealing with the qualitative identification of organic compounds also contain procedures for the preparation of derivatives on a small scale, i.e., McElvain's or Wild's "Characterization of Organic Compounds" and Shriner and Fuson's "Systematic Identification of Organic Compounds."

Hydroxyl groups, alcoholic or phenolic, may be esterified or etherified, acetylation [Eq. (4-1)] or methylation [Eqs. (4-2) and (4-3)] being the preferred reactions:

$$R-OH + (CH_3CO)_2O \xrightarrow{\text{Pyridine or } H_2SO_4} R-OCOCH_3 + CH_3COOH \qquad (4\text{-}1)$$

$$R-OH \text{ (phenols only)} + CH_2N_2 \longrightarrow R-OCH_3 + N_2 \qquad (4\text{-}2)$$

$$R-OH \text{ (phenols only)} + (CH_3)_2SO_4 \xrightarrow{OH^-} R-OCH_3 + CH_3SO_4H \qquad (4\text{-}3)$$

Some other functional groups also react with these reagents: Primary and secondary amines are acetylated by the anhydride used in the reaction in Eq. (4-1), unless performed in the presence of mineral acid. Diazomethane, a reagent preferred because of the simplicity of the procedure, gives rise to many side reactions—addition to triple and double bonds forming pyrazoles and pyrazolines, respectively; the reaction with carbonyl compounds to give higher homologs; methylation of amino groups, particularly when protonated. In addition, carboxyl groups are quantitatively esterified, a useful reaction [Eq. (4-8)] discussed later. Methylation of phenols with dimethyl sulfate [Eq. (4-3)] may lead to methylation (or quaternization) of additionally present amino groups. This may be prevented if trimethylanilinium hydroxide is used:

$$R-OH \text{ (phenols only)} + C_6H_5\overset{+}{N}(CH_3)_3 \xrightarrow{OH^-} R-OCH_3 + C_6H_5N(CH_3)_2 \quad (4\text{-}4)$$

This reaction was, for example, used [9] to convert sarpagine, a phenolic alkaloid, into a more volatile derivative (Chap. 8).

[9] K. Biemann, *J. Am. Chem. Soc.*, **83**, 4801 (1961).

A convenient reaction is the formation of trimethyl silyl ethers from phenols and alcohols on treatment with hexamethyldisilazane:

$$2R-OH + [(CH_3)_3Si]_2NH \longrightarrow 2R-OSi(CH_3)_3 + NH_3 \qquad (4\text{-}5)$$

These silyl ethers are well suited for mass spectrometry,[10] as they have a lower boiling point than the hydroxyl compound and give characteristic fragments such as a strong $M - 15$ peak exhibiting the silicon isotope ratios (Table 3-2). Gas chromatography can be employed for the isolation, purification, and separation of these derivatives. For mass spectrometric purposes silylation has been applied as yet only to alcoholic and phenolic hydroxyl groups and to one mercaptan.[10] It should be pointed out, however, that the reagent also converts free carboxyl and amino groups into silyl derivatives.[11] These silyl amines and esters are, however, very sensitive to water and hydrolyze very easily to the amines and acids.

Removal of the hydroxyl group is another possible way to eliminate its effect on the polarity of the compound. Conversion of an alcohol to the tosylate [Eq. (4-6)] or halide [Eq. (4-7)] followed by reduction with lithium aluminum hydride has been used for this purpose. Lithium alumi-

$$R-OH \xrightarrow[\text{in pyridine}]{(p)\ CH_3C_6H_4SO_2Cl} R-OSO_2-C_6H_4CH_3(p) \xrightarrow{LiAlH_4}$$

$$R-H + HSO_3-C_6H_4CH_3(p) \qquad (4\text{-}6)$$

$$R-OH \xrightarrow{SOCl_2} R-Cl \xrightarrow{LiAlH_4} R-H \qquad (4\text{-}7)$$

num deuteride is employed if the position of the hydroxyl group removed in this process is to be marked [9,12,13] (see Secs. 5-3B and 7-2).

Because of steric hindrance and ease of elimination it is not conveniently possible to acylate or remove a tertiary hydroxyl group by the reactions mentioned above. Fortunately, such a hydroxyl group contributes less to the polarity of a compound than do primary and secondary ones. Silylation [Eq. (4-5)] of tertiary alcohols is possible.[10]

Reduction of tosylates with Raney nickel leads to the elimination of phenolic hydroxyl groups. Specific replacement of these groups with deuterium cannot always be achieved by carrying out this reduction in the presence of D_2, because exchange of hydrogen for deuterium may take place simultaneously in other parts of the molecule. Catalytic desulfurization of cysteine with deuterated Raney nickel and D_2 in D_2O

[10] A. G. Sharkey, R. A. Friedel, and S. H. Langer, *Anal. Chem.*, **29**, 770 (1957).

[11] R N. Teeter. (Personal communication.)

[12] K. Biemann and M. Friedmann-Spiteller, *Tetrahedron Letters*, no. 2, p. 68, 1961; *J. Am. Chem. Soc.*, **83**, 4805 (1961).

[13] K. Biemann and W. Vetter, *Biochem. Biophys. Research Comm.*, **3**, 578 (1960).

led to the incorporation of up to four atoms of deuterium attached to carbon when performed in basic solution, while only one deuterium atom was introduced when alkali was omitted.[14]

Free carboxyl groups may be esterified with diazomethane [Eq. (4-8)], alcohol, and dry hydrogen chloride [Eq. (4-9)] or by conversion to the acid chloride followed by treatment with an alcohol [Eq. (4-10)].

$$R-COOH + CH_2N_2 \longrightarrow R-COOCH_3 + N_2 \qquad (4\text{-}8)$$

$$R-COOH + R'-OH \xrightarrow{\text{Dry HCl}} R-COOR' + H_2O \qquad (4\text{-}9)$$

$$R-COOH \xrightarrow{\text{SOCl}_2} R-COCl \xrightarrow{R-OH} R-COOR' \qquad (4\text{-}10)$$

The reaction in Eq. (4-8) is the most convenient one, as it requires only the addition of an ethereal solution of diazomethane to the free acid followed by evaporation of the solvent, leaving the ester behind. The variety of side reactions which may lead to a product other than the methyl ester of the original acid was pointed out earlier in this section. This reaction is thus most suitable for acids lacking other functional groups.

The safest reaction is, in general, acid-catalyzed esterification [Eq. (4-9)]. Treatment with thionyl chloride [Eq. (4-10)] may lead to the formation of anhydrides from dicarboxylic acids, to similar dehydrations, or to the formation of halides from alcohol groups [Eq. (4-7)].

Amides may be reduced to amines with lithium aluminum hydride; even polyamides can be made sufficiently volatile by reduction to polyamines: [15]

$$R-CONH_2 \xrightarrow{\text{LiAlH}_4} R-CH_2NH_2 \qquad (4\text{-}11)$$

Hydrolysis of the amide to the free acid followed by esterification [Eqs. (4-8) to (4-10)] is an alternative unless the amide group connects two parts of the molecule (as is the case in peptides).

Sulfonic acids are very polar and have to be esterified via the acid chloride:

$$R-SO_3H \xrightarrow{\text{PCl}_5} RSO_2Cl \xrightarrow{\text{CH}_3\text{OH}} RSO_3CH_3 \qquad (4\text{-}12)$$

Salts have to be converted into the free acid or base, whichever is to be investigated. This may be done in the conventional way, e.g., extraction of the acid with an organic solvent after acidification of an aqueous

[14] Unpublished experiments from the author's laboratory (by W. Vetter).
[15] K. Biemann, F. Gapp, and J. Seibl, *J. Am. Chem. Soc.*, **81**, 2274 (1959).

solution of the salt, or by a similar process for the isolation of the base. The solution obtained can be used as such, following the technique outlined in Sec. 2-5A. If only a very small amount of the salt is available, it is converted into the free base by heating it in a sealed evacuated ampoule with a base of low volatility, such as triphenylmethylamine. The more volatile amine can then be introduced directly into the mass spectrometer, using the techniques discussed on pages 25 or 298. The free acids may be produced by treating the salt with toluenesulfonic acid.

In zwitterionic molecules either the acidic or the basic group has to be removed to make even small molecules amenable to conventional techniques of introduction. Esterification of the acid group is the most convenient technique, and because of the reactivity of amino groups toward diazomethane mentioned earlier, esterification with alcohol and dry hydrochloric acid [Eq. (4-13)] is to be preferred. The hydrochloride of the ester is formed first and has to be converted to the free base. A technique which permits the isolation of the ester on a small scale, even if it is a somewhat unstable one, is discussed in Chap. 7.

$$R-\underset{\underset{NH_3^+}{|}}{CH}-COO^- + R'OH \xrightarrow{H^+} R-\underset{\underset{NH_3^+}{|}}{CH}-COOR' \xrightarrow{Base} R-\underset{\underset{NH_2}{|}}{CH}-COOR \quad (4\text{-}13)$$

The chemical conversions discussed above are useful, sometimes imperative, if the sample is to be introduced into a reservoir from which it streams, through a leak, into the ion source. Such conversions are not so necessary if the compound can be introduced directly into the ion source (Sec. 2-5E). Mass spectra of compounds normally existing as zwitterions have been obtained (Sec. 7-3), and even the spectra of both the acid and the base moiety of a salt can be obtained, provided both are volatile. The hydrochlorides or picrates of amines, for example, dissociate frequently without decomposition upon heating, thus leading to useful spectra.[15a]

B. Deliberate Degradation of the Molecule

An increase in size of the molecule leads inevitably to lower and lower volatility (with the exception of polyhalogenated compounds, which may have very high molecular weights and still be rather volatile). Removal of functional groups is then of little help, and degradation into smaller molecules is required. This may be done by a specific cleavage of the molecules, such as hydrolysis of an ester in a case where both the acid (in the form of the methyl or ethyl ester) and the alcohol are sufficiently

[15a] K. Biemann and J. A. McCloskey, *J. Am. Chem. Soc.*, **84** (1962).

volatile while the original ester is not. Partial hydrolysis of large peptides to small ones is another example.

More frequently employed is the deliberate pyrolysis of the compound, particularly in the case of polymers, the specific chemical degradation of which is difficult; this technique permits the identification of the monomeric units of which the substance exists. Extensive investigations of polymers have been carried out at the National Bureau of Standards by Madorsky et al.[16] One of the first examples was the pyrolysis of polystyrene followed by identification of the various fractions obtained by mass spectrometry. Styrene and a mixture of oligomers were obtained at 300 to 400° pyrolysis temperature. Such experiments are simplified if the pyrolysis of the material is done in a furnace located near the ionization chamber, eliminating the need for collection of the various fractions.[17] Polyethylene, polyvinylchloride, polyphenyl, and rubber have been pyrolyzed by this technique. The largest ion observed from rubber had a mass of 1,087.

Pyrolysis of the sample on a hot wire was employed by Zemany for the characterization of various polymers including Teflon, silicone gum, and also pepsin and albumin.[18] The products volatile at room temperature were investigated, which permitted the characterization of only the small fragments formed.

C. Chemical Conversions Aiding in the Interpretation of the Spectrum

Sometimes the mass spectrum is too complex to permit a conclusive interpretation in the absence of additional information. It is in such cases very helpful to perform a simple chemical reaction on the sample and to determine the spectrum of the substance before and after this reaction. From the differences in the two spectra, combined with a knowledge of the nature of the reaction used, one is frequently able to derive a considerable amount of information regarding the structure of the original molecule.

Reduction. The number of double bonds present in a molecule is usually determined by catalytic hydrogenation of a sample and accurate measurement of the volume of hydrogen gas consumed. By a mass spectrometric determination of the molecular weight before and after hydrogenation, the number of hydrogen atoms added and therefore the number of double bonds which are reduced under the conditions employed are determined. Of course, it is then not necessary either to weigh the sample

[16] S. L. Madorsky and S. Straus, *J. Research Natl. Bur. Standards*, **40**, 417 (1948).
[17] P. Bradt and F. L. Mohler, *J. Research Natl. Bur. Standards*, **55**, 323 (1955).
[18] P. D. Zemany, *Anal. Chem.*, **24**, 1709 (1952).

accurately or to measure gas volumes, to permit the determination of the number of double bonds with very small samples. Furthermore, if hydrogenation does not easily go to completion or does not cease because of the presence of other groups which are reduced very slowly, it is difficult to correlate the amount of hydrogen gas consumed with the exact number of double bonds present. If this is the case, the reduction product will be a mixture, but it is nevertheless possible to determine the molecular weight of the major component formed from the mass spectrum. Relatively large amounts of catalyst are used in such microhydrogenations, and saturation of the double bond occurs relatively fast. Figure 4-7a shows

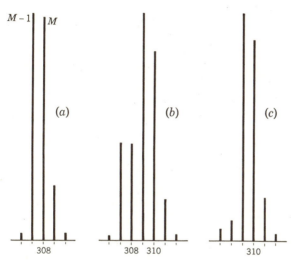

Fig. 4-7. Changes in the mass spectrum upon hydrogenation of an unsaturated compound. (See text for details).

the mass spectrum of O-methyldeoxysarpagine [19] in the region of its molecular weight [$C_{20}H_{24}N_2O$, mol. wt 308; for the structure of sarpagine see formula (10) in Chap. 8]. Two milligrams of this compound were hydrogenated, and after 10 and 25 min, respectively, one-tenth of the solution was withdrawn and evaporated. The mass spectrum of the residues shows the presence of a dihydroderivative of mol. wt 310 in the first sample (Fig. 4-7b) and complete reduction of the double bond in the second (Fig. 4-7c). After an extended period of time the reduction of the indole system became noticeable because of the presence of a peak at mass 312. The first mass spectrum had already shown the presence of only one double bond, which can easily be reduced.

[19] K. Biemann, *Tetrahedron Letters*, no. 15, p. 9, 1960.

Chemical reduction of heteroaromatic compounds has been used [20] for the purpose of resolving a complex mixture of homocyclic and hetero-cyclic aromatics found in petroleum distillates. Comparison of the mass spectrum of the mixture before and after treatment with tin and hydro-chloric acid, reaction conditions whereby heterocyclic aromatic rings are reduced, permitted the more accurate quantitative estimation of these compounds (mainly pyridines and quinolines) in very complex mixtures. The interference of fragment peaks of the nitrogen-containing compounds due to loss of an alkyl group with molecular-ion peaks of nitrogen-free aromatics of corresponding carbon number (e.g., both the M^+ peak of toluene and the $M - 15$ peak of ethylpyridine appear at m/e 92) is elim-inated upon reduction.

More detailed information regarding the structure of a compound may be obtained by its conversion into a molecule of quite different type, which then undergoes a different fragmentation, particularly at bonds at which the original compound is not split. In this manner much more in-formation can be obtained from these two compounds than from either one alone. An example of this type is the determination of the structure and size of alkyl chains attached to polyalkylpyrazines (1).[21] In such a molecule all side chains are necessarily attached to a carbon atom next to an aromatic nitrogen.

Such alkyl chains do not undergo simple fragmentation at the C_α—C_β bond because of the unfavorable carbonium ion formed (see page 134). Rather they are eliminated as an olefin molecule (rearrangement of Type H) if the side chain is at least three carbon atoms long. This peak indi-cates the total number of carbon atoms remaining with the pyrazine nucleus, but nothing can be learned regarding their attachment either to the ring or to C_α.

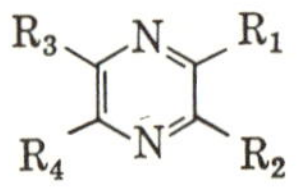

(1)

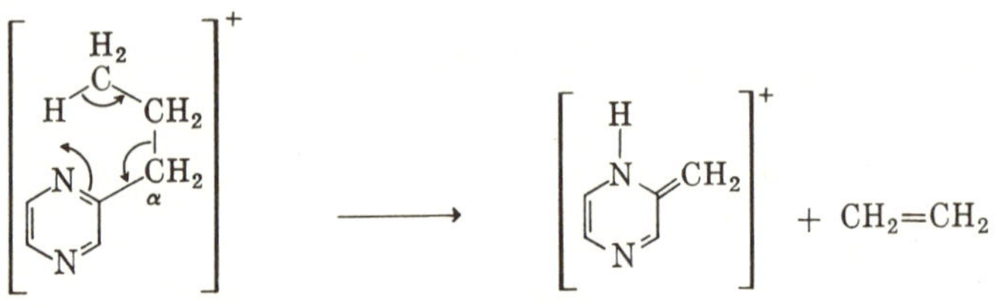

[20] C. La Lau, *Anal. Chim. Acta,* **22,** 239 (1960).
[21] K. Biemann and J. Seibl. (Unpublished.)

A pyrazine of mol. wt 150 exhibiting such a rearrangement peak at m/e 122 (Fig. 4-8a) must contain a C_3 side chain plus two additional carbon atoms, but a number of isomers are possible:

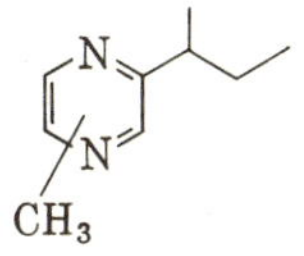

CH_3

(3 isomers, 2a, 2b, 2c)

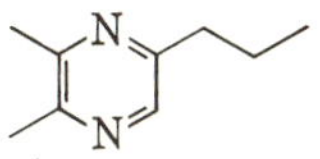

(2d)

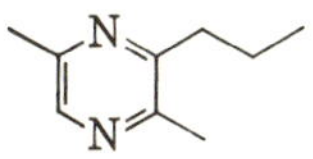

(2e)

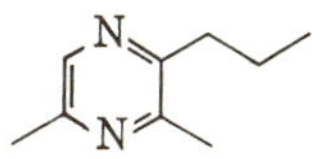

(2f)

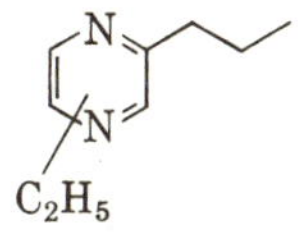

C_2H_5

(3 isomers, 2g, 2h, 2i)

Catalytic reduction of the compound with platinum in acetic acid results in the formation of a piperazine (3)

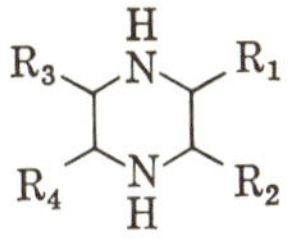

(3)

in which the alkyl groups are then attached to saturated carbon atoms next to an amino group, facilitating the loss of any one of the alkyl groups by simple cleavage (Type B). The loss of 43 mass units (Fig. 4-8b), which gives rise to the peak at mass 113, indicates the presence of a C_3 side chain and thus the absence of alkyl substituents at C_α. The remaining two carbon atoms must be present as methyl groups attached to the ring because of the absence of an $M - 29$ peak (loss of C_2H_5) and the presence of an $M - 15$ peak; the pyrazine in question is thus a dimethyl-n-propylpyrazine.

The fragmentation of the piperazine ring permits further differentiation between two of the three possible isomers, as it was found on the basis of a large number of spectra of polyalkylpiperazines that there were always peaks at mass $44 + 14n$ due to fragmentation of the piperazine ring itself, accompanied by rearrangement of one hydrogen atom. It was shown by deuteration experiments to be the one attached to the other nitrogen, and the following mechanism is proposed for its formation:

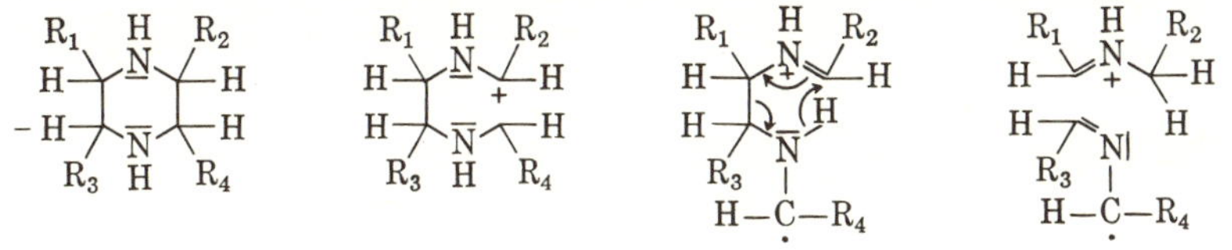

The mass of this fragment indicates the sum of alkyl substituents on this particular half of the piperazine ring. Such a peak is present at m/e 100 (Fig. 4-8b), indicating the attachment of four carbon atoms to this part of the molecule, i.e., the propyl group and one methyl group. The next highest peak of this kind ($C_nH_{2n+2}N$) is found at m/e 58, support-

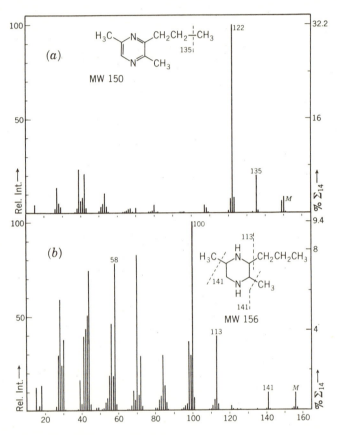

Fig. 4-8. Mass spectra of (a) 2,5-dimethyl-3-n-propylpyrazine and (b) 2,5-dimethyl-3-n-propylpiperazine.

ing the conclusion that there is one methyl group attached to the lower half of the ring. This eliminates isomer ($2f$) and narrows the choice to two possible pyrazines, ($2d$) and ($2e$). The mass spectrum shown in Fig. 4-8a was in fact obtained from a sample of ($2e$), and the corresponding piperazine is therefore represented by (3), ($R_1 = CH_3CH_2CH_2$, $R_2 = R_3 = CH_3$).

This principle is obviously applicable to other aromatic systems as well. The hydrogenation can be done with very small samples, and the products may be isolated by gas chromatography, thus making even minute amounts of material accessible.

More drastic reduction has been suggested for the determination of the position of alkyl substituents on thiophenes, namely, reductive desulfurization to hydrocarbons, the structure of which is indicative of the substitution pattern of the molecules.[22]

Oxidation. Just as the increase in molecular weight on hydrogenation, or the resulting change in the fragmentation of the molecule, can be used to obtain further structural information, so is it possible to use oxidation for principally the same purpose. The number of hydrogen atoms lost on oxidation would, for example, indicate the number of primary or secondary alcohol groups present because of their conversion to a carbonyl group.

Similarly, the change in fragmentation behavior which accompanies the conversion of an alcohol to a ketone is of value in the interpretation of certain spectra. The rearrangement of Type *H* occurring in ketones may give some insight regarding the extent of substitution at a carbon atom next to the carbinol group if the alcohol is oxidized to the ketone.

Number of Reactive Sites in a Molecule. Just as it is possible to determine the number of double bonds by saturation with hydrogen, one can also determine, for example, the number of carboxyl groups present in the molecule by esterification with two different alcohols. The mass difference between a compound obtained on esterification with methanol and that obtained with ethanol will always be $14 \times n$, where n is the number of carboxyl groups undergoing esterification. As esterification is frequently used to make complex carboxylic acids sufficiently volatile for mass spectrometry (Sec. 4-5A), it is very convenient to use this approach whenever the number of carboxyl groups present are in doubt. It is, of course, important to keep in mind that one actually determines the number of groups capable of reacting with a molecule of alcohol and simultaneous elimination of a molecule of water.

Similarly, the alkylation of amino groups gives an indication of the number of replaceable hydrogen atoms bound to nitrogen. Since in most cases it is possible to determine the mass spectrum of the free amino compound, it is not necessary to use two different alkylating agents in separate experiments. The simplest reaction is methylation, and since the formation of quarternary ammonium compounds has to be avoided, reductive

[22] I. W. Kinney and G. L. Cook, *Anal. Chem.*, 24, 1391 (1952).

alkylation using formaldehyde and a reducing agent (hydrogen and a catalyst or sodium borohydride) is the most convenient reaction: [23]

$$R—NH_2 + 2CH_2O \xrightarrow[\text{or NaBH}_4]{\text{Pd/H}_2} R—N(CH_3)_2$$

This technique will be outlined on a more complex problem, namely, the determination of the *N*-terminal amino acid in polypeptides or proteins. Although there are well-established chemical methods available for obtaining this information, it should be of advantage to have an additional technique at hand for at least any such cases in which the chemical methods give inconclusive results or need to be corroborated. The only disadvantage, if any, of those methods is the partial or complete destruction of the marked amino acid, in certain cases, upon hydrolysis of the peptide after reaction.

Alkylation of the free amino group produces dimethyl amino acid derivatives, which even on very drastic hydrolytic treatment do not lose these alkyl groups. Upon reaction of the polypeptide (4) with formaldehyde and sodium borohydride, one obtains compound (5), in which the *N*-terminal amino acid has been converted into a dimethyl derivative. Hydrolysis of the peptide leads now to a mixture of amino acids, one of which (in the case of an unbranched peptide chain) will be a dimethylamino acid (6).

$$
\begin{array}{cccccc}
R_1 & R_2 & R_3 & & R_{n-1} & R_n \\
| & | & | & & | & | \\
H_2NCHCO—&NHCHCO—&NHCHCO&\text{-------}&NHCHCO—&NHCHCOOH
\end{array}
$$

(*N*-terminal)   (4)   (*C*-terminal)

$$
\begin{array}{ccc}
& R_1 & R_2 & R_n \\
& | & | & | \\
(4) + 2CH_2O \xrightarrow{\text{NaBH}_4} (CH_3)NCHCO—&NHCHCO&\text{------} & NHCHCOOH \xrightarrow{H^+}
\end{array}
$$

(5)

$$
\begin{array}{cc}
R_1 & R_{2\text{-----}n} \\
| & | \\
(CH_3)_2NCHCOOH + & H_2NCHCOOH
\end{array}
$$

(6)

The mass spectrum of the ethyl ester of such a compound will reveal its nature because the major fragment of this dimethylamino ester is now found 28 mass units higher than the amine peak (see Sec. 7-1) of the corresponding primary amino ester (see Fig. 3-14). This peak can be spotted in the mass spectrum of the mixture of amino esters obtained on esterification of the total hydrolyzate if compared with a mixture of such

[23] W. Vetter and K. Biemann. (To be published.)

esters obtained from the unmethylated peptide. At least semiquantitative measurements are required if amino acids differing by C_2H_4 (e.g., alanine and valine) are present in the original peptide.

To facilitate the identification of the dimethylamino ester in the spectrum of a complex mixture, it is more convenient to use deuteroformaldehyde (CD_2O), which therefore introduces CD_2H groups into the amino group:

$$R_1$$
$$|$$
$$(CD_2H)_2NCHCOOH$$

The mass of the amine peak of such a deuteromethylamino ester is 32 mass units higher than the corresponding peak in the unalkylated amino ester, if the latter contains one NH_2 group.

Although this technique was originally designed for the particular purpose of end-group determination in polypeptides, it can of course be used for the determination of the number of free amino groups present in a molecule and perhaps also for locating the amino group within the molecule by its correlation with a certain peak in the mass spectrum. This approach will be preferable to the one outlined in Sec. 5-3A, namely, exchange of the hydrogens attached to nitrogen by deuterium, because the introduction of D_2O into the mass spectrometer may lead to complications in the use of the instrument for other purposes shortly thereafter (see Sec. 5-3A).

If there is present in the molecule a group which can be made to react with a halogenating agent, it is convenient to introduce bromine or chlorine at that point. Because of the characteristic doublets exhibited by fragments containing one of these halogens, it is easy to see which fragments of the molecule do contain the group that has reacted. Bromination of an aromatic ring in a complex molecule may be used to "label" that part of the molecule.

Degradation to a Hydrocarbon. The removal of all functional groups from the compound to determine the structure of the basic carbon skeleton present in the molecule has been discussed in Sec. 3-2A. The desulfurization of thiophenes mentioned above also falls into this group of reactions.

D. Derivatization to Increase the Intensity of the Molecular-ion Peak

For the determination of the molecular weight itself, but even more so for the estimation of the number and amount of stable isotopes incorporated into a molecule (Chap. 5), it is necessary that such a mass spectrum exhibit a peak of reasonable intensity due to the molecular ion. In Sec. 3-1A the factors leading to a high stability and therefore high abundance of the molecular ions, and vice versa, were discussed. This intensity is, for example, rather low for alcohols, while it is much higher for the corresponding ketones (see 3-nonanol versus 3-nonanone in Table 3-1). Oxidation of a secondary alcohol to a ketone thus appreciably increases the abundance of the molecular ion and makes it easier to determine the molecular weight of the alcohol, which would be 2 mass units higher. Oxidation can easily be achieved by treatment with chromic acid in pyridine:

$$R_1-\underset{\underset{OH}{|}}{C}H-R_2 \xrightarrow[\text{in pyridine}]{CrO_3} R_1-\underset{\overset{\|}{O}}{C}-R_2$$

It has also been pointed out that aromatic compounds are able to stabilize the molecular ion and that the conversion of an aliphatic substance into an aromatic derivative frequently is accompanied by the desired effect. Conversion of butyric acid into butyranilide

$$CH_3(CH_2)_2COOH \xrightarrow[\text{(2) } C_6H_5NH_2]{\text{(1) } PBr_3} CH_3(CH_2)_2CONH-\hspace{-0.3em}\langle\bigcirc\rangle$$

was used for the determination of the number of deuterium atoms in the acid.[24] Butyric acid itself shows only a very small peak at mass 88, and its high tendency to form an "$M + 1$" peak made any isotope determination impossible (Sec. 5-2B). The anilide, on the other hand, gives a very intense peak at its molecular weight and has very little tendency to form an "$M + 1$" peak.

E. Derivatives Used for Separation

In the chemical separation of very complex mixtures into groups of components use is frequently made of reagents converting a specific functional group to a derivative which can be separated more easily. These derivatives are then also used for the identification of the original substance on the basis of their physical constants, if they are known.

If the derivative is sufficiently volatile, the mass spectrum can be used for identification. For example, 3,5-dinitrobenzoates are useful for the isolation of alcohols from mixtures. These derivatives can be separated by paper chromatography [25] and are also quite volatile.

In Fig. 4-9 the mass spectrum of this derivative of 2-heptanol is shown.

[24] Unpublished experiments from the author's laboratory (by T. E. Dickelman).
[25] E. Sundt and M. Winter, *Anal. Chem.*, 29, 851 (1957).

The peaks at m/e 75, 103, 149, and 195 are characteristic for the dinitro-benzoyl group and are thus present in all these derivatives.[26] The molec-ular-weight peak is always small, but the presence of an $M - 30$ peak (loss of NO) helps to establish the molecular weight of the dinitroben-zoate and therefore of the alcohol. The elimination of dinitrobenzoic acid leads to an olefin-type fragment the mass of which necessarily corresponds to the molecular weight of the alcohol minus 18 mass units (m/e 98).

Fragmentation of the C—C bond next to the ester group (Type B) leads to characteristic peaks from which the position of the hydroxyl group of the alcohol can be deduced.

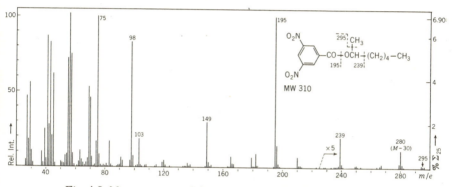

Fig. 4-9. Mass spectrum of the 3,5-dinitrobenzoate of 2-heptanol.

Obviously the same or more information can be obtained from the mass spectrum of the alcohol itself, and one will use it whenever possible. If, however, its isolation and purification involve such a derivative and paper chromatography, not enough material will be available to permit hydrolysis to the alcohol and its isolation. In such cases the spectrum of the derivative itself becomes very useful.

F. Physical Pretreatment

For the separation of mixtures prior to the introduction of the sample into the mass spectrometer, a number of physical tools may be used. The technique most ideally suited for combination with mass spectrometry is gas chromatography; its major applicability lies also in the field of compounds with a certain volatility, and one can safely state that any compound which survives passing through a high-temperature gas chro-matographic column without decomposition will be amenable to mass spectrometry. The experimental techniques employed have been dis-

[26] Unpublished experiments from the author's laboratory.

cussed earlier (Sec. 2-5C and D). A number of applications involving complex molecules of low volatility will be discussed in Chaps. 7 and 8.

Besides this method, most other chromatographic separation techniques can be used in a more or less direct combination with the mass spectrometer.

In the preparative separation of a mixture by aluminum oxide chromatography it may sometimes be of advantage to check the composition of certain fractions by mass spectrometry.

The individual fractions of a mixture separated by paper chromatography or paper electrophoresis may be eluted from the paper and subjected to mass spectrometry.[27] One difficulty encountered in other techniques, such as IR spectroscopy when used on substances eluted from paper—namely, the co-elution of components of the paper (hemicelluloses?)—interferes much less in the determination of the mass spectrum because of the nonvolatility of those substances. Particularly in the work with amino acids and peptides, separation of certain components by paper electrophoresis was frequently employed as an auxiliary tool.[14]

In a similar way, one may use fractions separated by thin-layer chromatography[27] by merely scraping off the adsorbent in the region of the plate where the compound is suspected and introducing the powder as one would a solid sample (Sec. 2-4). The volatile material sublimes into the mass spectrometer, while the solid support remains in the tube. It is, of course, important in such cases not to use adsorbents containing starch or other organic materials which would produce volatile decomposition products. Alternatively, the compound may be eluted with a suitable solvent and the resulting solution evaporated in the sample-introduction tube (Fig. 2-6 or 2-7). Blank experiments are advisable to avoid misinterpreations due to artifacts introduced with the support or the solvents.

Particularly for preliminary studies many of these simple separation techniques are very useful and lead to interpretable mass spectra.

4-6. HIGH-RESOLUTION MASS SPECTRA

To this point in our discussion we have considered only the approximate mass of a particle in integral mass numbers. This was done without difficulty, since all the atomic weights of pure isotopes are very close to integral numbers, which is also true for polyatomic arrangements of considerable size. In addition, the mass differences between adjacent peaks are always about 1 mass unit.

[27] Unpublished experiments from the author's laboratory.

However, if the mass of a given species is determined with considerable accuracy, it is found that it is, of course, not quite an integral number and furthermore that species of different elemental composition have slightly different masses, even though they have the same nominal mass. The exact mass of a species $C_{16}H_{22}O_2$ is 246.1620, while the mass of $C_{17}H_{26}O$ would be 246.1984, a difference of 0.0364 mass unit. Beynon recognized the potentialities of accurate mass measurement in the qualitative analysis of organic materials, using a single focusing mass spectrometer in his first experiment.[28] Such instruments can be used to obtain mass spectra of considerable resolution, particularly if the radius of deflection is large, but double-focusing mass spectrometers (see Sec. 1-2E) are more useful for this purpose and are now becoming commercially available.

Almost all the work done on the high-resolution mass spectra up to the present time stems from Beynon's laboratory and is discussed in his book.[29] Performance data of his instrument over a period of years have been presented recently.[30] Part of a spectrum determined with such an instrument is shown in Fig. 4-10.

In addition to the intrinsic resolving power of the instrument, one needs a method that permits the accurate measurement of the mass of a given particle. This can be achieved in one of three ways:

1. In a magnetic deflection instrument it should, in principle, be possible to measure both the magnetic field and the accelerating potential with high accuracy and compute the mass, using Eq. (1-1), after initial calibration of the instrument. Too many instrumental changes can take place, however, and it is therefore much more convenient and reliable to keep the magnetic field constant during the measurement, and measure the accelerating potential required to bring into focus the ion whose mass is to be measured. After repeating the measurement of the accelerating potential for an ion of known mass, the mass of the unknown species can be calculated by using Eq. (1-1). If the two masses differ for less than about 10 per cent of their absolute mass, quite accurate measurements can be obtained. (For one of the commercially available instruments an accuracy of 1 part in 100,000 is claimed.[31]) The accuracy may be even higher if a close but still resolved doublet of the same nominal mass can be meas-

---

[28] J. H. Beynon, *Nature,* **174,** 735 (1954).

[29] J. H. Beynon, "Mass Spectrometry and Its Applications to Organic Chemistry," Elsevier Publishing Company, Amsterdam, 1960.

[30] J. H. Beynon, in R. M. Elliott, "Advances in Mass Spectrometry," vol. II, Pergamon Press, London, 1962.

[31] R. D. Craig and G. A. Errock, in J. D. Waldron (ed.), "Advances in Mass Spectrometry," Pergamon Press, London, 1959.

ured, one peak of which is the known standard and the other one, the unknown species. It will be virtually always necessary to add a compound of known composition to the sample in order to produce a reference peak of accurately known mass.

2. Instead of accurately measuring the accelerating potential required to bring each one of the two peaks into register, the exact difference of these potentials can be measured electronically by the so-called "peak-matching technique" originally used by Nier for atomic mass determina-

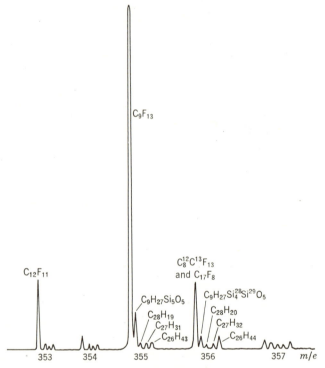

Fig. 4-10. Resolved multiplets in the region of mass 355. (*From Ref. 30.*)

tions.[32] The principle used in this method is that of employing the saw-tooth-like pulsing of the accelerating potential and display of the output signal of the collector on an oscilloscope; the peak will appear on the screen of the oscilloscope. If a square wave is superimposed on the pulse in such a manner that the sweep of the accelerating potential alternately starts at different values, two peaks will be shown on the screen which can be made to coincide if the difference in potential at the beginning of the alternate scans is equal to the difference in the accelerating potentials required to bring the two peaks into focus. Accurate measurement

[32] K. S. Quisenberry, T. T. Scolman, and A. O. Nier, *Phys. Rev.*, **102**, 1071 (1956).

of this potential difference can be expressed in terms of difference in mass, and the mass of the unknown ion may thus be calculated.

3. A radically different approach can be used with the Mattauch type of double-focusing mass spectrometer (see Fig. 1-6), which focuses all masses in one plane, in which a photographic plate is placed. The species of different mass are recorded as parallel lines, the distance of which varies linearly with the square root of their mass. With an accurate comparator it is possible to measure distances on the plate with high precision. Furthermore, the resolving power of photoplate detection is higher than the resolution attainable with an electronic detector, because no collector slit is necessary and the particles will produce separate lines as long as the ion beam is at all resolved while with electronic recording of two species two completely separated peaks will be obtained only if they are separated for more than the width of the slit.

There seem to be a number of additional advantages in using a photographic plate for the simultaneous recording of the entire mass spectrum under the highest possible resolution. If the spectrum of a compound of unknown structure is to be determined, no prior knowledge is available as to which peaks will have to be used later in the interpretation. All this information is recorded on the plate at once, whereas it would take a very long time to scan the entire spectrum under the highest resolution, a process also requiring a large amount of sample. The necessary mass measurements can then be made at leisure using a comparator, while the mass spectrometer is used for another sample. If a conventional record is desired, the lines can also be scanned with a recording microdensitometer at any time.

A small portion of such a spectrum,[32a] obtained in a preliminary experiment with a mixture of benzylbenzoate [(66), Chap. 3] with n-$C_{16}H_{34}$, is shown in Fig. 4-11. Figure 4-11a is an enlargement of the region of m/e 160 to 170. The exposure time was about three times longer for the upper set of lines. The separation of the center of each member of the doublet at m/e 168 was found to correspond to 0.1002 mass unit on the basis of their distance on the plate. The heavier particle must be $C_{12}{}^{12}H_{24}$ from the saturated compounds. The lighter ion is thus $C_{12}{}^{12}C^{13}H_{11}$, establishing the absence of oxygen in this fragment (see page 139). An automatic recording of the density of part of the lower set of lines is shown in Fig. 4-11b. It should be remembered that, in contrast to direct electronic recording, the height of the peaks is here not directly proportional to the abundance of the ions.

[32a] The author is indebted to R. Howard for providing the plate with the spectrum, which was taken on a CEC 21-110 mass spectrometer.

The integrating properties of the photoplate make it possible to use very small samples introduced directly into the ion source, as most of the difficulties otherwise encountered with these problems, namely, the fast decay of the sample and the fluctuations in its pressure (Secs. 2-3 and 2-2), do not change the relative intensities of the lines when recorded simultaneously.

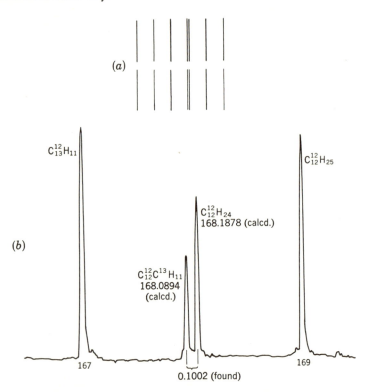

Fig. 4-11. (*a*) Part of a line spectrum (enlarged 9 times) obtained with a double-focusing mass spectrometer; (*b*) recording of the density of the doublet and adjacent lines. (For further details see text.)

Finally, most of the disadvantages of this method of recording are related to the difficulties in accurately measuring the density of the lines produced in the emulsion (i.e., the abundance of the ion). Fortunately, this is frequently unnecessary for an interpretation of the spectrum in terms of the structure of the compound, particularly since the accurate measurement of the intensity of the isotope peaks for the determination of the elemental composition (Sec. 3-1B) is made unnecessary by the much more reliable measurement of the accurate mass of the species.

The advantages of accurate mass determination for the interpretation of the mass spectrum are obvious. Knowledge of the empirical formula and not just the molecular weight decreases the number of possibilities to be considered at the outset. The compound of mass 246.1984, discussed on page 193, contains only one oxygen atom and therefore cannot possibly be a carboxylic acid or an ester, for example. With a resolving power of about 7,000 a mixture of $C_{16}H_{22}O_2{}^+$ and $C_{17}H_{26}O^+$ gives rise to two completely separated peaks and is thus easily recognized. In an actual experiment one would not deal with this particular doublet but rather with one of the two peaks and a peak of a reference compound which, if derived from a hydrocarbon, would be $C_{18}H_{30}$ of mass 246.2348. The resolving power indicated above is still required to resolve this reference peak from the species $C_{17}H_{26}O$, but half this resolution would only be necessary to distinguish it from $C_{16}H_{22}O_2$. In addition, it should be pointed out that it is, of course, not necessary to resolve the two peaks completely as long as the maximum of both can be identified in the unresolved doublet.

For many other species of the same nominal mass, however, a considerable resolving power is required to get at least a clearly visible shoulder as a doublet. To decide between $C_{17}H_{26}O$ and a fragment $C_{16}H_{24}NO$ (mass 246.1858), it is necessary to differentiate between a mass difference of 0.036 and 0.049 mass unit when comparing them with the $C_{18}H_{30}$ calibration peak. The distinction between most of the masses due to different elemental composition generally encountered in organic molecules should be possible with the now commercially available double-focusing mass spectrometers, which should have a clear resolution of at least 5,000. The measurement of mass can then be achieved with an accuracy of about 1 part in 60,000 [30] without difficulty, given reasonably good operation of the electronics of the instrument. Thus, ions differing by 0.005 mass unit at mass 300 could be distinguished. Although there are possible atomic combinations which differ less, most of these would be excluded on other grounds as, for example, consideration of the intensities of isotope peaks, which are much less prone to be in error due to contamination of the sample, because the impurity would have a quite different elemental composition in most cases. A brief interpretation of the mass spectrum and the elemental composition of smaller fragments frequently will also eliminate certain possibilities of the elemental composition of the molecule.

By the use of the above-mentioned peak-matching technique, accuracy in mass determination of a hundred times the clear resolution of the instrument is said to be possible.[29] It should, however, be pointed out that it is the mass difference of well-separated peaks only that can be determined with such high accuracy, while a doublet differing in mass for a factor of 1 in 500,000 of course cannot be resolved. Some of the smallest mass differences are encountered in combinations containing heavy isotopes; for example, the mass difference $CH - C^{13}$ is only 0.004471 mass unit. The difference between the mass of the molecular ion of mass 250 and the C^{13}-isotope peak of the fragment produced by loss of a hydrogen from the molecule would differ only for 1/55,750 of the total mass of the species, and the resolution of this doublet would be rather difficult. It is fortunate that in most cases the resolution of such peaks is of no great interest, unless one is concerned with molecules labeled with stable isotopes, which would make the differentiation between such species highly desirable.

Aside from the determination of the elemental composition of the molecule itself, one can of course also determine the elemental composition of fragment ions. Because their mass is necessarily lower, the resolving power required will be lower, but on the other hand more combinations will have to be considered, because many of the restrictions for the elemental composition of stable molecules do not, of course, hold for fragments formed upon electron impact.

The elemental composition of fragments, is, however, limited by the composition of the molecule from which they are derived. Multiplets of the same nominal mass frequently need not be measured accurately. For example, a doublet in the mass spectrum of compounds consisting of carbon, hydrogen, and only one oxygen atom has to be due to an ion containing C, H, and O (the ion of lower mass) and another one consisting of C and H only (found at slightly higher mass). The mass difference, 0.036 mass unit, need not be measured to arrive at this conclusion.

A mass spectrum determined with high resolution suffers less interference from impurities, and the spectra of mixtures consisting of compounds with quite different elemental composition should be much easier to interpret. Quantitative analysis of mixtures are facilitated for the same reason.[33] Peaks due to impurities, if their identity is known, may even facilitate the measurement of the mass of a species belonging to the major component, and the use of an internal mass scale, by deliberately adding a suitable substance, will considerably facilitate mass identification.

While a knowledge of the elemental composition of the fragments unquestionably aids in the interpretation of the mass spectrum, this

[33] E. G. Carlson, G. T. Paulissen, R. H. Hunt, and M. J. O'Neal, *Anal. Chem.*, **32**, 1489 (1960).

aspect seems sometimes to be overemphasized, particularly by those who are little acquainted with the problems arising in the interpretation of mass spectra. The accurate mass measurement indicates the number of carbon, hydrogen, nitrogen, and oxygen atoms retained in the fragment, but the major problem is the decision as to which of the carbon atoms originally present in the molecule are being retained in this particular fragment, and this, of course, cannot be decided by accurate mass measurement. Furthermore, the elemental composition of a fragment is not infrequently determined by its nominal mass, and the presence of other atoms like sulfur, chlorine, or bromine may be deduced from the characteristic isotope peaks. It is, however, difficult to make any generalizations in this respect. The mass spectra of aliphatic esters [34] have been interpreted correctly on the basis of low-resolution spectra as evidenced by a recent reinvestigation with a high-resolution mass spectrometer,[35] while on the other hand, the much simpler molecule, trimethylhydrazine, for which a detailed fragmentation mechanism based upon appearance potential measurements had been proposed,[36] was shown on the basis of the high-resolution mass spectrum [37] to give some quite unexpected fragments upon electron impact.

A combination of both techniques, namely the use of a single-focusing mass spectrometer for routine determination of the mass spectra and a double-focusing instrument for accurate measurement of the mass of certain peaks, might be the most powerful and most economical approach. In addition, labeling with stable isotopes will frequently be required to clarify many of the remaining details in a proposed fragmentation mechanism, or for the determination of the structure of a complex organic molecule.

4-7. IONIZATION AND APPEARANCE POTENTIALS

A. Basic Considerations

In Sec. 3-1 it was stated that a molecular ion is formed whenever the impinging electron transfers to the molecule an amount of energy equal

[34] A. G. Sharkey, Jr., J. L. Shultz, and R. A. Friedel, *Anal. Chem.*, **31**, 87 (1959).

[35] J. H. Beynon, R. A. Saunders, and A. E. Williams, *Anal. Chem.*, **33**, 221 (1961).

[36] V. H. Dibeler, J. L. Franklin, and R. M. Reese, *J. Am. Chem. Soc.*, **81**, 68 (1959).

[37] J. H. Beynon, R. A. Saunders, and A. E. Williams, *J. Am. Chem. Soc.*, **82**, 288 (1960).

to the ionization potential of this molecule. Furthermore, cleavage of a bond will occur if the energy transferred exceeds the ionization potential.[38]

Thus the ionization of a molecule XY requires merely the energy Q_i necessary for removal of an electron:

$$XY + Q_i = XY^+ + e^-$$

while for fragmentation, sufficient energy must be available to break the X—Y bond and to remove one electron from the fragment which becomes ionized. The appearance potential A of the ion X^+ is thus equal (or greater if the particles are formed with excess energy W) to the sum of the dissociation energy D of the bond X—Y and the ionization potential I of X to X^+:

$$A_{X^+} = D_{XY} + I_X + W$$

The excess energy W is frequently very small and can then be neglected. The equation holds only if I_X is smaller than I_Y.[39] In such a case X^+ is most preferably formed, and any Y^+ must arise by a different, more complex fragmentation process.[38b]

Electron-impact methods have therefore played an important role in the determination of ionization potentials and bond strength, because they permit one of the most direct measurements of these quantities (1 ev = 23.05 kcal/mole).

B. *Experimental Techniques*

One of the major difficulties, however, is the accurate determination of the potential itself. Both because of the relatively wide energy spread of a beam of electrons emitted from a hot filament and because of the presence of an electric field in the usual ion sources, the electrons may have energies differing up to ±1 ev from the mean energy of the beam. This fact leads to the tailing of the ionization efficiency curve shown in Fig. 3-1. It is somewhat difficult to choose the correct value from such data, and a number of ways have been suggested.

1. Selection of the potential at which the ion is first detectable ("initial-break method")[40]

[38] For a detailed discussion of this subject, see (*a*) F. H. Field and J. L. Franklin, "Electron Impact Phenomena," Academic Press, Inc., New York, 1957; (*b*) M. Krauss, A. L. Wahrhaftig, and H. Eyring, *Ann. Rev. Nuclear Sci.*, **5**, 241 (1955).

[39] D. P. Stevenson, *Discussions Faraday Soc.*, no. 10, p. 35, 1951.

[40] L. G. Smith, *Phys. Rev.*, **51**, 263 (1937).

2. Extrapolation of the linear part of the descending curve ("linear extrapolation method")[41]

3. Extrapolation to zero-ion current of the difference between the potentials required to produce the same abundance of the ion in question and an ion of known appearance potential ("extrapolated-difference method")[42]

4. A semilog plot of abundance of the ion versus electron energy, which results in a straight line ("critical-slope method"),[43] a technique that seems to be preferred by most workers in this field

Most of these difficulties are avoided if a nearly monoenergetic electron beam is used, and this can be accomplished[44] by determining the abundance of the ions produced with a beam from which the electrons of lower energy have been "filtered off" by a "retarding potential" on a grid placed between filament and ionization region. The difference in abundance obtained with two slightly differing retarding potentials (V_r' and V_r'') will correspond to an energy spread of only $V_r' - V_r''$.

To obtain an absolute value it is necessary to calibrate with a compound of known ionization potential (commonly Ar or Kr), using it, if possible, as an internal standard.

C. Use in the Interpretation of Spectra

The eminent importance of accurate appearance-potential measurements in the determination of bond dissociation energies or in physical-chemical investigations has been pointed out above, but this application will not be discussed here. Instead, the structural information derivable from ionization and appearance potentials will be illustrated in a few examples.

As the ionization potential of organic molecules varies widely (for example, 13.1 ev for methane[38a] and 7.6 ev for anthracene[45]), it should be possible to determine the class to which a compound belongs from its ionization potential. For example, a quite detailed conclusion regarding the substitution patterns of a benzene derivative could be made, as it was shown[46] that the electron-donating power of substituents influences the

[41] R. H. Vought, *Phys. Rev.,* **71,** 93 (1947).

[42] J. W. Warren, *Nature,* **165,** 810 (1950).

[43] R. E. Honig, *J. Chem. Phys.,* **16,** 105 (1948).

[44] R. E. Fox, W. M. Hickam, D. J. Grove, and T. Kjeldaas, *Rev. Sci. Instr.,* **26,** 1101 (1955).

[45] M. E. Wacks and V. H. Dibeler, *J. Chem. Phys.,* **31,** 1557 (1959).

[46] G. F. Crable and G. L. Kearns, Mass Spectrometry Conference, Chicago, June, 1961.

ionization potential (Table 4-1) and that these effects are additive and follow Hammet's σ^+ constant.[46]

Whether this effect will in fact be utilized more than occasionally remains to be seen, since other methods (UV, IR, NMR) are available and yield the same information in a much simpler way. Another application is the differentiation between isomers, one of which would have a lower ionization potential or contain a weaker bond than the other. This has

Table 4-1. Ionization Potentials of Substituted Benzenes [46]

Compound	Electron volts	Compound	Electron volts
Benzene	9.56	p-Bromotoluene	9.22
Toluene	9.18	p-Chlorotoluene	9.21
o-Xylene	9.04	Phenol	9.16
m-Xylene	9.05	p-Bromophenol	9.04
p-Xylene	8.99	o-Cresol	8.93
1,3,5-Trimethylbenzene	8.74	m-Cresol	8.98
Styrene	9.00	p-Cresol	8.97
Aniline	8.32	Methoxybenzene	8.83
Nitrobenzene	10.18	o-Nitroaniline	8.66
Benzonitrile	10.09	m-Nitroaniline	8.80
p-Nitrotoluene	9.82	p-Nitroaniline	8.85
p-Tolunitrile	9.76	o-Methylaniline	8.38
o-Dichlorobenzene	9.64	m-Methylaniline	8.27
Chlorobenzene	9.60	p-Methylaniline	8.14
Bromobenzene	9.52	o-Benzenediamine	8.00
p-Nitrophenol	9.52	m-Benzenediamine	7.96
o-Chlorophenol	9.28	p-Benzenediamine	7.58
p-Chlorophenol	9.07	p-Methoxyaniline	7.82

been suggested [47] for the differentiation of α- and β-glycosidic linkages in carbohydrates, where the former was found to give a lower value (for example, 14.2 ± 0.2 ev for the $C_6H_{11}O_5{}^+$ ion from maltose versus 14.7 ± 0.2 ev from cellobiose). A careful and critical investigation of this phenomenon would be desirable, as it could lead to valuable additional information.

In practice, however, one will always make use of the generally higher abundances of ions formed in a process requiring only small amounts of energy, which to a large degree reflects the ionization and appearance potential.

[47] P. A. Finan, R. I. Reed, and W. Snedden, *Chem. & Ind. London,* 1958, 1172.

One more important use of these potentials is in the formulation of fragmentation processes following electron impact. Two examples should be mentioned. For the removal of hydrogen from a methanol molecule two processes are to be considered:

1: $$CH_3OH \xrightarrow{-e^-} CH_3O^+ + H\cdot$$

2: $$CH_3OH \xrightarrow{-e^-} {}^+CH_2OH + H\cdot$$

On the basis of the appearance potential (11.8 ± 0.1 ev) of this ion and the known bond dissociation energies of C—H and O—H, process 1 was eliminated in favor of process 2, which involves the resonance form ($CH_2{=}O^+{-}H$) of the (CH_2OH)$^+$ ion discussed in Sec. 3-2A.[48]

Similarly, the postulated tropylium-ion structure of the C_7H_7 from alkylbenzenes is supported by arguments of this kind and resolved the problem of the "abnormal" appearance potential of the benzyl ion ($C_6H_5CH_2^+$).[49]

[48] C. S. Cummings and W. Bleakney, *Phys. Rev.*, **58**, 787 (1940).

[49] P. N. Rylander, S. Meyerson, and H. M. Grubb, *J. Am. Chem. Soc.*, **79**, 842 (1957).

5. The Mass Spectra of Isotopically Labeled Molecules

5-1. PRINCIPLE

The value of labeling techniques for the investigation of chemical or biological reaction mechanisms is too well known to need any further elaboration. While for many such experiments radioactive isotopes are preferred because their concentration may easily be measured by various counting techniques, stable isotopes frequently have to be used for various reasons. For their detection mass spectrometry is the only method available (with the exception of the measurement of the deuterium content of water). In most instances the molecule containing the stable isotope is degraded to small gaseous molecules, the isotope content of which is then measured in an isotope-ratio mass spectrometer (see Sec. 1-2F). This technique is generally known and need not be discussed here. This chapter will be devoted entirely to the detection and determination of stable isotopes in the intact molecule.

In addition to studies of mechanisms, isotopically labeled molecules are of interest for the determination of the structure of compounds into which a stable isotope can be introduced specifically by a reaction of known mechanism.

To solve such problems information is required for four general purposes: (1) to recognize the presence of a heavy isotope in the molecule; (2) to determine the concentration of a heavy isotope in the molecule;

(3) to determine the number of such stable isotopes incorporated into the molecule; and (4) to follow any changes in isotopic composition of a compound in the course of a chemical reaction.

The discussion in Chap. 3 on the relationship between the structure of a molecule and its mass spectrum makes it rather obvious that the incorporation of a heavy isotope will result in certain specific changes in a mass spectrum because the mass of a given particle is increased if a light atom is replaced by a heavy isotope. The shifts in mass will, of course, correspond to the mass difference between the two isotopes, and this difference will be multiplied by the number of such heavy isotopes present in this particular molecule or fragment.

Ordinary methane exhibits an intense peak at mass 16, the molecular ion, and peaks of decreasing intensity at masses 15, 14, 13, and 12 due to the loss of one to three or four hydrogen atoms. A small peak at mass 17 is due to naturally occurring C^{13} and D. If one hydrogen atom is replaced by deuterium, the most abundant peak will shift to mass 17, and others will be found at mass 16, 15, 14, 13, and 12 that are due to the loss of hydrogen or deuterium in any combination from H to H_3D. The small isotope peak at mass 18 would still be present, since the concentration of C^{13} has not changed, but the peak will be slightly lower, since there are only three hydrogen atoms left, one of which may be an additional deuterium atom. Dideuteromethane would have its most abundant peak at mass 18, and tetradeuteromethane gives rise to such a peak at mass 20. This molecule will now exhibit fragment peaks only at mass 18, 16, 14, and 12, because all that can be lost is one, two, three or four deuterium atoms. In Table 5-1 the mass spectra of $C^{12}H_2D_2$, $C^{12}HD_3$, and $C^{12}D_4$ are compared with the spectrum of $C^{12}H_4$. Since these are corrected for the naturally occurring isotopes, the peaks due to species containing C^{13} are not shown in the table.

Various points are illustrated by this simple example: the number of deuterium atoms present in the molecule can be deduced from the mass of the molecular-weight peak; an equimolar mixture of nondeuterated methane and tetradeuterated methane will give a mass spectrum very different from that of dideuterated methane, although the total content of deuterium in both samples is the same; the appearance of the mass spectrum of a partially deuterated molecule will be quite different from that of the ordinary molecule, because the number of fragments possible is greatly increased while the mass spectrum of a completely deuterated compound is again rather similar to the spectrum of the ordinary molecule with the exception of the wider spacing of the peaks; and, finally, fragment peaks of the labeled species may interfere with the molecular-weight peak of the unlabeled one.

Table 5-1. Mass Spectra of Deuterated Methanes *

$C^{12}H_4$			$C^{12}HD_3$		
Ion	m/e	$\% \Sigma_1$	Ion	m/e	$\% \Sigma_1$
H	1	3.19	H	1	0.96
H_2	2	0.15	D	2	0.87
C	12	1.16	HD	3	0.51
CH	13	3.72	D_2	4	0.04
CH_2	14	7.38	C	12	1.08
CH_3	15	39.00	CH	13	0.67
CH_4	16	45.30	CD	14	3.00
			CHD	15	3.17

$C^{12}H_2D_2$			CD_2	16	6.20
			CHD_2	17	24.00
Ion	m/e	$\% \Sigma_1$	CD_3	18	13.00
			CHD_3	19	46.95
H	1	2.00			

$C^{12}D_4$		
H_2, D	2	0.56			
HD	3	0.08	Ion	m/e	$\% \Sigma_2$
D_2	4	0.02			
C	12	1.08	D	2	1.40
CH	13	1.27	D_2	4	0.10
CH_2, CD	14	2.90	C	12	1.05
CH_3, CHD	15	4.44	CD	14	3.53
CH_2D, CD_2	16	13.93	CD_2	16	6.00
CHD_2	17	28.32	CD_3	18	39.84
CH_2D_2	18	45.38	CD_4	20	48.00

° Determined at 70 ev; corrected for C^{13}. Per cent Σ values calculated from *Mass Spectral Data*, API Project 44, serial nos. 455–457.

A somewhat more complex situation is shown in Fig. 5-1, in which part of the mass spectra of butadiene, partially deuterated butadiene, and tetradeuterobutadiene are presented. From the peaks at m/e 58 in both *b* and *c* of Fig. 5-1 it can be inferred that both samples contain tetradeuterobutadiene (the peaks at mass 59 in both spectra are about 4.4 per cent as intense as the peaks at mass 58 and are, therefore, due only to the natural abundance of C^{13} and not to pentadeuterobutadiene). It is, however, impossible to conclude whether or not there are present molecular species of lower deuterium content because of the peaks present at mass 57 and below, although the high peak at mass 56 in Fig. 5-1*b* would seem to indicate the presence of an appreciable amount of less deuterated material.

Even the subtraction of the contributions of the fragments due to the loss of one through six hydrogen atoms from the molecular ion as indicated by the mass spectrum of undeuterated butadiene is impossible, since there is no reason to assume that the probability of loss of hydro-

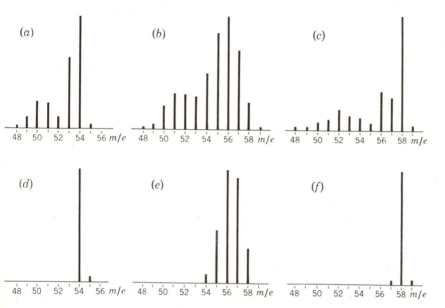

Fig. 5-1. Mass spectra of butadiene. (*a*) Undeuterated; (*b*) partially deuterated; (*c*) mainly 1,1,4,4-tetradeuterated butadiene, using 70-volt electrons; (*d*) to (*f*) same as *a* to *c*, using 9.5-volt electrons. Relative intensities in terms of the highest peak in each group.

gen would be exactly equal to the probability of loss of deuterium. That such is definitely not the case has been found in many instances, some of which have been discussed by Stevenson.[1] It was shown that hydrocarbons, for example, if partially deuterated, had a higher tendency to lose hydrogen than deuterium,[2] an effect borne out also by the data in Table 5-1. For example, statistical loss of H or D from CHD_3 would lead to a peak at m/e 17 (CHD_2) with three times the intensity of the peak at m/e 18 (CD_3) while it is found to be only 1.85 times as intense.

[1] D. P. Stevenson and C. D. Wagner, *J. Chem. Phys.*, **19**, 11 (1951).
[2] F. L. Mohler and V. H. Dibeler, *Phys. Rev.*, **72**, 158 (1947).

If the molecular ion of the compound to be investigated tends to lose one or more hydrogen atoms, a process which would interfere in a simple analysis of such substances, then it is necessary to prevent this fragmentation from occurring. For this purpose the spectrum is determined at an electron energy sufficient for the production of molecular ions, but not of these fragments.[1] This technique applied to our sample of butadiene produces the spectra shown in Fig. 5-1d through f. At an electron energy of about 9.5 volts butadiene still produces a peak due to the molecular ion of appreciable intensity, while the abstraction of one or more hydrogen atoms no longer occurs. The spectrum is thus very much simplified; i.e., it contains only the peaks of the molecular species at mass 54 and 55. A spectrum determined on isotopically labeled material will also consist only of peaks due to the individual molecular species and not to fragments, since both the ionization potential of the molecule and the appearance potential of the fragments do not appreciably change on isotopic substitution.[1] Figure 5-1f indicates that this sample is almost entirely tetradeuterated, containing only a small amount of trideuterated impurity, while the absence of pentadeuterated butadiene is shown by the fact that the peak at mass 59 is of the same relative intensity as the peak at mass 55 in nondeuterated butadiene.

Returning to Fig. 5-1e now makes possible the calculation of the individual concentration of the various deuterated butadiene molecules present in this sample. Since all these peaks are due to molecular ions, it is necessary merely to correct for the abundance of heavy molecules due to the presence of C^{13}. This can be done by applying the correction factor obtained from the intensity ratios of the peaks at mass 54 and 55 in Fig. 5-1d, starting with the peak of lowest mass, namely, the one at mass 54 in Fig. 5-1e. On the basis of such calculations it can be shown that one of the samples (Fig. 5-1e) consists of 3.5 per cent d_0-, 18.0 per cent d-, 36.8 per cent d_2-, 31.6 per cent d_3-, and 10.2 per cent d_4-butadiene, while the other, the more highly deuterated sample (Fig. 5-1f), contains 4.5 per cent d_3- and 95.5 per cent d_4-butadiene.

A few points which are borne out by this simple example should be emphasized: First, if it is of interest to determine the number of hydrogen atoms exchangeable under the conditions of a certain reaction, then it is not necessary to carry this reaction to completion. The isotopic distribution deduced from the spectrum shown in Fig. 5-1e is sufficient indication that by the particular reaction employed[3] only four of the six

[3] A. C. Cope, G. A. Berchtold, and D. L. Ross, *J. Am. Chem. Soc.*, **83**, 3859 (1961).

hydrogens of butadiene are exchangeable, since otherwise a small but measurable amount of pentadeuterated butadiene would necessarily be observed.

Second, the method is most sensitive in terms of absolute values if the sample consists mainly of one species, in which case the small amounts of other species present can be determined with much higher accuracy than with the otherwise quite precise technique involving the combustion of the sample to water and measuring the deuterium content of the water on the basis of its density.

Third, if the average deuterium content of the whole sample is to be measured rather than the individual concentrations of the various deuterated species, then the combustion method would be more accurate in the case of the partially deuterated sample, such as the one shown in Fig. 5-1b and e. The total deuterium content of the sample as determined by mass spectrometry would be the result of the summation of the deuterium content of the individual species and therefore subject to considerably greater errors. The latter situation arises only if one needs to detect small differences in deuterium content between starting material and final product of a chemical reaction, because these two compounds now would be entirely different entities. On the other hand, such changes are easily detected in the mass spectrum of the intact molecule if the samples to be compared consist of the same compound.

5-2. EXPERIMENTAL TECHNIQUES

A. Selection of Operating Conditions

The quantitative determination of the isotope distribution in a sample requires the following steps:

The first step is the choice of the optimal electron energy at which the molecular-ion peak is still high enough to be measured accurately while the fragmentation resulting in the loss of one or more hydrogen atoms is negligible. It is of extreme importance to reduce such fragmentation to a level below the desired limit of error. It is not possible arithmetically to eliminate the contribution of such peaks on the basis of the mass spectrum of the nonlabeled standard, because in the deuterated molecule this fragment may involve loss of hydrogen or loss of deuterium or undergo both fragmentations; the magnitude of the peaks at $M - 1$ and $M - 2$ can, therefore, not be estimated with certainty. It would also be incorrect to assume a statistical chance for the removal of hydrogen or deuterium, because it is known that hydrogen is lost with greater ease than deuterium from equivalent positions (see Table 5-1). Secondly, the $M - 1$ fragment may arise by loss of a specific hydrogen atom of the molecule, and in such a case the deuterated species would lose either hydrogen or deuterium exclusively. As an example, the mass spectra of benzaldehyde and benzaldehyde-α-d are shown in Fig. 5-2. The equal intensity of the peak at mass 105 in both spectra indicates clearly that it is the aldehyde hydrogen which is lost and not a hydrogen atom from the aromatic ring. While this behavior is useful if the problem

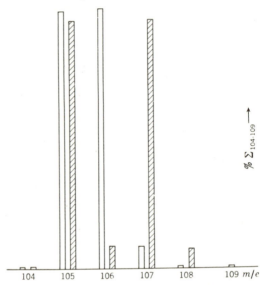

Fig. 5-2. Mass spectra of benzaldehyde (light) and benzaldehyde-α-d (shaded) in the region of the molecular weight.

is one of locating the deuterium atom either at the α position or in the ring, it makes impossible the analysis of a mixture of differently deuterated benzaldehyde species unless the position of the deuterium atoms is known.

The electron energy most suitable for each individual compound is found empirically, by scanning the mass region of interest repeatedly while stepwise decreasing the potential of the bombarding electrons (Fig. 5-3). Intervals of 0.5 ev in the region of the ionization potential of the molecule are in general sufficient, permitting good interpolation if necessary. The potential at which the M^+ peak is still reasonably intense but at which the peaks one or more mass units lower have disappeared is then chosen for the spectrum of the labeled compound (i.e., 12.5 ev for aniline). The recording obtained in this way may also be used for the detection of an $M + 1$ peak due to an ion-molecule collision which could give rise to errors in the deuterium determination (see Sec. 3-1A).

The mass spectrum of the labeled sample is then determined without changing any one of the operating conditions of the ion source. It is, in general, advisable to flush the inlet system with the sample a few times before actually measuring, to ensure the complete removal of unlabeled sample which was used for calibration. The intensity of all the peaks in the region of the molecular weight must then be measured and corrected for the presence of the other naturally occurring isotopes by subtracting

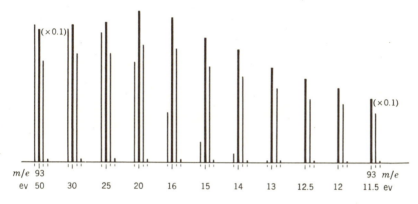

Fig. 5-3. Mass spectrum of aniline in the region of the molecular weight versus decreasing ionizing potential. Note that the peak for the monoisotopic molecular ion (mass 93) is shown one-tenth actual size in all scans.

this contribution of the peak at lowest mass from the next one in the ratio of the peak intensities at M, $M + 1$, and $M + 2$ exhibited by the spectrum of the calibration compound. Summation of all the corrected intensities and expression of the individual peak heights in per cent of this sum results in the determination of the composition of such a mixture (see sec. 5-2C and Table 5-3).

Utmost care has to be taken to identify the mass numbers of these peaks correctly, since an error of 1 mass unit would, of course, give an entirely wrong composition. This may be done by counting the peaks, beginning at the low-mass end of the spectrum, as outlined in Chap. 2, but it is much easier instead to inject, after the spectrum has been run but before it is pumped off, a small amount of the nondeuterated standard compound and to rescan this region of the spectrum. This operation provides an additional peak of unambiguously known mass very close to, or superimposed on, the ones to be identified, and is thus the safest check possible.

There are, of course, many compounds which do not appreciably lose hydrogen on electron impact, and in such a case the determinations are simplified, because the spectra may be taken at the usual 70 ev. On the other hand, there will be compounds which are not suited at all for such a determination, either those which do not exhibit an appreciable peak at the mass of the molecular weight or those which give a fragment corresponding to the loss of hydrogen, the appearance potential of which is very close to the ionization potential of the molecule. Reducing the electron energy is then of no help, because it would only lead to a decrease in the intensity of both peaks.

The calculation of the isotopic distribution in a labeled sample is to some extent an approximation based on the following assumptions:

1. The molar intensity of the molecular-weight peak is equal for all labeled species of the same molecule.
2. The intensity of the isotope peaks at $M + 1$ and $M + 2$ is the same in both the standard and the labeled substance.
3. There is no fractionation of the labeled molecules in the mass spectrometer.
4. There is no loss of isotope in the mass-spectrometer inlet system.
5. There is no "$M + 1$" peak due to ion-molecule collisions.
6. The electron energy does not change from one sample to another.
7. There are no background or other impurities present that contribute to the peaks to be measured.

Many of these assumptions are not entirely justified, but the resulting errors are in most cases not large and are also quite reproducible. Relative ratios will, therefore, be more nearly correct than the determination of absolute abundances. Fortunately it is the former result which is sought in most experiments. The accuracy required for such determinations varies widely. Only a qualitative indication of the number of stable isotopes incorporated during a given reaction is needed for certain structural arguments, while in the investigation of a reaction mechanism it is sometimes necessary to obtain quite accurate quantitative results. It is for this reason that the magnitude of the errors introduced by the assumptions mentioned above have to be evaluated, and these phenomena need, therefore, to be discussed in more detail.

B. Sources of Error

Assumption 1 will hold for most practical purposes, but for more accurate measurements on molecular species differing appreciably in mass a few factors have to be considered which may lead to *different molar intensities of the molecular-ion peaks*. Those factors fall into two groups, namely, those influencing the number of molecular ions initially formed and those influencing the number of ions actually collected. Stevenson [1] has pointed out that no difference in ionization efficiency is to be expected between light and heavy molecules. Since the bonds connecting light isotopes are, however, more easily cleaved than bonds connecting heavy isotopes, the light molecular ions will decompose more easily than heavy ones, and the remaining light and heavy molecular ions may thus differ in abundance. For this reason the abundance of $(CH_4)^+$ is lower (see Table 5-1) than that of $(CD_4)^+$.

Use of an electron energy at which no fragmentation takes place therefore ensures that the abundance of molecular ions, after acceleration, is still the same for both light and heavy species. The ionization potentials of light and heavy molecules seem also to be identical within experimental error, with the exception of a somewhat larger diversity between CH_4 and CD_4, which may be due to the relatively large mass difference between two species. The ionization potentials of methane and monodeuteromethane are sufficiently different to give rise to a lower ionization efficiency of CD_4 compared with CH_4 at the same electron energy, if the measurement is made in the region near the ionization potential, where this curve is very steep (Fig. 3-1). A value up to 15 per cent low was obtained [4] in an analysis of a mixture of CH_4 and CD_4. For the other compounds listed in Table 5-2 no such errors are possible, and the same will be true of even more complex molecules.

Unfortunately, no ionization efficiencies of labeled versus unlabeled complex organic molecules seem to have been measured under conditions which would result in sufficiently accurate values. The ones obtained by Natalis [5] for cyclopentanone and cyclopentanone-d_4 indicate an ionization cross section for the nondeuterated molecule twice that of the deuterated ketone at 9 ev. Such a large difference is somewhat improbable and may be due to the difficulties in reproducing ionizing conditions at low electron energies. Any measurement of this kind should be done, if possible, on a mixture of the deuterated and nondeuterated material rather than consecutively on the individual substances, particularly if a mass spectrometer not specially modified for such measurements is employed.

The difference in the molar intensity of the molecular ions accelerated

[4] F. P. Lossing, A. W. Tickner, and W. A. Bryce, *J. Chem. Phys.*, **19**, 1254 (1951).
[5] P. Natalis, *Bull. soc. chim. Belges*, **67**, 599 (1958).

before decomposition will also depend on the nature of the fragmentation still taking place. This difference will be appreciable if a bond at the heavy isotope is broken. For examples, the ratio of H^+/H_2^+ in hydrogen gas is 0.013, compared with 0.007 for D^+/D_2^+ and 0.0036 for T^+/T_2^+ in the heavy molecules.[6] Similarly, the loss of D from C_2D_2 is less pronounced than the loss of H from $C_2H_2^2$. On the other hand, if the

Table 5-2. Ionization Potentials of Labeled Molecules

Compound	Ionization potential, ev
CH_4	13.07,° 13.04 †,‡
CH_3D	13.12 °,†
CH_2D_2	13.14 °,†
CHD_3	13.18 °,†
CD_4	13.25,° 13.21 †,‡
C_2H_2	11.40 °,†
C_2D_2	11.39 °,†
C_2H_4	10.60 °,†
C_2D_4	10.59 °,†
$CH_3C≡CH$	10.54 ± .03 §
$CD_3C≡CH$	10.62 ± .05 §
CH_3COOH	10.7 ¶
CD_3COOH	10.7 ¶

° ± 0.02 ev.
† F. P. Lossing, A. W. Tickner, and W. A. Bryce, *J. Chem. Phys.*, **19**, 1254 (1951).
‡ R. E. Honig, *J. Chem. Phys.*, **16**, 105 (1948).
§ J. Collin and F. P. Lossing, *J. Am. Chem. Soc.*, **80**, 1568 (1958).
¶ K. Hirota, K. Nagoshi, and M. Hatada, *Bull. Chem. Soc. Japan*, **34**, 226 (1961).

heavy isotope is far removed from the site of bond breaking, the isotope effect on the cleavage reaction will be very small, or negligible, and therefore will not influence the intensity of the molecular ion.

As far as collection efficiency is concerned, one must take into account the mass discrimination in the instrument leading to the collection of fewer particles, if accelerated at a lower potential. A particle of higher

[6] O. A. Schaeffer and J. M. Hastings, *J. Chem. Phys.*, **18**, 1048 (1950).

mass thus always gives rise to a smaller peak than the one of lower mass, even if their abundance is the same when leaving the exit slit of the ion source. This may be of the order of a few tenths of a per cent of the intensity for a mass difference of 1 per cent between the two particles, but this value depends very much on the geometry of ion source and ion path and whether magnetic or electric scanning is employed. Nier [7] has measured this value on his isotope-ratio instrument and found that the intensity of $(Ar^{36})^+$ was about 0.6 per cent higher than the intensity of $(Ar^{40})^+$. The difference in collection efficiency is much larger in single-collector instruments employing electrical scan of the spectrum. Preliminary experiments using trideuteroaniline versus aniline indicate that the intensity appears to fall off about 1 per cent per deuterium atom at mass 93. This value includes any change in isotopic composition due to a faster rate of diffusion through the leak of the light species (see below). At higher masses the relative differences in mass caused by the incorporation of a stable isotope are generally much lower, except for highly deuterated compounds.

Assumption 2, the constancy of the *natural-isotope peaks*, will always be justified if both the standard and the labeled compound come from the same source and if the label consists of only one or a few deuterium atoms substituted for hydrogen. Since any changes in the isotopic abundance of other elements present in the molecule would lead to differences in the intensities of the isotope peaks, one must make sure that the standard comes from the same carbon source (if possible from the same bottle) and that no isotopic fractionation occurs during the reaction by which the labeled substance is produced. Errors can occur if, for example, changes in deuterium concentration are monitored, while the reaction proceeds, by taking samples at certain time intervals. Isotope effects on the reaction rates could lead to enrichment or depletion of the reactant or product in C^{13}, N^{15}, or O^{18}. In most cases, the mass spectrum cannot distinguish such changes from a variation in the concentration of mono- or dideuterated species. A resolving power of 50.000 would be required at mass 150 (a reasonable value) if species differing by $C^{13}H$ versus $C^{12}D$ ($\Delta = 0.00302$ mass unit) are to be resolved. For $N^{15}C^{12}$ versus $N^{14}C^{13}$ and $N^{15}H$ versus $N^{14}D$, resolving powers of 30.000 and 16.000, respectively, are required at mass 150. For all these reasons the most conclusive results are obtained if a control reaction that does not involve labeled reagents is used, producing samples of comparable history as standards for all measurements.

[7] A. O. Nier, *Phys. Rev.*, 77, 789 (1950).

To obtain very accurate values for samples of high deuterium content one has to consider the small decrease in the intensity of the natural-isotope peak. The unlabeled standard always contains more hydrogen atoms which may contribute to the isotope peak to the extent of the natural abundance of deuterium. The peak 1 mass unit above the major molecular species was found, for example, to have 6.72 per cent of the intensity of mass 78 in C_6H_6 but only 6.60 per cent of the intensity of mass 84 in C_6D_6.[8]

Contrary to assumption 3, *fractionation* of a mixture of light and heavy molecules may occur before or after the sample has been introduced into the mass spectrometer. Because of the relationship between rate of effusion and molecular weight discussed in Sec. 4-4, the sample in the reservoir will slowly be depleted of light molecules while the compound passes through the leak into the ion source. This effect will be the more serious, the larger the mass difference between the species and the longer the sample is allowed to stream through the leak before the measurement is taken. In the case of the relatively large molecules with which we are concerned here, this effect will be almost negligible if the peaks are scanned within 1 or 2 min after introduction into the reservoir and the opening of the valve leading to the leak. The magnitude of fractionation may either be calculated from Graham's law or measured experimentally by extrapolation to zero time of the ratios found, whenever the desired accuracy of the measurement necessitates such corrections.

Much more serious is fractionation of the mixture before introduction of the compound into the mass spectrometer. While normal purification processes hardly lead to any noticeable change in isotopic composition, it is necessary to consider this possibility if highly efficient techniques are used. For example, it is often overlooked that gas chromatography, a technique frequently used for the purification of samples for mass spectrometry, may lead to considerable fractionation. Almost complete separation of C_6H_{12} and C_6D_{12} on a 4-m column has been achieved by Wilzbach.[9] This separation is, of course, facilitated by the large mass difference between those two species and the use of a relatively long column, but it shows that isotopic fractionation is possible by gas chromatography.

Less efficient separation owing to the use of shorter columns and a lower degree of isotopic substitution is even more likely to lead to unexpected errors, as one would not expect a single peak to represent par-

[8] G. A. Semenov and M. Ya. Turkina, *Zavodskaya Lab.*, **24**, 1084 (1958); (cf. *Chem. Abstr.*, **54**, 13942c (1960)).

[9] K. E. Wilzbach and P. Riesz, *Science*, **126**, 748 (1957).

tially separated isotopic species. The extent of fractionation achieved with a mixture of aniline and aniline-2,4,6-d_3 (in a 1:0.9 proportion) is shown in Fig. 5-4. The shape of the gas chromatographic peak is not noticeably different from the one obtained with ordinary aniline. Upon separate collection of different parts of the peaks, a widely differing isotopic distribution is found. In the first part of the peak, trideuteroaniline is enriched (Fig. 5-4c shows a ratio of 1:1.22 for d_0/d_3); the center cut (Fig. 5-4d) is similar to the total mixture (1:0.85), while in the last part, the light species predominates (1:0.64).

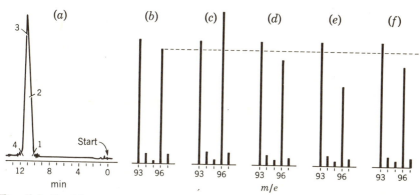

Fig. 5-4. Partial separation of a mixture of aniline and aniline-2,4,6-d_3 by gas chromatography (10 per cent silicone oil on Chromosorb W, 90°, 12 lb helium). (*a*) Gas chromatogram; (*b*) mass spectrum of the mixture before gas chromatography; (*c*) spectrum of front of peak collected between 1 and 2; (*d*) spectrum of center cut collected between 2 and 3; (*e*) spectrum of tail, collected between 3 and 4; (*f*) spectrum of entire peak collected, without efficient cooling, between 1 and 4. Spectra determined at 12.5-ev ionizing potential. All intensities in terms of m/e 93 = 1.

If the compound is to be purified by gas chromatography, great care has to be taken to collect the entire fraction quantitatively. An efficient trapping device will be necessary to ensure condensation of even the first trace of material, which is particularly easily lost because of the tendency of many compounds to form a fog rather than to condense on dry, cold glass walls. Figure 5-4*f* shows the mass spectrum of the mixture obtained when collected in a small plain glass tube. Loss of part of the fast-moving component is indicated by the 1:0.82 ratio for d_0/d_3.

This extent of fractionation is not serious if merely the number of incorporable isotopes is to be determined (see Sec. 5-3), but it can be detrimental if it occurs during an experiment in which small changes in isotopic distribution are of significance. Obviously, a sample containing species differing only by one heavy isotope, i.e., 1 mass unit, will be less affected. For very accurate determinations of low levels of N^{15} or D, the possibility of a fractionation of naturally occurring C^{13} also has to be taken into account, as the concentration of molecular species containing one C^{13} is appreciable in organic molecules of the usual size (see Sec. 3-1*B*).

Whenever accurate isotope determinations are to be done on samples purified by gas chromatography, it is worthwhile to check whether any such fractionation occurs with the particular column employed.

Large errors may be due to *loss of the isotope* while in the inlet system. Water and traces of other hydroxyl-containing substances are always adsorbed on the walls of both inlet system and ion source, and any compound containing exchangeable deuterium atoms such as ROD, RCOOD, RND_2, $RCOND_2$, or RSD will lose some of or all the deuterium by reaction with those substances. It is therefore, in general, not possible to determine the deuterium content of such samples unless repeated equilibration of the instrument with the sample or with D_2O precedes the actual determination. Even deuterium bound to carbon in an easily enolizable position may exchange fast enough to lead to serious errors. An example is cyclodocanone; Fig. 5-5 shows the variation in the intensity of masses 186, 185, and 184, the molecular ions of tri-, and di-, and mono-deuterocyclododecanone versus the time elapsed after introduction of the sample into the inlet system. The loss of deuterium from the trideuterated species with formation of di- and some monodeuterated molecules is apparent. It is therefore worthwhile to scan the mass region of interest repeatedly. If the intensity ratios vary in a manner indicating exchange, one has to extrapolate the ratio to zero time in order to obtain the correct result.

Very labile deuterium atoms can be retained, however, if the sample is introduced directly into the electron beam, thus minimizing the chance for a collision with other molecules containing labile hydrogen. Examples of the application of this technique will be discussed in Sec. 10-2.

The most erratic and unpredictable, and perhaps the least suspected, source of error is the tendency of a compound to give rise to an "*M* + 1" *peak* caused by abstraction of a hydrogen radical from another molecule during an ion-molecule collision. If this were a reproducible process, it then would be automatically corrected along with the subtraction of the natural-isotope peak taken from the calibration spectrum. For a number of reasons the intensity of this peak is, however, not reproducible. As was pointed out in Sec. 3-1A, this process is not directly proportional to the sample pressure but to the square of it, and therefore care must be taken to determine the spectrum of the calibration compound at the same sample pressure as that used for the actual run of the deuterated specimen.

It has also been pointed out earlier that the intensity of this peak, produced in a bimolecular reaction, is very sensitive to the residence time of the ions in that region of the ion source where neutral molecules are rather abundant. Any variation of the potential in this region will

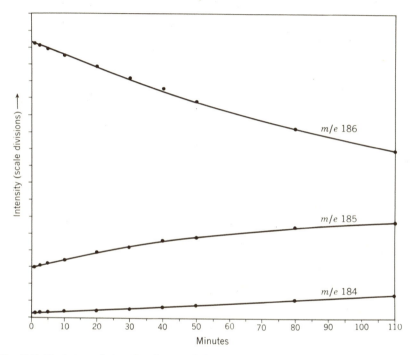

Fig. 5-5. Variation of the abundance of the molecular ion of tetra- (m/e 186), tri- (m/e 185), and dideuterated cyclododecanone (m/e 184) versus residence time of sample in inlet system.

change the velocity with which the ions travel out of this area. Variation of the repeller potential itself, of course, would produce such a change, and it is important to keep the potential applied to this plate constant while determining both the calibration spectrum and the spectrum of the isotopically labeled sample. This potential should be relatively high to decrease the residence time of the ions in the ion source. Variation of the ionizing current also influences the so-called "space charge," which is more negative if more electrons travel through the source, as is the case at higher ionizing current. The magnitude of the space charge is affected, in addition, by the pressure of the sample in the ion source, since at higher pressures more positive ions are produced, leading to a more positive value of the potential at the ionization region. Some of these factors may account, at least in part, for the irreproducibility of the magnitude of the "$M + 1$" peak. It is also rather sensitive to the electron energy near the ionization potential of the molecule, the region in which one frequently determines mass spectra for isotope measurements. Figure 5-6 shows the variation of the relative ratio $(M + 1)^+/M^+$ versus electron energy. Some of the other effects too are discussed in more detail by Beynon.[10]

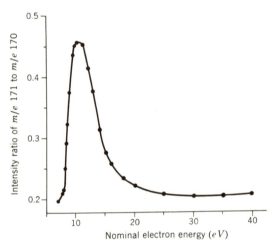

Fig. 5-6. Variation of $(M + 1)/M$ ratio for undecanone due to a change in ionizing potential. (*From Ref.* 10.)

Thus, the tendency of a substance to give rise to an appreciable "$M + 1$" peak via ion-molecule collisions introduces a number of complications in the determination of the isotope content of a sample. It is advisable first to check on the extent to which this process occurs with the particular sample to be investigated, and the record obtained in the course of the evaluation of the optimum electron energy (discussed earlier in this section) may be used for this purpose. If the ratio $(M + 1)^+/M^+$ is constant over a wide range or at least changes only slowly, without exhibiting maxima, it then is possible to obtain rather accurate results. If there is any indication of an appreciable "$M + 1$" peak, one has to take

[10] J. H. Beynon, G. R. Lester, R. A. Saunders, and A. E. Williams, *Trans. Faraday Soc.*, **57**, 1259 (1961).

great care not to vary any one of the conditions discussed above. One would assume that such an "$M + 1$" peak leads only to errors in the concentration of the species containing one deuterium atom (or C^{13} or N^{15}) more than the major component, and this is correct for compounds containing little or no deuterium.

For highly deuterated substances, this species becomes in part a particle of mass "$M + 2$." In the extreme case of a perdeuterated compound such as hexadeuteroacetone, an appreciable peak is found at m/e 66, corresponding to a species $(CD_3COCD_3 \cdot D)^+$, which could be confused with hexadeuteroacetone-O^{18}. In addition, such a perdeuterated molecule cannot exhibit an "$M + 1$" peak, and the use of the 58:59 ratio of ordinary acetone for the computation of the deuterium content of

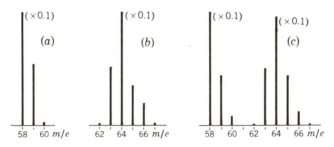

Fig. 5-7. Mass spectra of (a) acetone, (b) acetone-d_6, and (c) a mixture thereof, obtained with low-energy electrons (the peaks at m/e 58 and m/e 64 are, in fact, ten times higher than shown).

perdeuteroacetone would result in a negative value for "heptadeuteroacetone." This is because the contribution of the protonated acetone species of mass 59 ($C_3H_7O^+$) is thus subtracted from mass 65 although there can be no protonated deuteroacetone ($C_3D_6HO^+$) present. If the samples are run under exactly the same conditions, including sample pressure, one can calculate (Sec. 3-1B) the theoretical intensity of the isotope peak of acetone and apply the remaining intensity of the 59 peak as a correction to the peak at m/e 66 and arrive at reasonable values. Figure 5-7 shows the mass spectra of acetone and hexadeuteroacetone in the region of their molecular weight. It is of interest to note that if both samples are mixed and the spectrum of the mixture is determined, a decrease in the intensity of m/e 59 and 66 is observed, while peaks at m/e 60 and 65 increase to the same extent, indicating that the undeuterated acetone ion may subtract a deuterium radical from perdeuteroacetone and vice versa.

Some of the factors influencing the "$M + 1$" peak may also lead to *changes in electron energy*. While it is easily possible to keep the potential between filament and anode constant, the electron energy may still change because of changes in space charge. It is for this reason that a change in sample pressure also changes the actually applied electron energy, and thus the relative intensity of the peak. At a given potential (near the ionization potential of the molecule or appearance potential of the fragment) applied to filament and anode, the intensity of a peak per unit pressure will increase because of the added potential due to the positive space charge. A plot of the intensity of mass 78 of benzene at

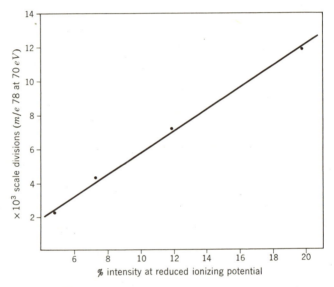

Fig. 5-8. Variation of effective ionization energy with sample size.

70 ev versus the intensity of the same peak at constant but much lower potential applied between filament and anode gives a fairly straight line with a positive slope (Fig. 5-8), indicating that at higher sample pressure (for which the intensity at 70 volts is a measure) the actual energy of the bombarding electrons is higher than at lower pressure. If the spectrum for isotope determination is run at a potential near the appearance potential of the fragment formed by loss of hydrogen, one must be very careful not to use a sample pressure very different from the one employed when the optimum electron energy was selected. Otherwise fragments will be formed that simulate the presence of species of lower isotope content.

The absence (assumption 7) of *instrument background or impurities* contributing to any one of the peaks to be measured is of obvious importance. A pure sample and the determination of the background spectrum are necessary. Nevertheless, the latter can be subtracted from the actual determination without hampering the accuracy. As far as impurities are concerned it should be noted that they are of little consequence if of lower molecular weight than the compound to be investigated, unless the impurity is a large amount of a substance (such as H_2O or D_2O) particularly suited to donate a hydrogen atom (or deuterium atom) to the molecular ion to be measured, which would lead to an excessive "$M + 1$" or "$M + 2$" peak, causing considerable errors.

The principle of the determination of the isotope content on the basis of the mass spectrum of the intact molecule has been discussed in great detail, including all the possible sources of error, because the technique is already being used rather frequently and will be used even more so in the near future. As all the early work was done on small and simple hydrocarbons, one has to be aware of additional complications when using more complex molecules containing functional groups and other heteroatoms. Particular care has to be taken to minimize all the sources of error discussed above, and it is necessary to estimate their magnitude. This is most important if the conclusions to be drawn rest on the detection of small differences in isotope content, as is often the case in the investigation of reaction mechanisms. Accurate quantitative results are much less important if the isotope has been incorporated for the purpose of structure determination, in which case frequently a qualitative estimate suffices, indicating the number of isotopes incorporated into the molecule.

C. Calculation of Analysis

The isotope content of a uniquely labeled molecule, such as CH_2D_2 or $C_{10}H_{16}D_4O$, is simply derived from its molecular formula (for example, 50 atom per cent and 20 atom per cent, respectively, for the compounds mentioned).

More frequently, the determination of the composition of a mixture, consisting of species of the same molecule but containing a varying number of heavy isotopes, is required. The principle of this calculation, the necessary assumptions which have to be made, and the possible errors have been discussed earlier. The rather simple arithmetical manipulation involved in the conversion of the intensities as taken from the record to the distributions of the various species (in mole per cent) in the mixture is outlined in the following examples.

Example 1. In this example no fragments of mass $M - 1$, $M - 2$, and $M - 3$ are formed. The isotope is 1 mass unit heavier than the light one.

Peak heights (arbitrary units) in unlabeled standard (M denotes its molecular weight):

Mass:	M	$M + 1$	$M + 2$	
Intensity:	1.000	0.0671	0.0039	(A)

Peak heights (scale divisions) in labeled sample:

Mass:	M	$M + 1$	$M + 2$	$M + 3$	$M + 4$	$M + 5$	
Intensity:	225	591	890	690	45.6	2.5	(B)

The entire peak at mass M, 225 div, must be due to unlabeled species

Compute the contributions of the unlabeled species to M, $M + 1$, and $M + 2$ by multiplying the peak height at mass M with the abundance of M, $M + 1$, and $M + 2$ in standard [see (A)]:

$$225 \times 1.00 = 225 \quad 225 \times 0.0671 = 15.10 \quad 225 \times 0.0039 = 0.88 \quad (C)$$

Subtract (C) from (B):

225	591	890	690	45.6	2.5
−225	15.10	0.88			
0	575.9	889.12	690	45.6	2.5 (D)

The peak height due to singly labeled species is thus 575.9 div. Compute its contributions to $M + 1$, $M + 2$, and $M + 3$:

$$575.9 \times 1.00 = 575.9 \quad 575.9 \times 0.0671 = 38.64$$
$$575.9 \times 0.0039 = 2.25 \quad (E)$$

Subtract (E) from (D):

575.9	889.12	690	45.6	2.5
−575.9	38.64	2.25		
0	850.48	687.75	45.6	2.5 (F)

The peak height of doubly labeled species is 850.5 div. Compute its contributions to $M + 2$, $M + 3$, and $M + 4$:

$$850.5 \quad 850.5 \times 0.0671 = 57.07 \quad 850.5 \times 0.0039 = 3.32 \quad (G)$$

Subtract (G) from (F):

850.48	687.75	45.6	2.5
−850.48	57.07	3.32	
0	630.68	42.28	2.5 (H)

The peak height of triply labeled species is 630.68 div. Compute its contribution to $M + 3$, $M + 4$, and $M + 5$:

$$630.68 \quad 630.68 \times 0.0671 = 42.31 \quad 630.68 \times 0.0039 = 2.46 \quad (I)$$

Subtract (I) from (H):

630.68	42.28	2.5
−630.68	42.31	2.46
0	−0.03	0.04

No species containing more than three heavy isotopes are present. The sum of all corrected intensities is

$$225 + 575.9 + 850.5 + 630.7 = 2{,}282.1$$

The distribution in mole per cent is

$$225/2{,}282 \times 100 = 9.86 \text{ mole per cent unlabeled species}$$

Values of 25.2_4 mole per cent singly, 37.2_7 mole per cent doubly, and 27.6_3 mole per cent triply labeled species are obtained in a similar manner. These results are, at best, precise to three significant figures since the experimental data (A) and (B) are not more precise. The absolute accuracy may be considerably lower owing to one or more of the causes of errors discussed in the previous section.

Example 2. In this example a fragment of mass $M - 1$ of moderate abundance is present but no $M - 2$, $M - 3$, or $M - 4$. The isotope is 1 mass unit heavier than the light one.

Peak heights (arbitrary units) in unlabeled standard:

Mass:	$M - 1$	M	$M + 1$	$M + 2$
Intensity:	1.00	10.45	1.15	0.058

Peak heights (scale divisions) in labeled sample:

Mass:	$M - 1$	M	$M + 1$	$M + 2$	$M + 3$	$M + 4$	
Intensity:	86.7	1,075	1,998	1,585	163.2	7.9	(J)

The peak at $M - 1$, 86.7 div, is due to only unlabeled species.

Compute contributions of unlabeled species to the peaks at $M - 1$, M, $M + 1$, and $M + 2$ by multiplying the peak height at $M - 1$ with the abundance values of the standard:

$$86.7 \times 1.00 = 86.7 \quad 86.7 \times 10.45 = 906.0 \quad 86.7 \times 1.15 = 99.70$$
$$86.7 \times 0.058 = 5.03 \qquad (K)$$

Subtract (K) from (J):

86.7	1,075	1,998	1,585	163.2	7.9	
−86.7	906	99.7	5.03			
0	169	1,898.3	1,580	163.2	7.9	(L)

The peak height at M due to singly labeled species is thus 169 div. Compute the contributions of singly labeled species:

$$169 \quad 169 \times 10.45 = 1{,}766 \quad 169 \times 1.15 = 194.4$$
$$169 \times 0.058 = 9.80 \qquad (M)$$

Subtract (M) from (L):

169	1,898.3	1,580.0	163.2	7.9	
−169	1,766.0	194.4	9.80		
0	132.3	1,385.6	153.4	7.9	(N)

The peak height at $M + 1$ due to doubly labeled species is 132.3 div. Compute contributions of doubly labeled species:

$$132.3 \qquad 132.3 \times 10.45 = 1,381.5 \qquad 132.3 \times 1.15 = 152.0$$
$$132.3 \times 0.058 = 7.67 \qquad\qquad\qquad (O)$$

On subtraction of (O) from (N), peaks of 4.1 div at $M + 2$, 1.4 div at $M + 3$, and 0.23 div at $M + 4$ are left over. As these are not in the expected ratio and the one at $M + 3$, the molecular weight of the triply labeled species, is very small, one can conclude that this species is absent.

The composition of the mixture in mole per cent as above, using either the abundances of the species due to loss of one hydrogen (86.7, 169, and 132.3 scale divisions, respectively) or, better, the values of the molecular species is

$$906 + 1,766 + 1,386 = 4,058$$
$$906/4,058 \times 100 = 22.3_3 \text{ mole per cent unlabeled species}$$

Values of mole per cent 43.52 singly and 34.15 mole per cent doubly labeled species are obtained in a similar manner.

A few aspects of Example 2 should be discussed. First, as one uses a small peak (87.6 div) to begin the calculation, some error may result from the lower accuracy with which this peak can be measured. Relatively large residuals or negative values may be found in the last step. It is then best to use the calculation above as an approximation and repeat it in *reverse order*, i.e., starting with the assumption that 1385.6 div is a more reliable value than 1381.5 for the abundance of the molecular ion of the doubly labeled species.

Second, this type of a calculation will be reliable only for compounds labeled, not with deuterium, but with C^{13} or N^{15}. In a deuterated compound, as was pointed out in Sec. 5-2B, one cannot assume that the spectrum of the labeled compound will be merely shifted for one or more mass units while the intensities remain constant. The intensity of the $M - 1$ peak may be lower in the deuterated species owing to the possibility of the removal of deuterium rather than hydrogen. Nevertheless, if one has reasons to assume that loss of deuterium is unlikely, one can obtain reasonable values by this technique. It should, however, be used only in cases where the $M - 1$ peak cannot be eliminated by lowering the ionizing potential.

Third, the results can also be calculated using a set of simultaneous equations. This is rather complex for more than three unknowns, and the stepwise method outlined above is preferred because it can be continued through as many steps as necessary and permits easier detection of irregularities (due to impurities, "$M + 1$" peaks, etc.) giving rise to excessive or negative values before the process of calculation is completed.

It should be remembered that the calculations would be simplified and many of the assumptions discussed above would be unnecessary if calibration spectra of each specifically labeled single component of the mixture were available. The computation of the results would then be as simple as any quantitative analysis by mass spectrometry of a multicomponent mixture, and all the complications introduced by working with low-energy electrons would be eliminated also. These specifically labeled pure substances will, however, not be available in most instances, and their synthesis will frequently be rather difficult, if not impossible. In practice it is thus almost always necessary to use the approach discussed in this section. There may be cases where insurmountable difficulties (mostly too intense $M - 1$ or "$M + 1$" peaks) will still require the synthesis of one or more of the pure labeled species if reliable results are to be obtained.

D. Distribution of Isotopes within the Molecule

One of the most useful aspects of determining the isotope content on the undegraded molecule is the possibility of learning a considerable amount about the distribution of the stable isotopes within the molecule. The information deduced from a single mass spectrum of deuterated N-benzoylproline ester may be mentioned as an example.[11] The sample had been prepared by catalytic deuteration of N-benzoyldehydroproline (1) and was esterified by briefly boiling it with ethanolic hydrogen chloride. This treatment not only converted the free acid (2) to the ethyl ester (3) but also led, to a small extent, by alcoholysis to proline ethyl ester (4) and ethyl benzoate (5).

$$
\begin{array}{ccc}
\text{N-COOH} & \quad & \text{N-COOH} \\
| & & | \\
\text{CO} & & \text{CO} \\
| & & | \\
\text{C}_6\text{H}_5 & & \text{C}_6\text{H}_5 \\
(1) & & (2)
\end{array}
\longrightarrow
$$

[11] Unpublished measurements (by G. G. J. Deffner) on a sample kindly provided by A. V. Robertson.

$$174 \quad [\text{ring}]\text{N}-\text{COOC}_2\text{H}_5 \quad + \quad 70 \quad [\text{ring}]\text{N(H)}-\text{COOC}_2\text{H}_5 \quad + \quad C_6H_5COOC_2H_5$$

$$105 \quad \overset{|}{CO} \quad \overset{|}{C_6H_5}$$

$$(3) \qquad\qquad (4) \qquad\qquad (5)$$

The mass spectrum of the free amino esters, introduced into the instrument by the technique described in Sec. 7-1, was determined at an ionizing energy of about 9.5 volts. Table 5-3 lists the intensities of the

Table 5-3. Deuterium Determination in a Sample of Benzoylproline

Peak, m/e	N-Benzoyl-proline intensity[a]	Deuterated N-benzoylproline intensity[b]			Composition	
		Uncor-rected	Correction	Corrected	Found, %	Calcd.[c]
(1)	(2)	(3)	(4)	(5)	(6)	(7)
70	100	68.5	...	68.5	59.4 d_0	
71	5.5	41.9	−3.8	38.1	33.0 d_1	
72	...	9.2	−2.2[d]	7.0	6.1 d_2	
73	...	2.1	−0.4	1.7	1.5 d_3	
				115.3		
105	100	3,660	...	3,660	89.7 d_0	
106	7.9	637	−289.1	347.9	8.5 d_1	
107	0.7	107.1	−27.5[e], −25.6[f]	54.0	1.3 d_2	
108	...	15.9	−4.3, −2.4	9.2	0.2 d_3[g]	
				4,071.1		
174	100	678	...	678	56.1 d_0	53.3
175	13	499	−88.1	410.9	34.0 d_1	34.7
176	1.0	163	−53.4, −6.8	102.8	8.5 d_2	9.4
177	...	34.2	−13.4, −4.1	16.7	1.4 d_3	2.2
178	...	3.2	2.1, −1.0	0.1	0 d_4	
				1,208.5		

[a] Relative to most intense peak ($= 100$) in this group.
[b] Scale divisions.
[c] Calculated from the results of first and second group.
[d] For example, 38.1×0.055.
[e] For example, 347.9×0.079.
[f] For example, $3,660 \times 0.007$.
[g] Omitted in the calculation of the results given in column 7.

peaks in the region of mass 70 [from (4)] and of mass 105 and 174 [from (3)]. Also included in the table are the values obtained from an unlabeled sample of N-benzoylproline. The amount of free proline ester formed in each case differed, of course, but this has no bearing on the results of the analysis (column 6, Table 5-3).

It could be concluded from this experiment that the sample contained deuterium in the proline moiety of the molecule not only as a result of the saturation of the double bond but also because of exchange of some hydrogen on saturated centers. In addition, catalytic exchange had taken place in the aromatic ring of the benzoyl group. These results can be summarized as follows:

$$
\begin{array}{ll}
A \quad \text{(proline ring)} & \begin{array}{l} 59.4\% \ d_0 \\ 33.0\% \ d_1 \\ 6.1\% \ d_2 \\ 1.5\% \ d_3 \end{array} \\
\text{N—COOH} & \\
\hline
B \quad \text{CO} & \begin{array}{l} 89.7\% \ d_0 \\ 8.5\% \ d_1 \\ 1.3\% \ d_2 \end{array} \\
\quad C_6H_5 &
\end{array}
$$

It is possible to check the correctness of the determination and of the assignment of the fragments by calculating the isotope distribution in the entire molecule from the distributions in the two individual parts A and B. Those two parts of the molecule can be treated like two elements, A and B, consisting of isotopes differing by 1 mass unit and of abundance a_1, a_2, a_3, a_4 and b_1, b_2, and b_3, respectively. As was outlined in Sec. 3-1B, the product

$$(a_1 + a_2 + a_3 + a_4)(b_1 + b_2 + b_3)$$

gives the abundances of the peaks for the species containing one atom each of A and B, if one considers that the product a_1b_1 equals the relative abundance of the monoisotopic molecules M while both a_2b_1 and a_1b_2 together produce the species of $M + 1$, and so on, to a_4b_3, which results in the species at $M + 5$. For the above example, the product of abundances is

$$(59.4 + 33.0 + 6.1 + 1.5) \times (89.7 + 8.5 + 1.3)$$

leading to the values presented in Table 5-3, column 7.

In the course of this discussion only the molecular-weight peak was used for the measurement of the isotope distribution in the sample, with the exception of the last example. In principle, fragment peaks may be used as well for the determination of the isotope distribution in the particular part of the molecule from which this peak arises. In such a case, however, it is of extreme importance to know exactly from which part of the molecule this fragment is formed and by which mechanism. In the case of N-benzoylproline one could rely on the correctness of the assumptions made regarding the nature of the fragments of mass 70 and 174 on the basis of the extensive investigations which had been carried out on the mass spectra of amino acid esters (see Chap. 7).[12] A peak at mass 105 in a derivative of benzoic acid must be due to the benzoyl ion, and only one such group is present in (3). Finally, the agreement between the values obtained from the peaks in the region of mass 174 and the ones calculated from the two other fragments (70 and 105) indicates the correctness of all the assumptions. Nevertheless, not too much confidence should be placed in the assignment of certain peaks to a given part of the molecule on the basis of the fragmentation processes discussed in Chap. 3. While most of the signal producing a peak at a given mass number will be due to a favorable mode of fragmentation of the molecule, the remaining part of the signal may be due to a less favored and unsuspected fragmentation process not involving all or any of the heavy atoms present in the major fragment.

A striking example of an unexpected fragmentation is the loss of 43 mass units from methyl esters of long-chain fatty acids. One would intuitively suspect that such a peak is due to the loss of the three terminal carbon atoms, and one might be tempted to use this peak for the determination of the number and amount of deuterium atoms (or C^{13}) in the terminal propyl group of the molecule. An extensive investigation of labeled molecules of this type by Stenhagen et al.[13] has, however, shown that the majority of the $M - 43$ fragments are produced by the elimination of C_2, C_3, and C_4 from (6)

$$\overset{4}{C}H_3(CH_2)_n\overset{3}{C}H_2\overset{2}{C}H_2CH_2COOCH_3$$
$$(6)$$

accompanied by the abstraction of an additional hydrogen atom. The mass spectrum of methyl stearate-18-d_3 is shown in Fig. 5-9 (cf. Fig. 6-1).

If fragment peaks have to be used, either because the intensity of the molecular-ion peak is too low or because the isotope distribution in a particular part of the molecule has to be measured, one must make sure that the assumptions regarding the origin of this fragment are entirely correct. This may best be tested by the synthesis of the molecule labeled in this particular way. Whether this is necessary or not will depend on one's

[12] K. Biemann, J. Seibl, and F. Gapp, *J. Am. Chem. Soc.*, **83**, 3795 (1961).

[13] Ng. Dinh-Nguyen, R. Ryhage, S. Ställberg-Stenhagen, and E. Stenhagen, *Arkiv Kemi*, **18**, 393 (1961); R. Ryhage and E. Stenhagen, *Arkiv Kemi*, **15**, 291 (1959).

experience and ability to predict mass spectra and on the accuracy requirements for this determination. Nevertheless, the possible pitfalls in the use of fragment peaks cannot be overemphasized.

While deuterated molecules have been used as examples throughout, the same technique applies to the determination of C^{13} and N^{15}. The problem is even somewhat simplified, because, for example, loss of the isotope by exchange during the handling of the sample is very improbable and in general it is only one such isotope that is incorporated into a molecule while not infrequently many deuterium atoms are present in a single molecule. The difficulties in obtaining samples containing a very

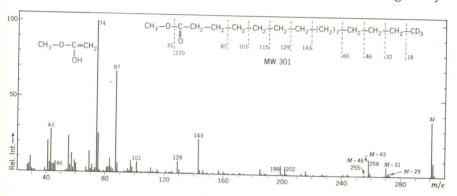

Fig. 5-9. Mass spectrum of methyl stearate-18-d_3. (*From Ref. 13.*)

high concentration of C^{13} or N^{15} make it more often necessary to rely on peaks of relatively low intensity in the presence of high peaks due to unlabeled species.

Compounds labeled with O^{18} are in some respects easier to analyze, because the peak to be measured will always be 2 mass units higher than the one due to the unlabeled species. The normal isotope peak of organic molecules, mainly due to C^{13}, therefore does not interfere, and the one due to the presence of two C^{13} atoms is generally of very low intensity. This advantage is partly offset by the fact that O^{18} labeling is done mostly at relatively low isotope concentrations.

5-3. INCORPORATION OF STABLE ISOTOPES FOR STRUCTURE DETERMINATIONS

The fact that in mass spectrometry a method is available for determining the number and location of stable isotopes within a molecule makes it an attractive technique for determining the structure of a molecule by incorporating such isotopes, using specific chemical reactions. Deuterium may be introduced in a molecule (1) by exchange of labile hydrogen atoms, (2) by replacement of a functional group with deuterium, and (3) by the saturation of multiple bonds with deuterium.

A. Incorporation by Exchange

Determination of the number of hydrogen atoms attached to a carbon alpha to a carbonyl group is a good example for the first group. Treatment of cyclohexanone with D_2O and alkali (carbonate or hydroxide) converts it to tetradeuterocyclohexanone:

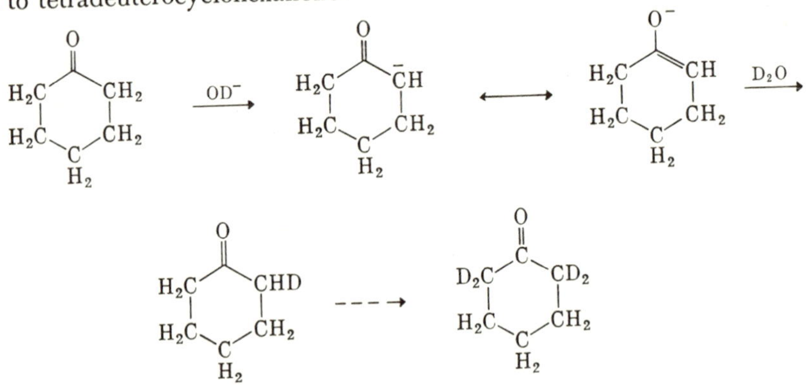

For compounds insoluble in boiling water, it is necessary to use CH_3OD or C_2H_5OD as a solvent, or mixtures of these or dioxane with D_2O. The isolation of the deuterated product is rather simple, requiring only the evaporation of most of the alcohol and extraction of the product with ether, after addition of D_2O to dissolve any remaining inorganic material. Ordinary water or proton-containing acids must be avoided in the working up of such reaction mixtures to prevent the exchange of deuterium by hydrogen. The number of deuterium atoms incorporated in the molecule is determined from the mass spectrum of the compound, as discussed in Sec. 5-1. The advantages of this technique over a deuterium determination through combustion of the sample, followed by a density measurement of the water formed, are, as outlined earlier, that the equilibration does not have to be carried to completion, that the product of the reaction does not have to be extensively purified, that any change occurring in the compound other than deuteration is disclosed by the mass spectrum, and that a small amount of material suffices for both the exchange and determination. In addition, it is frequently possible to draw valuable conclusions from the mass of fragment peaks that indicate the location of the deuterium atom(s) within the molecule.

A few examples may serve as an illustration for some of these points.

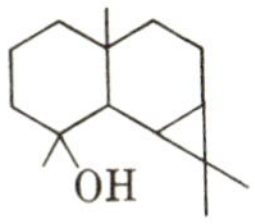

(7) 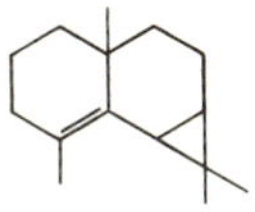　　　　　　(8) 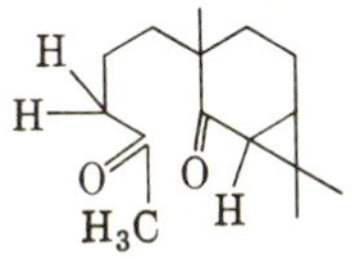　　　　　　(9)

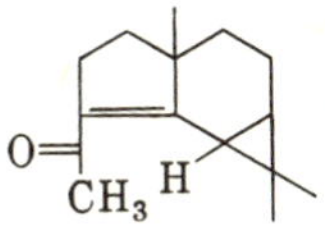

(12)　　and/or　　(13) 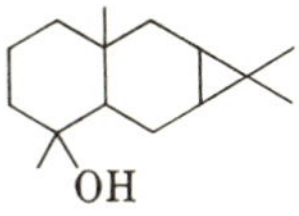　　　　(10) 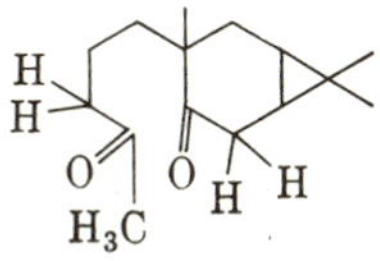　　　　(11)

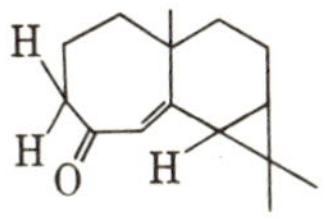

In the course of elucidating the structure of maaliol (7) [14] it was necessary to determine the site of the attachment of the three-membered ring. Upon dehydration of maaliol and oxidation of the olefin (8), the diketone (9) was obtained. This molecule would have a total of six hydrogen atoms alpha to a carbonyl group if structure (7) were correct. If maaliol, on the other hand, were (10), for example, the resulting diketone (11) would contain seven such hydrogen atoms. Treatment of the diketone with deuteroethanol and alkali gave a product, the mass spectrum of which showed that the compound had gained five and six atoms of deuterium because, instead of the single peak at mass 236 in the undeuterated sample, there are now present two peaks, at mass 241 and 242. This result indicated that (9) rather than (11) was the correct expression for this diketone and that five of the deuterium atoms had exchanged faster than the sixth one, probably the hydrogen atom attached to the ring junction.

In the spectrum of the reaction product there appeared, however, two additional peaks at mass 221 and 222 which could not be correlated with any peak in the undeuterated starting material. Their intensity indicated that they are most probably peaks of molecular ions, and the mass difference from the other pair of peaks of 20 units led to the conclusion that the diketone has in part undergone base-catalyzed elimination of water. The product of such a condensation, (12) or (13), would have molecular weight 218, and it follows that under the conditions of deuteration three and four hydrogen atoms, respectively, were replaced by deuterium either before or after cyclization.

It should be noted that neither the incomplete exchange which led to

[14] G. Büchi, M. Schach Von Wittenau, and D. M. White, *J. Am. Chem. Soc.*, **81**, 1968 (1959).

a mixture of penta- and hexadeuteroketone nor the extensive cyclization of the product containing a different D/H ratio had any influence on the results; the conclusion is that in the starting diketone six hydrogen atoms may be exchanged. An earlier experiment in which the deuterium content was determined by combustion to water led to values in very close agreement with the incorporation of five deuterium atoms, a result rather puzzling at that time.

A similar situation arose in the course of the determination of the structure of aromadendrene, for which structure (14) was finally proved correct.[15] Acid-catalyzed opening of the three-membered ring could lead to four possible isomers (15a, b, c, and d). Ozonization of the olefin gave a diketone which upon deuterium exchange incorporated six atoms of deuterium, as borne out by the shift of the molecular weight from mass 208 to 214. This result would seem to rule out structures (16a) and (16b) in favor of (16c) and (16d). The presence of a peak both at mass 43 and 165 ($M - 43$) in the undeuterated diketone, however, indicated the presence of a CH_3CO group. This was confirmed by the shift of these peaks to mass 46 and mass 168, respectively, in the deuterated sample. While the formation of either one of those fragments might possibly be due to a rearrangement peak of a molecule not containing the acetyl group, the presence of both those peaks which on deuteration specifically retain three deuterium atoms makes such a rearrangement extremely unlikely and corroborates the presence of an acetyl group.

(14)

a

b

c, d

(15) R=CH_2
(16) R=O

It would seem that both (16a) and (16b) would exchange seven hydrogen atoms, since it has seven such atoms alpha to a carbonyl group. Inspection of a model shows, however, that the enol form of (16a), the intermediate in the exchange reaction, is greatly hindered because of the interference of the methyl group on the five-membered ring with the methyl or hydroxyl of the enol grouping, since all these atoms are forced into nearly one plane. It was thus possible to deduce even the position of the acetyl group in this molecule, which must have structure (16a).

[15] G. Büchi et al. (To be published.)

Also in this case a nonspecific deuterium determination would have led to erroneous results.

A further example, the locating of a carbonyl group in a more complex degradation product [(20a), Chap. 8] of an alkaloid, will be discussed later.

It has been pointed out on page 218 that it is difficult to determine deuterium bound to oxygen, nitrogen, or sulfur because of exchange taking place in the mass spectrometer. This can, in part, be prevented by saturating the instrument with D_2O; while it is difficult to obtain accurate quantitative results, it is nevertheless possible to determine in this way the number of active hydrogens in a molecule.

This approach was used [16] in the investigation of a substance obtained in the course of the isolation of biologically active constituents of a plant. It was a hydrochloride of a base $C_6H_{13}ON$, but the amount of material available was insufficient for a further chemical investigation. The free base obtained from 1 mg of the salt, on addition of aqueous sodium carbonate and extraction with ether, was introduced into the spectrometer using the technique outlined for dilute solutions in Sec. 2-5A, and the spectrum shown in Fig. 5-10a was obtained. The very small peak at m/e 115 (not visible in Fig. 5-10) could not be used as an argument for the molecular weight, because it was not much higher than the background. However, the characteristic changes of the intensity of the peak at 116, which could be observed when the spectrum was determined in the "nonfocused" position (see page 56), corroborated the mol. wt 115. It is made even more plausible by the presence of a considerable peak at mass 100, which could be due to the loss of a methyl group.

The most intense peak at mass 58 could represent either $(C_3H_8N)^+$ or $(C_3H_6O)^+$. The latter possibility, however, seems to be excluded, as the peak at m/e 60 was only 0.19 per cent as intense as mass 58, which would exclude the presence of oxygen. The occurrence of a nitrogen-containing fragment was also plausible, since the compound was known to be a base, and the structure of the species of mass 58 could thus be any one of the following:

$$
\underset{(17a)}{\overset{\displaystyle CH_3-CH_2-\overset{+}{C}H}{\underset{\displaystyle NH_2}{|}}}
\qquad
\underset{(17b)}{\overset{\displaystyle CH_3}{\underset{\displaystyle CH_3-\overset{+}{C}}{\underset{\displaystyle NH_2}{|}}}}
\qquad
\underset{(17c)}{\overset{\displaystyle CH_3-\overset{+}{C}H}{\underset{\displaystyle NHCH_3}{|}}}
\qquad
\underset{(17d)}{\overset{\displaystyle \overset{+}{C}H_2}{\underset{\displaystyle N(CH_3)_2}{|}}}
$$

[16] Unpublished experiments from the author's laboratory (by G G. J. Deffner) on a sample kindly supplied by F. C. Steward.

Although the intensity of the peak indicated fragmentation at a highly substituted carbon atom, which would point to structure (17b), it was thought to be advantageous to determine, if possible, the number of hydrogen atoms bound to nitrogen. This was done by converting another specimen of the hydrochloride to the free base, using a solution of sodium

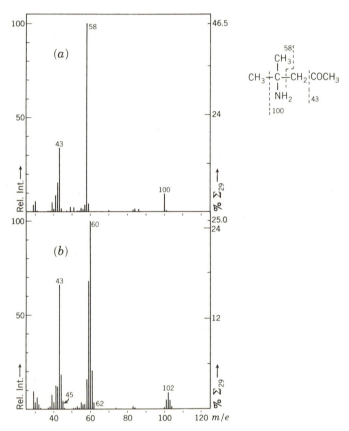

Fig. 5-10. Mass spectra of diacetoneamine (a) before and (b) after treatment with D$_2$O.

carbonate in D$_2$O, and determining the mass spectrum of the product after injection of D$_2$O into the instrument to displace any ordinary water present. If the peak at mass 58 corresponded to (17a) or (17b), it would shift to mass 60; if it were (17c), it would become mass 59; and if it were (17e), it would remain at mass 58. Surprisingly, the mass spectrum obtained (Fig. 5-10b) showed peaks up to mass 62, indicating the incorporation of up to four deuterium atoms into this fragment. Similarly, the fragment, originally of mass 100, was spread over the region m/e 100 to 105, and surprisingly enough, also the peak at mass 43 was spread up to mass 46. These findings indicated the presence of another group in the molecule containing exchangeable hydrogen atoms, and the whole spectrum could be explained on the basis of a methyl ketone, which may undergo rearrangement of Type H to form a fragment of mass 58. Any deuterium incorporated in this ketonic fragment, plus the one acquired in the course of the rearrangement, would manifest itself in a corresponding increase of the mass of this fragment. The only two structures in agreement with these spectra are the amino ketones (18) and (19):

$$
\begin{array}{cc}
\underset{\substack{|\\ NH_2}}{CH_3-\underset{|}{\overset{CH_3}{\underset{|}{CH}}}-CH_2-\underset{\parallel}{\overset{}{C}}-CH_3}
& CH_3-CH_2-\underset{\substack{|\\ NH_2}}{CH}-CH_2-\underset{\parallel}{\overset{}{C}}-CH_3 \\
O & O \\
(18) & (19)
\end{array}
$$

The peak at mass 58 is due, therefore, to two different fragments—one of them containing oxygen while the other one does not—thus accounting for the low intensity of the isotope peak at mass 60 in Fig. 5-10a. Expression (18) seemed the more probable one, and was proved to be correct by comparison of the spectrum shown in Fig. 5-10a with the spectrum of diacetoneamine. A reinvestigation of the isolation procedure indicated that this compound was formed as an artifact.

While such a technique would be very useful for the determination of active hydrogen in a molecule, it should be used with caution, because obviously any compound containing hydrogen attached to oxygen, nitrogen, or sulfur will also exchange some hydrogen if run immediately after such a deuteration experiment. Great care must be taken to remove all D_2O from the instrument and replace it with water. This requires repeatedly introducing ordinary water or methanol, warming of the cold traps, and perhaps even baking of the ion source and analyzer tube.

All these labeling experiments for structure determination have been done with deuterium. While the incorporation of C^{13} and N^{15} by exchange or another simple reaction is not easily possible, O^{18} may be incorporated in an organic molecule containing carbonyl groups by treatment with H_2O^{18} and the addition of some acid or base as a catalyst if necessary. Carbonyl groups present in the molecule can be labeled by this technique:

$$
\underset{-O-}{\overset{O^{16}}{\overset{\parallel}{}}} \xrightarrow{+H_2O^{18}} \underset{-C-}{\overset{HO^{18} \quad O^{16} H}{\diagdown \diagup}} \xrightarrow{-H_2O^{16}} \underset{-C-}{\overset{O^{18}}{\overset{\parallel}{}}}
$$

Such experiments [16a] are generally performed with relatively low concentrations (5 to 20 per cent) of O^{18} because of the high price of water containing O^{18} almost exclusively. The number of carbonyl or other exchangeable groups is therefore best deduced from the intensity of the $M + 2$ peak and not from the increase in molecular weight. After complete exchange, the relative intensities of M, $M + 2$, $M + 4$, etc., must obey Eq. (3-16) ($a = H_2O^{16}/H_2O^{16} + H_2O^{18}$; $b = H_2O^{18}/H_2O^{16} + H_2O^{18}$, n = number of exchangeable oxygens).

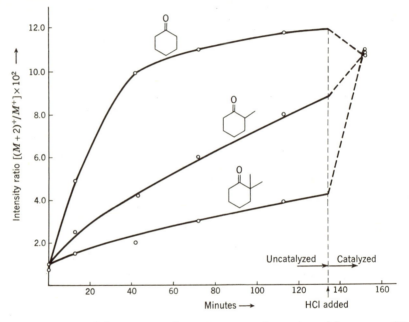

Fig. 5-11. Increase of the $M + 2$ peak upon oxygen exchange in cyclohexanones. (For details see text.)

Equilibration of cyclohexanone with water containing a total of 11.4 per cent H_2O^{18} leads to an intensity ratio of m/e 100:m/e 98 of 1:0.118 (Fig. 5-11). The theoretical value of 0.131 (0.129 for O^{18} plus 0.002 for C_2^{13}) is not quite reached, owing to dilution of the H_2O^{18} during the reaction unless used in large excess. On the other hand, for a compound containing two carbonyl groups, the intensity ratio for M, $M + 2$, $M + 4$ should be 1:0.257:0.0165.

These values can be quite easily determined experimentally; often it suffices to merely mix the compound with an excess of water containing O^{18}. In most cases it will be necessary to use a water-miscible organic

[16a] Unpublished experiments from the author's laboratory.

solvent—tetrahydrofurane or a bulky alcohol such as isopropanol, for example—which cannot successfully compete with water in the addition to the carbonyl group. After a suitable period of time, part of the entire mixture is introduced into the mass spectrometer, and the spectrum is determined in the region of the molecular weight to obtain the intensities of M^+ and $(M+2)^+$.

The exchange of oxygen in a carbonyl group involves a change both in bond angle and in the space requirement when the molecule of water is added in the first step, and the rate of this reaction is thus greatly influenced by the structural environment of the carbonyl group. Alkyl substituents attached to the α carbon decrease the rate of exchange considerably, as shown in Fig. 5-11 which represents data obtained in a single experiment—the exchange of a mixture of cyclohexanone, 2-methylcyclohexanone, and 2,2-dimethylcyclohexanone; water (11.2 per cent excess O^{18}); and isopropanol, containing about equal weights of total ketones, water, and isopropanol. At suitable time intervals the spectrum of small samples is determined. If necessary, the reaction can be accelerated by the addition of a trace of hydrochloric acid.

Although information regarding the number of α substituents can also be obtained from deuterium exchange, oxygen equilibration is more sensitive to the size of the substituents and, in the case of cyclic ketones, of the ring.

Thus oxygen exchange has considerable potential as an indicator of the presence of carbonyl groups and as an aid in the elucidation of their environment, especially if more than one such group, with different rates of exchange, are present in the molecule. In addition, the information obtainable from the mass spectrum of a compound labeled with O^{18} aids in the interpretation.

The ease in which competition experiments, such as the one leading to the data in Fig. 5-11, can be performed greatly facilitates the determination of relative exchange rates, because all species are by necessity subjected to identical conditions throughout the experiment.

B. Incorporation by Replacement

Deuterium may also be introduced into a molecule by replacement of a functional group. The reactions most suitable are reduction with lithium aluminum deuteride or decomposition of Grignard reagents with DCl. Such a replacement of a functional group by deuterium may be used for one of two reasons: First, if a functional group decreases the volatility of the material so much that the spectrum of the parent compound cannot be obtained, the removal of the functional group by a reaction which introduces deuterium in its place makes it possible to obtain a more volatile derivative in which the position of the functional group can still be recognized. The conversion of an alcohol grouping into a CD group or of carboxyl into —CD_3 was used, for example, in the conversion of peptides containing hydroxyamino acids or aminodicarboxylic acids into the much more volatile polyamines (Sec. 7-2).[17] A methyl group derived from a primary alcohol will then correspond to 16 mass units (CH_2D), while a methyl group derived from a carboxyl group will be —CD_3 (18 mass units). In the mass spectrum such methyl groups may be easily distinguished from each other.

The other reason for the replacement by deuterium is the conversion of the unknown material by this reaction into a known compound with a mass spectrum which has already been interpreted in detail. It is then generally possible to locate the heavy isotope in this molecule, thus revealing the structure of the original compound. For determining the structure of iboxygaine, an alkaloid which was suspected to be a hydroxy derivative of ibogaine (20), the hydroxy group was replaced by deuterium.[18]

(20) R = H
(21) R = D
(22) R = OH

This conversion, which involved a reduction of iboxygaine tosylate by lithium aluminum deuteride, in fact produced ibogaine, thus proving the first assumption to be correct. The mass spectrum of this sample was very similar to the one of ibogaine (Fig. 8-5), which had been determined previously, with the exception of a shift of 1 mass unit of certain peaks including the molecular weight, indicating that, as expected, one atom of deuterium had been specifically incorporated.

Some of the peaks of the two mass spectra are compared in Fig. 5-12, showing that the methyl group in the deuterated sample is still lost as CH_3 (15 mass units) while the ethyl group is lost as C_2H_4D (30 mass units). The deuterium atom is, therefore, not located in the methyl group but is present in the ethyl group, and it follows that the deuterated ibo-

[17] K. Biemann and W. Vetter, *Biochem. Biophys. Research Comm.*, 3, 578 (1960),
[18] K. Biemann and M. Friedmann-Spiteller, *Tetrahedron Letters*, no. 2, p. 68, 1961; *J. Am. Chem. Soc.*, 83, 4805 (1961).

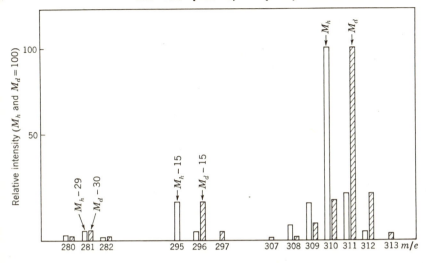

Fig. 5-12. Mass spectra of ibogaine (light) and ibogaine-20-*d* (shaded) in the region from mass 280 to 320. (*From Ref. 18.*)

gaine obtained in this reaction is represented by (21) and iboxygaine is, therefore, (22). A more detailed discussion of the mass spectra of deuterated ibogaine molecules will be presented in Sec. 8-2A. A number of other deuteration experiments have been done in the course of the work on the structure of sarpagine.[19]

C. Incorporation by Addition to Multiple Bonds

The saturation of multiple bonds with deuterium would seem to be one of the most straightforward reactions for incorporating deuterium in a molecule to locate a double bond. This is especially desirable in that, as pointed out in Sec. 3-2A, it is frequently impossible to determine the position of a double bond on the basis of a mass spectrum of the olefinic compound because of the mobility of such multiple bonds within the molecular ion or the fragments. Treatment of an unsaturated molecule with deuterium and a hydrogenation catalyst in a proton-free solvent leads not only to the addition of two deuterium atoms to the double bond but in the majority of cases to extensive exchange of hydrogen at saturated centers. One example, the catalytic deuteration of *N*-benzoylproline, has already been mentioned in Sec. 5-2.

It has also been shown[20] that methyl oleate incorporates up to 18

[19] K. Biemann, *J. Am. Chem. Soc.*, **83**, 4801 (1961).

[20] Ng. Dinh-Nguyen and R. Ryhage, *Acta Chem. Scand.*, **13**, 1032 (1959); *J. Research Inst., Hokkaido Univ.*, **8**, 73 (1960).

atoms of deuterium into the molecule, borne out by the mass spectrum of the reduction product (methyl stearate) shown in Fig. 5-13. Obviously, it is not possible to determine the number and position of double bonds present in such a molecule by catalytic deuteration. Chemical reduction involving deuterated reagents lead, however, to a specific addition of deuterium on the double bond, and deuterohydrazine (N_2D_4) has been used for locating the double bond in methyl oleate and some of its isomers.[21]

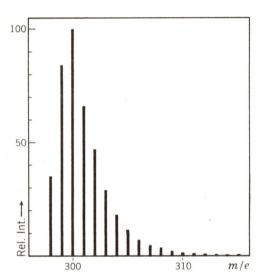

Fig. 5-13. Mass spectrum of methyl polydeuterostearate. (*From Ref. 20.*)

The recent discovery of diimide (N_2H_2) as the active agent in the reduction of double bonds [22-24] opens a much simpler way to saturate a double bond with deuterium. Reaction of the olefin with anthracene-9,10-biimine in D_2O-dioxane solution leads to saturation of the double bond with deuterium.[24a] These techniques make it unnecessary .to prepare deuterohydrazine and, in addition, increase the rate of reduction. Tri- and tetrasubstituted double bonds are, however, not attacked by diimide. Tri-

[21] Ng. Dinh-Nguyen, R. Ryhage, and S. Ställberg-Stenhagen, *Arkiv Kemi*, 15, 433 (1960).

[22] E. J. Corey, W. L. Mock, and D. J. Pasto, *Tetrahedron Letters*, no. 11, p. 347, 1961.

[23] S. Hünig, H. R. Müller, and W. Thier, *Tetrahedron Letters*, no. 11, p. 353, 1961.

[24] E. E. van Tamelen, R. S. Dewey, and R. J. Timmons, *J. Am. Chem. Soc.*, 83, 3725 (1961).

[24a] E. J. Corey and W. L. Mock, *J. Am. Chem. Soc.*, 84, 685 (1962).

substituted olefins require prolonged heating (up to a few days) with hydrazine for appreciable reduction.

The unspecific exchange of hydrogen by deuterium in the course of catalytic deuteration seems, however, to be very dependent on the structure and stereochemistry of the olefin. A derivative (23) of sarpagine, an alkaloid containing an exocyclic ethylidene group, incorporated only up to six deuterium atoms,[19] five of which were located in the resulting ethyl group and must therefore be attached to the carbon atoms marked with an asterisk in structure (23); the sixth one must have been on the six-membered ring, as deduced from the mass spectrum.

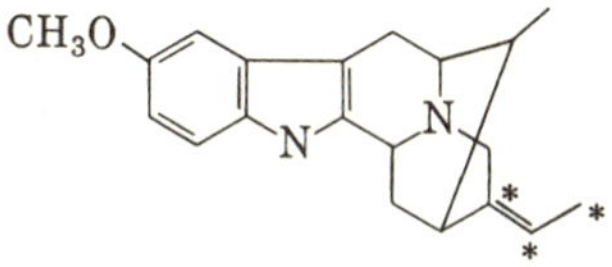

(23)

The particular geometry of this polycyclic ring system seems to prevent the molecule from attaining a position on the catalyst in which more than these carbon atoms come close to the metal surface.

The presence in the molecule of fully substituted carbon atoms also seems to prevent hydrogen exchange beyond that point. Catalytic deuteration of β,β-di-*tert*-butylacrylic ester leads mainly to the saturation of the double bond with deuterium but very little deuterium incorporation in the methyl groups,[25] in marked contrast to the exchange taking place in methyl oleate. The type and extent of catalytic exchange of hydrogen by deuterium may thus be used for the purpose of gaining some insight into the environment of the double bond.

From the few examples cited in the discussion it is obvious how useful the mass spectra of specifically labeled derivatives are for determining the structure of a complex molecule. It is very helpful and revealing to have at hand the spectrum of the unlabeled substance as well, which may be readily available or may be prepared in the course of an identical reaction not involving labeled reagents.

5-4. APPLICATIONS IN THE INVESTIGATION OF REACTION MECHANISMS

While the use of stable or radioactive isotopes for the elucidation of reaction mechanisms is a well-known and widely applied technique, a few particular aspects of the use of the mass spectra of the intact molecule

[25] Unpublished spectra of samples kindly provided by A. Mehta.

will be discussed in detail. There are in principle two situations in which only the mass spectrum of the entire, undegraded molecule permits drawing definite conclusions: in some problems it is important to determine the location of the isotope within the molecule rather than the average concentration in the sample; for other investigations it is necessary to incorporate two isotopes in the molecule and to determine whether they both remain in the same molecule or become separated during the reaction. The latter technique is frequently called "double labeling." In addition, there are situations where it is desired to follow a small increase or decrease in the isotope content of a molecule during the course of a reaction which may extend over a long period of time. Such measurements can be made most easily and without requiring much time and material by measuring the mass spectrum of the product of the reaction at different time intervals.

The position of the deuterium atom introduced on reduction of a halohydrin (24) with lithium aluminum deuteride had to be known in order to distinguish direct replacement from the alternative, elimination of HBr prior to reduction: [26]

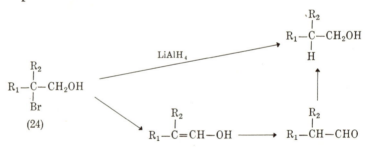

When 2-bromo-1-butanol $[(24), R_1 = C_2H_5, R_2 = H]$ was reduced to 1-butanol, the mass spectrum of the product still exhibited an intense peak at mass 31 and therefore had to be 1-butanol-2-d (25):

$$CH_3-CH_2-CHD\dashv CH_2OH$$
$$\vdots 31$$

(25)

The isomeric 2-bromo-2-methyl-1-propanol $[(24), R_1 = R_2 = CH_3]$ led, however, to a mixture of isobutanol molecules, 85 per cent of which were deuterated at C-1, indicating elimination, while 15 per cent contained the deuterium at C-2 and are therefore the product of the normal reaction. The same results can, of course, be obtained by oxidation of the alcohol to the corresponding acid, the deuterium content of which, determined

[26] E. L. Eliel and T. J. Prosser, *J. Am. Chem. Soc.*, 78, 4045 (1956).

by combustion, would also indicate how much deuterium is present at C-2. It is obvious how much more involved this procedure would be compared with determining the mass spectrum of the original reduction product.

The Hofmann degradation of carboxamides was shown to be an intramolecular reaction by a double-labeling experiment.[27] On treatment of a mixture of *m*-deuterobenzamide (26) and N^{15}-labeled benzamide (27)

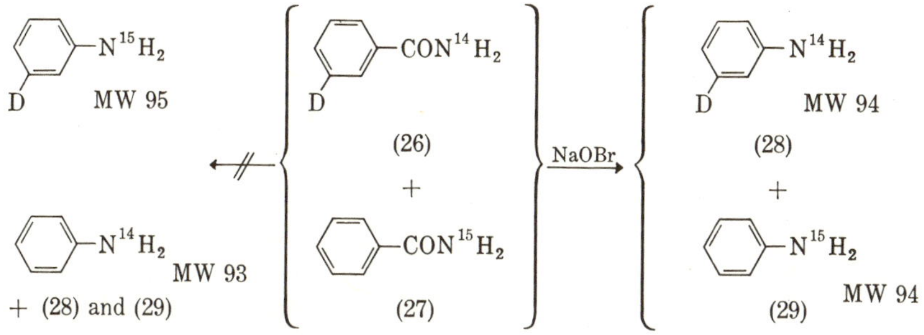

with sodium hypobromite, aniline was formed which, according to the mass spectrum, consisted only of species of mol. wt 94. If at any stage of the reaction the nitrogen should become separated from the aromatic ring as, for example, in an intermolecular reaction, both nonlabeled and double-labeled aniline would have to be formed, and the mass spectrum would then show the presence of species of mol. wt 93, 94, and 95. Since neither the total deuterium content nor the total N^{15} content changes during the reaction, the two mechanisms cannot be distinguished by any technique which involves merely the determination of the average concentration of these two isotopes in the sample. Even specific degradation would be useless.

Double labeling may also be used in all instances in which a symmetrical dimer is thought to be an intermediate which can decompose in two ways to a monomeric product. Such an experiment was used [28] to eliminate the following mechanism for the photoisomerization of *trans*-benzalacetone (30):

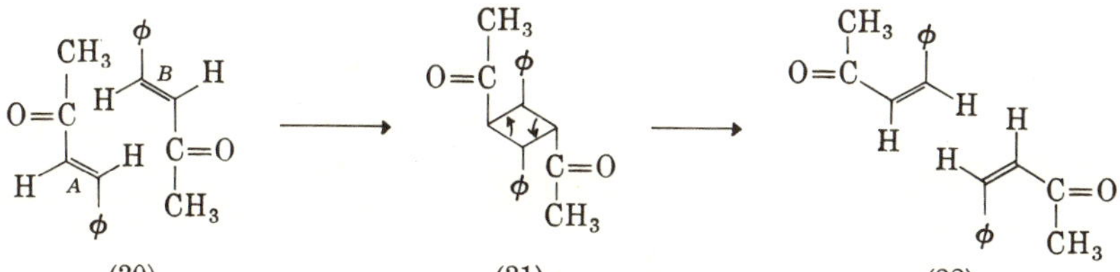

[27] T. J. Prosser and E. L. Eliel, *J. Am. Chem. Soc.*, 79, 2544 (1957).
[28] H. O. House, *J. Org. Chem.*, 24, 1374 (1959).

If the two molecules A and B would dimerize to (31), which then would decompose to two molecules of *cis*-benzalacetone (32), each one of the two molecules formed would consist in part of the original molecule A and in part of B. When a mixture of ordinary *trans*-benzalacetone and its pentadeutero derivative ($C_6H_5CD{=}CDCOCD_3$) was irradiated, the mass spectrum of the isolated product showed the absence of any species of mol. wt 148 or 149, which could be formed each time the isomerization proceeded through the dimer (31). It should be pointed out that in such an experiment it is not necessary to isolate the desired reaction product—in this case *cis*-benzalacetone—in pure form.

Some experiments concerned with the validity of Bredt's rule in bicyclic systems of medium ring size involved determining the exchangeability of bridgehead hydrogens. There is no reason to assume an abrupt change at a particular ring size when proceeding from small rings to large ones but rather that the rate of exchange—that is, the rate of enolization—will become consecutively faster. Most of the experiments published in this area are based on preparative reactions. It seemed of interest to use a more subtle approach, namely, the detection of even small amounts of deuterium incorporated during a long reaction period into those bicyclic ketones said not to enolize at all.

(33)   (34)

When the bicyclic ketone (33) containing eight carbon atoms in the larger ring was treated with sodium methoxide and methanol-*O-d* for 1 hr at room temperature, complete exchange of two hydrogen atoms by deuterium had taken place, as evidenced by the mass spectrum, which indicated a mol. wt 154 compared with 152 for the standard.[29] Under those conditions the lower homolog (34), in which the larger of the two rings contains only seven carbon atoms, did not incorporate any deuterium, as evidenced by the unchanged ratio of the peak intensities at m/e 138 and 139 before and after this treatment. When the reaction mixture, however, was heated to reflux and a small amount withdrawn after 24 hr, the material isolated had incorporated some deuterium and consisted of a mixture of 84 per cent undeuterated, 15 per cent monodeuterated, and 1 per cent dideuterated ketone (34). Another sample, with-

[29] Unpublished experiments from the author's laboratory (by M. Friedmann-Spiteller).

drawn after 48 hr, consisted of 41 per cent, 47 per cent, and 13 per cent of these species. This simple experiment clearly shows that the ketone (34) is able to enolize, even though at a very slow rate. The reliability of this technique is illustrated by the fact that Gutsche [30] had performed essentially the same experiments but had to rely on the detection of incorporated deuterium by combustion of the product to water and concluded that the bicyclic ketone (34) does not incorporate any deuterium. These investigators ascribed the 0.14 atom equivalent of deuterium found in the sample to an impurity rather than to deuterated ketone.

In view of the important position of Bredt's rule in certain structural and mechanistic arguments, a clear definition of its qualitative and quantitative validity would be desirable and may be achieved by a number of experiments of this kind performed on different ketones related to (33) and (34).

5-5. APPLICATIONS IN THE INVESTIGATION OF BIOCHEMICAL MECHANISMS

The exploration of chemical reactions occurring within the living cell or in isolated enzyme preparations also frequently calls for the specific location of an isotope rather than the measurement of the total amount of isotope incorporated. One of the most elegant examples for the use of this technique is the investigation of the biosynthesis of squalene [undeuterated (37)] from farnesyl pyrophosphate by Cornforth et al.[31] Enzymatic synthesis using mevalonic acid-5-d_2 (35) surprisingly led to squalene

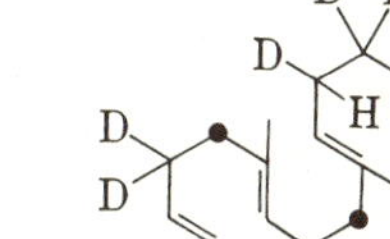

$$
\begin{array}{c}
HO \diagdown \quad CH_3 \\
 C \\
H_2C \diagup \diagdown CH_2 \\
| | \\
HO-CD_2 COOH
\end{array}
$$

(35)

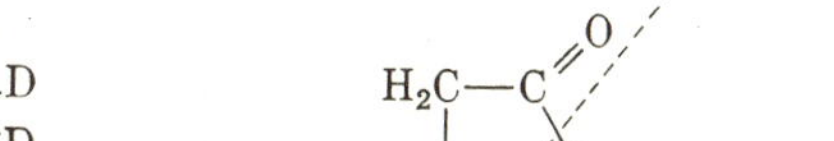

(36)

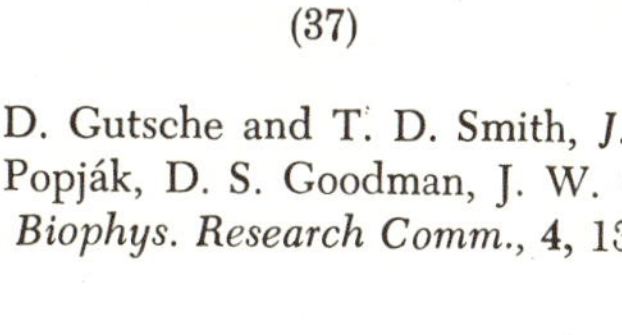

(37)

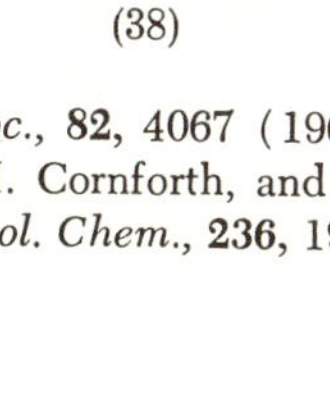

(38)

[30] C. D. Gutsche and T. D. Smith, *J. Am. Chem. Soc.*, **82**, 4067 (1960).
[31] G. Popják, D. S. Goodman, J. W. Cornforth, R. H. Cornforth, and R. Ryhage, *Biochem. Biophys. Research Comm.*, **4**, 138 (1961); *J. Biol. Chem.*, **236**, 1934 (1961).

containing 11 atoms of deuterium rather than 12 (or 10) as expected if the intermediate, farnesyl pyrophosphate (36), which in this case must contain 6 deuterium atoms, would enzymatically couple to squalene by a symmetrical mechanism.

The number of deuterium.atoms and their distribution in the central part of the squalene molecule was determined on the basis of the mass spectrum of a sample of succinic anhydride obtained on ozonization of the squalene, isolation of the succinic acid formed, and cyclization to the anhydride. While only about 1.5 to 2.5 mg of succinic acid was formed in such an experiment, usable mass spectra were still obtained. Although succinic anhydride (38) does not exhibit an intense peak for the molecular weight, it was possible to deduce the total amount of deuterium from the fragment due to the loss of carbon dioxide, which is found at m/e 56 in the nondeuterated sample while it is at mass 60 in the tetradeuterated derivative prepared for comparison. This fragment clearly showed that in the succinic anhydride derived from squalene three atoms of deuterium were present. All the other fragment peaks corroborated the assignment. The correctness of the assumptions regarding the fragmentation of succinic anhydride was supported by the mass spectra of authentic symmetrically and unsymmetrically dideuterated anhydride in addition to the already mentioned tetradeuterated compound.

The evaluation of the spectrum of the sample derived from the degradation of squalene was complicated by the fact that succinic acid is also formed to a lesser extent from other parts of the molecule. It was for this reason that in the experiment a small amount of mevalonic acid-2-C^{14} also had been added, thereby introducing a radioactive label in all the positions marked with a heavy dot in structure (37). Any radioactive succinic acid found thus arises from the periphery of the molecule and will contain only two atoms of deuterium. By measuring the radioactivity of this sample of succinic anhydride it was possible to subtract the contributions of dideuterated anhydride which would otherwise interfere with the molecules arising from the center.

On the basis of these experiments it was concluded that the deuterium distribution in this sample is as shown in expression (37).

Recently these investigators have further confirmed [32] the loss of one deuterium atom during the enzymatic coupling of two molecules of farnesol-1,1-d_2 to trideuterosqualene. The sample of squalene isolated in the incubation experiment exhibited prominent peaks at both m/e 410

[32] G. Popják, J. W. Cornforth, R. H. Cornforth, R. Ryhage, and D. S. Goodman, *J. Biol. Chem.*, **237**, 56 (1962).

and m/e 413, corresponding to nondeuterated (35.7 per cent) and trideuterated (64.3 per cent) species. The absence of other isotopic species was shown by correction of the spectra for the natural abundance of C^{13} and D. From the groups of peaks due to loss of 43 and 69 mass units, respectively, similar results were obtained (67.5 per cent and 65.2 per cent squalene-d_3), indicating that about two-thirds of the isolated squalene was synthesized from labeled farnesol while the rest had been present in the substrate.

A few possible biosynthetic mechanisms in agreement with such an unsymmetrical dimerization of farnesyl pyrophosphate have been suggested by these investigators. Earlier experiments from another laboratory,[33] which involved dilution of the labeled compound with unlabeled material and deuterium analysis by combustion, had led to results which indicated the incorporation of only 10 atoms of deuterium.

For studies concerning the metabolism of amino acids it is of interest to determine N^{15} in these compounds. This may be done by determining the mass spectrum of the corresponding ethyl ester, since the "amine fragment" formed by loss of the carbethoxy group (cleavage of Type *B*) contains the nitrogen atom (see Sec. 7-1). Even rather small amounts of N^{15} (above 0.3 per cent excess) can be detected. The major advantage is the possibility of determining the individual isotope content of all the components of a mixture of amino acids without prior separation.[34]

5-6. APPLICATIONS IN THE INVESTIGATION OF ELECTRON-IMPACT MECHANISMS

For the elucidation of electron-impact–induced fragmentation reactions as they occur in the mass spectrometer, the extensive use of labeled molecules is of extreme importance. Many examples of such experiments were discussed in Chap. 3, and additional ones will be mentioned in later sections. It is therefore neither necessary nor possible to repeat all these here, but it should be pointed out that such experiments should be done whenever conceivably possible and wherever any detailed fragmentation mechanism is proposed. Only in this way can the accumulation of incorrectly formulated fragmentation processes in the published literature be prevented.

It is of equal importance in such experiments to use samples which

[33] H. C. Rilling and K. Bloch, *J. Biol. Chem.*, 234, 1424 (1959).
[34] K. Biemann and G. G. J. Deffner, *Biochem. Biophys. Research Comm.*, 4, 283 (1961).

are specifically labeled for this particular purpose rather than those which are available by chance in connection with other experiments. Particular emphasis must be placed upon the use of fully labeled groups if more than purely qualitative conclusions are to be drawn. Statements concerning the extent to which two or more competing reactions proceed are likely to be in error if the abstraction or rearrangement of hydrogen is involved and a compound incompletely deuterated at the position in question is used. The magnitude of the isotope effects, which, in general, facilitate removal of hydrogen rather than deuterium, is not known, thus making a correction impossible.

On the other hand, a study of the spectra of partially and completely labeled species would be an interesting approach to the evaluation of such isotope effects in electron-impact reactions.

6. Fatty Acids and Related Substances

6-1. LONG-CHAIN ALIPHATIC ACIDS AND ESTERS

Detailed investigations of the mass spectra of fatty esters, unsubstituted and substituted, by Ryhage, Stenhagen, and their collaborators [1] resulted in a thorough knowledge of the behavior of these compounds upon electron impact.

The main features of the mass spectrum of the methyl ester of a long-chain fatty acid are a result of the fragmentation reactions discussed in Sec. 3-2A and B, particularly fragmentations of Type A_1 and the rearrangement of Type H involving the ester group. The mass spectrum of methyl stearate [2] shown in Fig. 6-1 exhibits the intense peak at m/e 74 expected of a methyl ester of a long-chain acid, unsubstituted at C_α (see Type H, Sec. 3-2B).

It is of interest to note that the majority of the intense peaks are oxygen-containing fragments; i.e., the positive charge is more easily retained on the species containing the carbomethoxy group. Furthermore, there is a peculiar periodicity with respect to the cleavage of carbon-carbon bonds further along the chain, as fragments which have retained, in addition to the carbomethoxy group, 6, 10, 14 CH_2 groups (m/e 143, 199, and 255) are particularly abundant. A "transhelical" reaction involving the elimination of C_4 fragments has been suggested as an explanation.[1]

The mass spectra of free fatty acids are analogous to the spectra of the methyl esters with the exception that the peaks due to fragments con-

---

[1] For a review of this work and references in addition to the ones cited in this chapter, see R. Ryhage and E. Stenhagen, *J. Lipid Research*, **1**, 361 (1960).

[2] R. Ryhage and E. Stenhagen, *Arkiv Kemi*, **13**, 523 (1959).

taining the carbomethoxy group are found 14 mass units lower, e.g., at m/e 60, 129, 185, and 241, depending on the length of the chain. The spectrum of myristic acid is shown in Fig. 6-2.

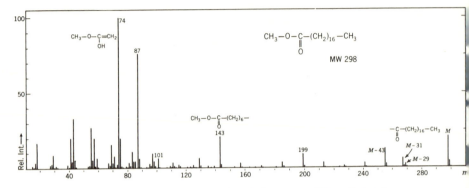

Fig. 6-1. Mass spectrum of methyl stearate. (*From Ref.* 1.)

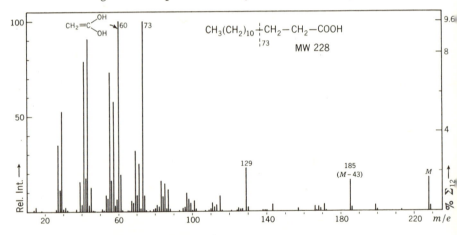

Fig. 6-2. Mass spectrum of myristic acid.

The molecular ions of these acids and esters are relatively abundant and the determination of the molecular weight of an unsubstituted fatty acid or ester is thus easily possible. The intensity of the molecular ions seems to increase with chain length.[2]

If additional substituents are introduced into the hydrocarbon chain, they will influence the fragmentation of the molecule, and, depending on the character of the functional group, the changes may be slight or more drastic. Upon introduction of an alkyl side chain at a carbon atom other than C-2 the character of the spectrum remains more or less unchanged with the exception of an increased tendency of the alkyl chain to fragment at the carbon atom bearing the additional substituent, as discussed in regard to hydrocarbons (Type A_1, Sec. 3-2A). The peak at m/e 157 in the mass spectrum of methyl 7-methyloctadecanoate (Fig. 6-3) indicates higher branching at C_7.[3] Because of the above-mentioned periodicity of certain peaks of even the unbranched esters, care must be taken not to confuse these peaks with the ones indicating branching of the chain.

A quaternary carbon atom increases the tendency for fragmentation at that point even more; in the spectrum of methyl 3,3-dimethylhenei-cosanoate (1) the peak at m/e 115 is the most intense one, and the re-arrangement ion of mass 74 is only slightly higher than the one at m/e 295, which results from the hydrocarbon fragment.[4] An alkyl substituent at C-2 makes itself felt in the mass of the Type H rearrangement ion, as discussed on page 126.

$$CH_3-(CH_2)_{17}-\overset{\overset{115}{|}\;\;\;\overset{CH_3}{|}}{\underset{\underset{295}{|}}{\underset{CH_3}{C}}}-CH_2-CO_2CH_3$$

(1)

The introduction of a double bond into the aliphatic chain gives rise to a somewhat less characteristic spectrum as borne out by a comparison of the spectrum of methyl oleate (Fig. 6-4)[1] with Fig. 6-1. In such a molecule the olefin fragment eliminated in the Type H rearrangement is in fact a diolefin which has a greater tendency[5] to retain the positive charge, and a peak at $M - 74$ therefore appears in the spectrum of methyl oleate. The similarity of the double-bond isomers of such molecules has been discussed earlier (Type A_3, Sec. 3-2A).

Thus, upon introduction of an alkyl substituent or even a double bond the basic peaks of an ester still dominate the spectrum. The presence of groups leading to cleavage of Type B or C gives rise, however, to very intense peaks of that type. The spectrum of methyl 4-methoxyocta-decanoate (Fig. 6-5)[6] has by far the most intense peak at m/e 131, cor-responding to cleavage of the carbon-carbon bond next to the methoxy group, and the analogous fragment of mass 241 is also very intense. How-ever, the rearrangement peak otherwise so characteristic of aliphatic esters (m/e 74) has almost disappeared. The presence of a ketone group

[3] *Ibid.*, **15**, 291 (1960).
[4] *Ibid.*, p. 333.
[5] S. Meyerson, Mass Spectrometry Conference, Atlantic City, N.J., June, 1960.
[6] R. Ryhage and E. Stenhagen, *Arkiv Kemi*, **15**, 545 (1960).

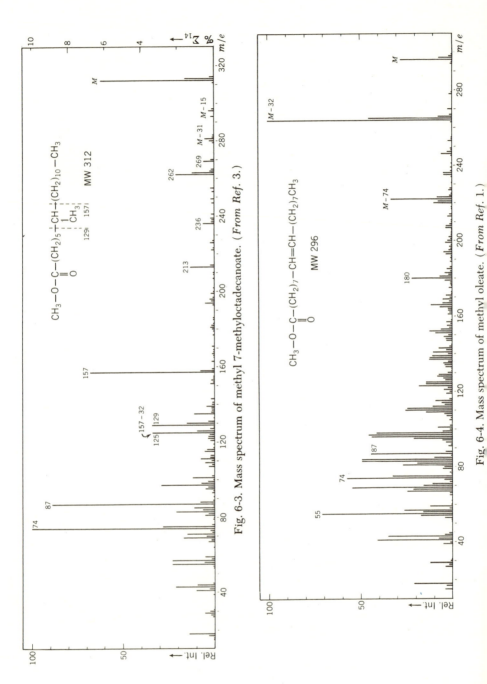

Fig. 6-3. Mass spectrum of methyl 7-methyloctadecanoate. (*From Ref. 3.*)

Fig. 6-4. Mass spectrum of methyl oleate. (*From Ref. 1.*)

254

along the side chain makes itself felt by the appearance in the spectrum of fragments of even mass number, which are due to the Type *H* rearrangement caused by the carbonyl group. The peaks at mass 158 and m/e 212 in the spectrum of methyl 6-oxooctadecanoate (Fig. 6-6)[6] are due to such a fragmentation; the peak at m/e 74 is only a very small one.

Many of these fragment ions containing the carbomethoxy group eliminate the elements of methanol, which gives rise to additional fragments 32 mass units lower.

These few examples taken from the work of the Swedish group may suffice as an illustration of the sensitivity of the mass spectra of fatty acids and their esters to structural variations in the aliphatic chain. In addition to the groups mentioned, esters of dibasic acids,[7] polyalkyl-substituted esters,[4] hydroxy and epoxy esters,[6] and esters involving long-chain alcohols [8] also have been investigated in detail.

All these compounds in general follow the behavior which one would expect on the basis of the discussion in Sec. 3-2A and in the present chapter, but there are also a number of more peculiar fragments formed, such as the ones of mass 143, 199, and 255 mentioned on page 251, the elimination of three carbon atoms from the chain (see page 230), the fragment of mass 98 in many methyl esters of dibasic acids,[7] etc. These processes must be kept in mind in the interpretation of mass spectra of this type of compound and also deserve further investigation as to the mechanism of their formation.

6-2. GLYCERIDES

The mass spectra of glycerides would be of interest in the investigation of fats and related materials. However, because of the molecular size and polarity of such molecules, it is difficult to introduce them into the mass spectrometer and even more difficult to remove them from the ion source after the experiment. Preliminary experiments have been reported,[1] and it seems that useful information could be derived from the mass spectrum of such a compound, as borne out by Fig. 6-7. The acyl ions at m/e 155 and 183 permit the identification of the acid moieties present in the glyceride, while the one at $M - (171 + 14)$ indicates that decanoic acid rather than the lauric acid component is attached to positions 1 and 3. It seems thus to be possible to distinguish between positional isomers of glycerides, an otherwise rather difficult task.

[7] *Ibid.*, **14,** 497 (1959).
[8] *Ibid.*, p. 483.

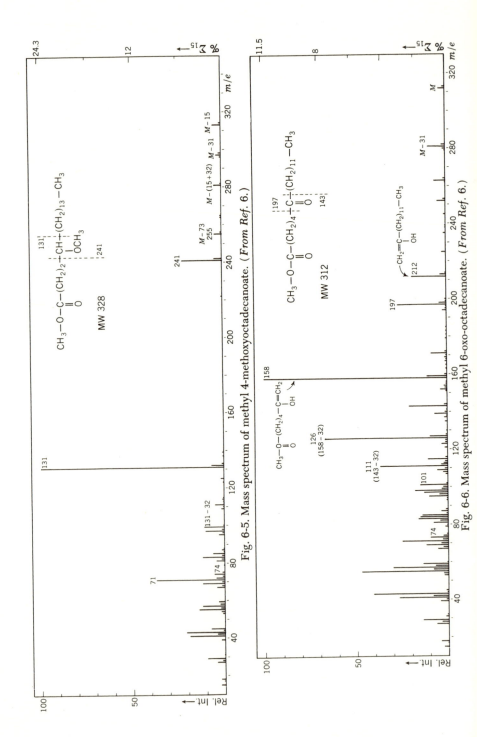

Fig. 6-5. Mass spectrum of methyl 4-methoxyoctadecanoate. (*From Ref. 6.*)

Fig. 6-6. Mass spectrum of methyl 6-oxo-octadecanoate. (*From Ref. 6.*)

256

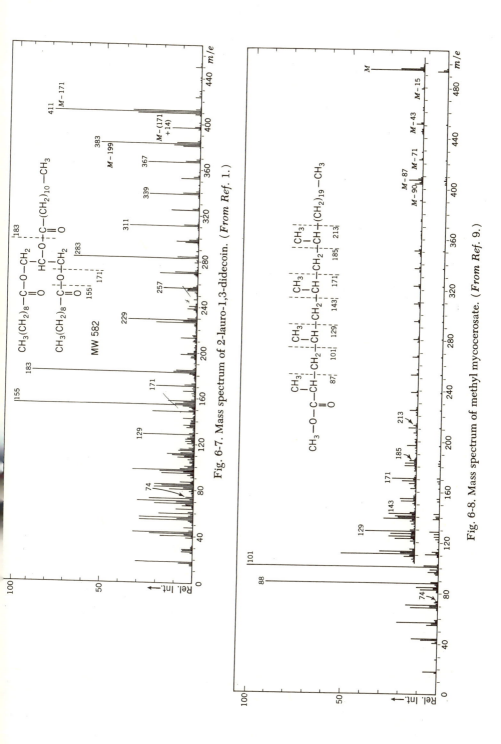

Fig. 6-7. Mass spectrum of 2-lauro-1,3-didecoin. (*From Ref. 1.*)

Fig. 6-8. Mass spectrum of methyl mycocerosate. (*From Ref. 9.*)

257

6-3. OTHER NATURAL PRODUCTS

As an example of the determination of the structure of a natural product related to long-chain fatty acids discussed in Sec. 6-1, mycocerosic acid should be mentioned.[9] This compound, which occurs in the lipids of tubercle bacilli, has been shown on the basis of the mass spectrum of its methyl ester (Fig. 6-8) and of the corresponding alcohol to have structure (2):

$$CH_3(CH_2)_{19}-CH-CH_2-CH-CH_2-CH-CH_2-CH-COOH$$
$$\underset{CH_3}{|} \quad \underset{CH_3}{|} \quad \underset{CH_3}{|} \quad \underset{CH_3}{|}$$

(2)

The rearrangement ion of mass 88 in such a methyl ester indicates the presence of a methyl group at C-2, and the alternating intensities of the $(CO_2CH_3 +14n)^+$ ions indicate methyl substitution at alternating carbon atoms. Structure (2) for mycocerosic acid was in agreement with this spectrum and furthermore was corroborated by the mass spectrum of the corresponding alcohol [CH_2OH in (2) instead of COOH]. As can be gleaned from Fig. 6-8, the spectrum of the ester is more characteristic of the environment of the carbomethoxy group, while the peaks due to fragmentation farther along the chain become less and less intense and thus less reliable.

The alcohol grouping does not dominate the fragmentation so much (see Fig. 3-13*a*). Peaks become more pronounced, thus yielding more conclusive information with respect to the other end of the molecule. The spectrum of the alcohol indicated clearly that there is a methyl branch 21 carbon atoms from the terminal CH_3 group of the molecule.

The structure of another constituent of the lipid fraction of tubercle bacilli, phthiocerol, was also finally elucidated by mass spectrometry and shown [10] to consist of a mixture of (3) and (4):

$$CH_3(CH_2)_n-CHOH-CH_2-CHOH-(CH_2)_4-\overset{\overset{\textstyle CH_3}{|}}{C}H-CH-CH_2-CH_3$$
$$\underset{OCH_3}{|}$$

(3, *n* = 20)
(4, *n* = 22)

[9] C. Asselineau, J. Asselineau, R. Ryhage, S. Ställberg-Stenhagen, and E. Stenhagen, *Acta Chem. Scand.*, 13, 822 (1959).

[10] L. Ahlquist, R. Ryhage, E. Stenhagen, and E. Von Sydow, *Arkiv Kemi*, 14, 211 (1959).

The basic carbon skeleton and the position of the methyl group was derived from the mass spectrum of the hydrocarbon to which the substance was degraded. It was shown after separation by gas chromatography to be 4-methyldotriacontane and 4-methyltetratriacontane, indicated by a preferred loss of 43 mass units from the molecule, in both cases [11] (see page 79).

The most conclusive evidence for the position of both the hydroxy groups and the methoxy group was obtained from the mass spectra of the acids formed on drastic oxidation of the molecule followed by esterification of the acidic fractions.[12] The mixture contained both methyl docosanoate and methyl tetracosanoate, which could be readily identified from their mass spectra, and indicated the presence of unsubstituted C_{21} and C_{23} chains. The more polar esters turned out to contain, among other products, methoxy esters of mol. wt 202 and 216, respectively, as deduced from the characteristic "$M + 1$" peak. The mass of the most intense peak was 73 and indicated the presence of the methoxy group at the third carbon atom from the methyl terminus in these esters. Structures (5) and (6) follow on the basis of this peak, the molecular weight of the esters, and consideration of the position of the methyl group in phthiocerane.

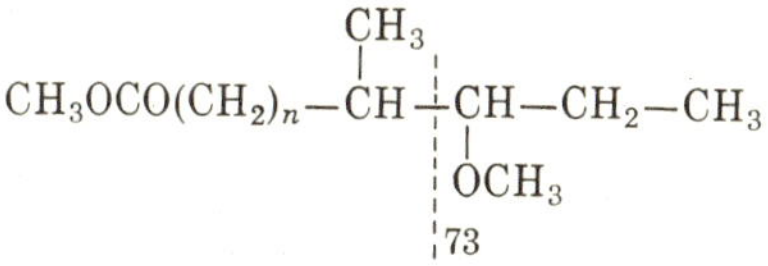

$$CH_3OCO(CH_2)_n-CH-\overset{\overset{\displaystyle CH_3}{|}}{CH}-CH_2-CH_3$$
$$\underset{\underset{73}{OCH_3}}{|}$$

(5, $n = 3$)
(6, $n = 4$)

[11] R. Ryhage, S. Ställberg-Stenhagen, and E. Stenhagen, *Arkiv Kemi*, 14, 259 (1959).
[12] *Ibid.*, p. 247.

7. Amino Acids and Peptides

7-1. DERIVATIVES OF AMINO ACIDS

A. The Mass Spectra of Amino Acid Esters

The characterization and structure determination of amino acids by spectroscopic methods are difficult, because these compounds differ not so much in the types of functional groups present as in the size and structure of alkyl side chains and the arrangement of functional groups in the molecule. Thus it is difficult to obtain specific information from the IR spectrum; also, the absence of chromophores in most amino acids greatly limits the application of UV spectroscopy. For these reasons and because of the small amount of sample usually available in this field, paper chromatography and paper electrophoresis have been used almost exclusively for the identification and characterization of amino acids. The determination of the structure of a new amino acid is of course also hampered; this becomes more and more serious as new amino acids are discovered relatively often in plants or as products of microorganisms, making the identification by paper chromatographic R_f values more uncertain and increasing the need for new techniques for structure determination on a small scale.

On the basis of the fragmentation of organic molecules upon electron impact outlined in Sec. 3-2 it might be expected that the mass spectra of amino acids or their derivatives would be very characteristic and would permit identifying an amino acid or deducing a few of or all structural characteristics of a new compound of this class. However, the zwitterionic character of these molecules(1)

$$\underset{\underset{(1)}{\overset{\alpha}{NH_3^+}}}{R-CH-COO^-} \longrightarrow \underset{\underset{(2,\ R=CH_3)}{\underset{(3,\ R=C_2H_5)}{NH_2}}}{R-CH-COOR'} \quad \overset{Slowly}{\longrightarrow} \quad \left[\begin{array}{c} R-CH-CO \\ HN \qquad NH \\ OC-CH-R \end{array}\right]$$

$$\begin{array}{c} R-CH-COOR' \\ | \\ NHCHO \\ (4,\ R'=CH_3) \end{array}$$

leads to a very low vapor pressure and hampers the study of free amino acids by mass spectrometry. While it is still possible to obtain mass spectra of free amino acids, as will be pointed out in Sec. 7-3, it is desirable to convert the free amino acids into simple derivatives thereof, which would exhibit a sufficient vapor pressure to be analyzed by conventional techniques.

As was briefly pointed out in Sec. 4-5A, such zwitterions may be converted into much more volatile compounds by destroying either the acidity of the carboxyl group or the basicity of the amino group, or both. The methyl esters (2)[1,2] and also the ethyl esters (3)[3] of amino acids have been shown to be suitable for mass spectrometric investigations, and recently N-formyl methyl esters (4)[4] have also been used for this purpose. These derivatives seem to be the most suitable although a number of others would conceivably lead to volatile substances having structures which are still indicative of the structure of the original amino acid; but if the major advantage of mass spectrometry in this area—namely, the small sample required—is to be retained, the reaction has to be very simple and applicable to amounts as small as a few tenths of a milligram of the free amino acid.

The mass spectra of the ethyl esters of amino acids have been studied [3] most thoroughly, and these investigations have resulted in a detailed knowledge of the behavior of such molecules upon electron impact, so that it is now possible to use this technique with considerable confidence to solve a number of problems in this field, particularly to determine the

[1] C. O. Andersson, *Acta Chem. Scand.*, **12**, 1353 (1958).

[2] E. Stenhagen, *Z. anal. Chem.*, **181**, 462 (1961).

[3] K. Biemann, J. Seibl, and F. Gapp, *Biochem. Biophys. Research Comm.*, **1**, 307 (1959); *J. Am. Chem. Soc.*, **83**, 3795 (1961).

[4] K. Heyns and H.-F. Grützmacher, *Z. Naturforsch.*, **16b**, 293 (1961).

structure of new amino acids. A priori one might think that for this purpose free amino esters are too unstable with respect to the formation of
diketopiperazines (5), but it must be kept in mind that in the mass spectrometer the sample is present at a relatively low pressure, and dimerization reactions are very slow under such conditions. To minimize this side
reaction further, it is of advantage to use the ethyl ester (3) rather than
the methyl ester (2), because the latter dimerizes faster, and to keep the
free ester in the form of a dilute solution or at low temperature prior to
vaporization.

The conversion of an amino acid (as little as a few tenths of a milligram) into the free ethyl ester is accomplished by heating it with ethanol
HCl (see Sec. 4-5A), evaporation, dissolution of the remaining hydrochloride in dichloromethane, and brief saturation with gaseous ammonia.
Upon filtering, a solution of the free ester is obtained, and the ester is
introduced into the spectrometer by means of the distillation tube and
technique discussed in Sec. 2-5A.

The mass spectra of α-amino acid ethyl esters (6)

$$
\begin{array}{cc}
b & a \\
\end{array}
$$
$$
R\text{---}CH\text{---}COOC_2H_5
$$
$$
NH_2
$$

(6)

exhibit characteristic peaks which are due to fragmentation of either one
of the two carbon-carbon bonds to which the amino group is attached
(fragmentation of Type B) and to fragmentation of the group R if it
contains any one of the structural features leading to preferred fragmentation, as discussed in Sec. 3-2A. In Figs. 7-1 through 7-10 a few
mass spectra of such esters are shown, and in almost all cases one can
observe a very intense peak, due to fragmentation at a in (6).

The "amine fragment" $(R\text{---}CH\text{---}NH_2)^+$ is the most intense peak in
the mass spectra of at least those amino acid esters which do not contain
other functional groups in R. The size of the side chain is therefore
easily deduced from this peak by subtraction of 29 mass units. This peak
alone, in simple cases, is sufficient for the identification of the substance.

Fragments due to further decomposition of the amine fragment or
peaks due to fragmentation of the molecule at certain bonds within
group R give rise to a number of peaks characteristic of the structure
of the original amino acid. The effect of simple alkyl branching is illustrated by the mass spectra of the isomeric leucines shown in Fig. 7-1a
to c. The preferred loss of an ethyl group from isoleucine versus the loss

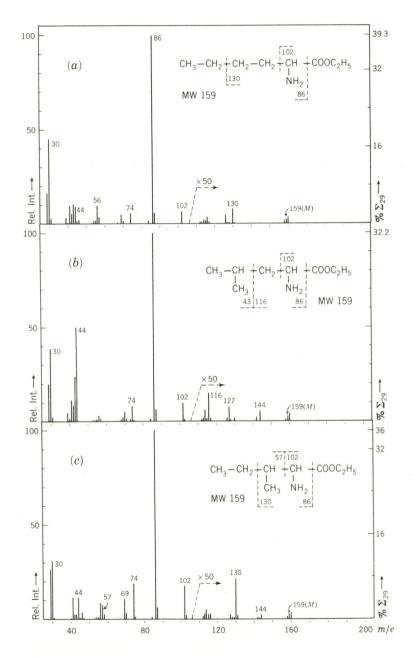

Fig. 7-1. Mass spectra of (a) norleucine ethyl ester, (b) leucine ethyl ester, (c) isoleucine ethyl ester.

of an isopropyl group from leucine is due to the different points of attachment of a methyl group in the side chain. It has been pointed out in Sec. 3-2A that such fragmentation of Type A_1 is much less effective than fragmentation of Type B, and the peaks at mass 116 and 130 in Fig. 7-1*b* and *c* are, therefore, of very low intensity. They occur, however, in a region otherwise completely free of fragments and may be easily detected. Retention of the positive charge on the alkyl fragment gives rise to more intense peaks (m/e 43 and 57) which also can be used to distinguish these two isomers, although they occur in a part of the spectrum in which other peaks are also found.

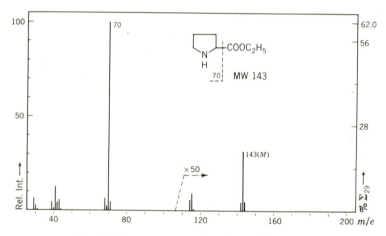

Fig. 7-2. Mass spectrum of proline ethyl ester.

The cyclic nature of the "side chain" of proline reduces markedly the tendency for fragmentation of the molecular ion at bonds other than *a* in (6) or for further cleavage of the amine fragment. The mass spectrum of proline ethyl ester (Fig. 7-2) consists, therefore, chiefly of one very intense peak at m/e 70.

The presence of functional groups in group R aids the fragmentation of carbon-carbon bonds to which the functional group is attached or leads to further decomposition of the amine fragment by eliminations of Type *E* or *H*. The peaks at mass 42 in the spectra of serine ester (Fig. 7-3) and cysteine ester are due to fragments formed by elimination of H_2O and H_2S, respectively, from the amine fragments of these amino esters:

$$\underset{\substack{| \quad \quad | \\ OH \quad NH_2}}{CH_2-CH^+} \xrightarrow{-H_2O} \underset{\substack{| \\ NH_2}}{CH_2=C^+} \xleftarrow{-H_2S} \underset{\substack{| \quad \quad | \\ SH \quad NH_2}}{CH_2-CH^+}$$

$$m/e\ 42$$

Similarly the amine fragments of threonine and hydroxyproline lose the elements of water to form the species of mass 56 and 68, respectively. Metastable peaks at m/e 29.6 and 42.6 (calcd. 29.4 and 42.4) in the spectra of serine and threonine ester support the fragmentation sequence

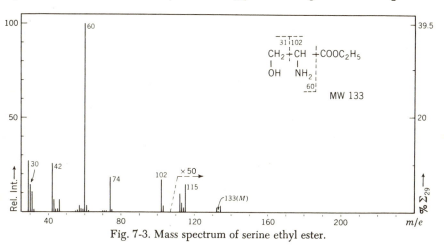

Fig. 7-3. Mass spectrum of serine ethyl ester.

suggested above, namely, cleavage of bond a in (6) followed by elimination of water, and not the reverse.

The amino group is eliminated from the amine fragment (in analogy to alcohol fragments, Type E_1) only to a small extent, giving rise to peaks

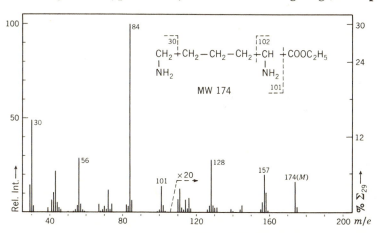

Fig. 7-4. Mass spectrum of lysine ethyl ester.

of relatively low intensity. The loss of NH_3 is, however, a very important process in the mass spectrum of lysine ester, in which the fragment of mass 84 is the most abundant one (Fig. 7-4). Participation of the second amino group is suggested in this elimination:

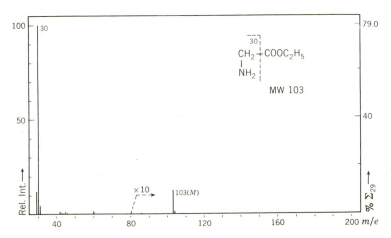

That both these mechanisms are operative is borne out by the mass spectra of $N_\alpha{}^{15}$-labeled lysine, in which either one of the two amino groups may be eliminated, giving rise to peaks at mass 84 and 85.

Fig. 7-5. Mass spectrum of glycine ethyl ester.

Esters of amino acids with side chains longer than two carbon atoms exhibit a peak of considerable intensity at m/e 30, due to the elimination of an olefin molecule (Type F) from the amine fragment:

$$R—CH—CH_2—CH^+ \longrightarrow R—CH{=}CH_2 \ + \ CH_2^+$$
$$\overset{|}{H} \qquad\qquad\qquad\qquad\qquad \overset{|}{NH_2}$$
$$\overset{|}{NH_2} \qquad\qquad\qquad\qquad\qquad m/e\ 30$$

The peak at m/e 30 is therefore virtually absent from the spectrum of the esters of alanine (Fig. 7-6), the prolines (e.g., Fig. 7-2), and the aromatic amino acids (e.g., Figs. 7-7 and 7-8c). In glycine ester (Fig. 7-5) the peak at m/e 30 is, of course, due to the amine fragment itself.

The elimination of ethylene (Type H) or ethanol (Type E_1) from the carbethoxy group remaining in the amine fragment of aspartic ester leads to the peaks at mass 88 and 70, respectively; similar processes occur in glutamic ester (7). The latter is also prone to eliminate ethanol

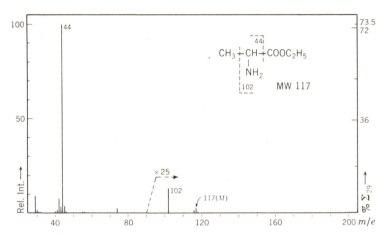

Fig. 7-6. Mass spectrum of alanine ethyl ester.

thermally by cyclization to ethyl 2-pyrrolidone-5-carboxylate in a uni-molecular reaction

$$\underset{m/e\ 84}{\overset{+}{\underset{H}{\left[\begin{array}{c}\ \end{array}\right]}}N{\overset{}{\diagup}}O} \longleftarrow \underset{m/e\ 130}{\overset{CO_2C_2H_5}{\underset{+\ \cdot CO_2C_2H_5}{(\overset{|}{C}H_2)_2}}} \overset{-\ e^-}{\longleftarrow} \underset{(7)}{\overset{CO_2C_2H_5}{\underset{CO_2C_2H_5}{(\overset{|}{C}H_2)_2}}} \overset{\Delta}{\longrightarrow} \underset{84}{O{\overset{}{\diagdown}}N\overset{|}{\underset{H}{\ }}CO_2C_2H_5}$$

and the peak at m/e 130 therefore decreases much faster with time than m/e 84, a fact which has to be taken into account for quantitative spectra.

Fragmentation at bond b in (6) and retention of the positive charge at C_α leads to the "ester fragment" of mass 102; it is of much lower intensity than the amine fragment due to the destabilizing effect of the neighboring carbonyl group (see page 122). This fragment of mass 102 is found in all primary α-amino acids bearing no additional substituents in this part of the molecule. An exception is glycine ester (Fig. 7-5), which does not exhibit such a peak, because loss of hydrogen is much less favorable. The peak is absent, of course, from the mass spectra of the ethyl esters of proline (Fig. 7-2), hydroxyproline, or aminoisobutyric acid. In the latter the ester fragment has mass 116. The structural significance of this peak is obvious.

The peak at mass 102 is always accompanied by one at m/e 74, formed by elimination of C_2H_4 from the ester fragment (Type *H*). The metastable peak at mass 53.9 (calcd. 53.8) again is an indication of this sequence rather than elimination of ethylene from the molecular ion as the first

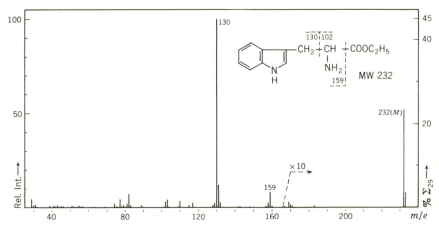

Fig. 7-7. Mass spectrum of tryptophan ethyl ester.

step. While the intensity of the ester fragment is not very high in most cases, it is increased if a functional group or an aromatic system is attached to C_β. Phenylalanine ester (Fig. 7-8c) is an extreme example of this kind.

$$\overset{\alpha}{^+CH}-\overset{O}{\underset{O-CH_2}{\overset{\nwarrow}{C}}}\overset{H}{\underset{CH_2}{\diagdown}} \quad \longrightarrow \quad {^+CH_2}-C\overset{OH}{\underset{O}{\diagup}} \quad + \quad \overset{CH_2}{\underset{CH_2}{\|}}$$

$$\underset{NH_2}{}$$

m/e 102 m/e 74

In contrast to other aliphatic esters, the rearrangement of Type *H*, which would give rise to a peak at mass 103, does not take place, mainly because the free electron pair on the amino group offsets the destabilization of the positive charge at C_α to a considerable extent (see Sec. 3-2B). Only in the spectrum of threonine ester is an intense peak found at 103 instead of 102.

Fragmentation of the molecular ion at the R group or at bond *b* in (6) with retention of the charge at C_β is observed if a functional group which is able to stabilize the positive charge particularly well is present in this part of the molecule. The mass spectrum of methionine ester (Fig. 7-13) is a good example of an instance in which the most intense peak is due to such a fragment: CH_3—S—$CH_2{}^+$ (m/e 61). In this case the resulting carbonium ion is stabilized by the sulfur atom while in the spectrum of tryptophan ester (Fig. 7-7) the particle of mass 130, by far the most abundant one in the whole spectrum, obtains its stabilization from the indole ring system. Elimination of neutral molecules from the molecular ion is also observed, and the formation of m/e 131 and m/e 129 in the spectrum of methionine ester is due to the loss of ethanol and methyl mercaptan, respectively.

A number of the particular fragmentation mechanisms leading to certain peaks in the mass spectra of ethyl esters of amino acids have been discussed in earlier chapters; for example, m/e 44 from leucine ester and aspartic ester (page 125) and mass 102 and 86 in β- and γ-amino butyric ester (page 142). A more detailed discussion is found in the original paper.[3]

Because of the presence of a number of easily cleaved bonds in these molecules, the molecular-weight peak is in general of rather low intensity. It is always accompanied, however, by an "$M + 1$" peak, thus easily identified (Fig. 3-2). The molecular ions of N, N-dimethylamino acid esters are considerably more abundant (Fig. 3-14b).

The correctness of these mechanisms proposed for the fragmentation of amino esters was shown on the basis of a number of N^{15}-labeled derivatives. Two examples are presented in Fig. 7-8. As the labeling in these compounds was not complete, nitrogen-containing fragments gave rise to doublets spaced 1 mass unit apart. From Fig. 7-8b it can be deduced that almost all important fragments formed from aspartic ester do contain the nitrogen atom with the exception of mass 29, which arises from the ethyl group of the ester moiety. This peak only appears to be more intense in Fig. 7-8b than in 7-8a, because in the two spectra the peak height is expressed in terms of the highest peak (m/e 116 and m/e 117, respectively). In terms of total ionization their intensity is about the same. The mass spectrum of N^{15}-labeled phenylalanine ester (Fig. 7-8d) shows more peaks devoid of nitrogen, namely, 29, 77, 91, and 131. The first three are indicated in the figure; the last one is due to the cinnamoyl ion,

$$\langle \bigcirc \rangle\text{—CH}=\text{CH}-\overset{\overset{\displaystyle O}{\|}}{C}{}^+$$

formed by elimination of ammonia from the molecular ion, followed by the loss of the ethoxy group.

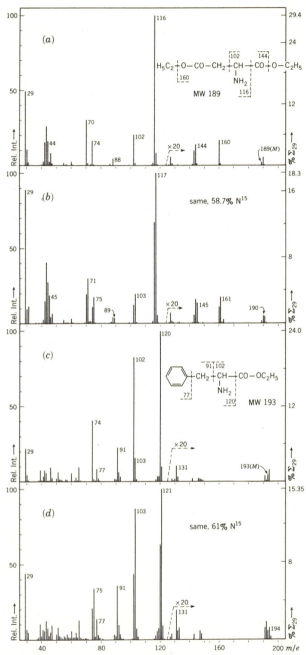

Fig. 7-8. Mass spectra of (a) aspartic acid ethyl ester, (b) N^{15}-labeled aspartic acid ethyl ester, (c) phenylalanine ethyl ester, (d) N^{15}-labeled phenylalanine ethyl ester.

The methyl esters of amino acids show a very similar behavior upon electron impact,[2] with the exception of those processes in the ethyl esters that involve the elimination of ethylene from the ester moiety of the molecule (Figs. 7-9 and 10). An analogous elimination is not possible in methyl esters, and the ester fragment of mass 88 is therefore not ac-

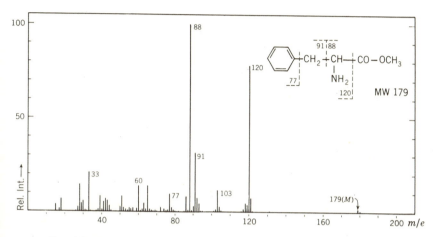

Fig. 7-9. Mass spectrum of phenylalanine methyl ester. (*From Ref. 2.*)

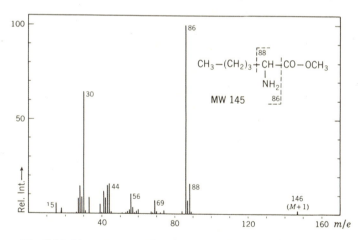

Fig. 7-10. Mass spectrum of norleucine methyl ester. (*From Ref. 2.*)

companied by a peak corresponding to the species of m/e 74 in the ethyl esters. All the fragments containing the ester group are found at masses 14 units lower as compared with the ethyl esters.

For the purpose of structure determination it may sometimes be of advantage to prepare both the methyl and the ethyl ester, to identify the ester fragments definitely or to determine the number of carboxyl groups present (see page 187).

The mass spectra of a number of N-formyl-α-amino acid methyl esters (4) have been reported,[4] and these too basically follow the fragmentation processes outlined in Sec. 3-2 and are in many respects similar

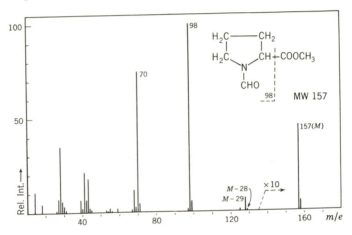

Fig. 7-11. Mass spectrum of N-formylproline methyl ester. (*From Ref.* 4.)

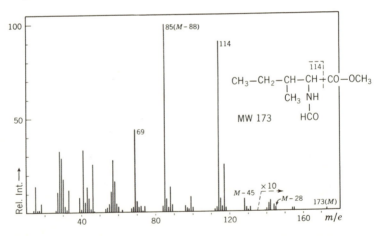

Fig. 7-12. Mass spectrum of N-formylisoleucine methyl ester. (*From Ref.* 4.)

to the process discussed for the free esters. The loss of 59 mass units ($COOCH_3$) is a predominant process. The mass spectra (Figs. 7-11 and 7-12) are more complex, since the loss of CO from the formyl group seems to be involved quite frequently, thus giving rise to two peaks of the same type differing by 28 mass units (e.g., $M - 59$ and $M - 87$). Somewhat puzzling are some peaks at $M - 88$, particularly abundant in the derivatives of the isomeric leucines and phenylalanine; the proposed [4] mechanism, namely, cleaving off both the $COOCH_3$ (mass 59) and CHO group (mass 29), is difficult to visualize and should operate in the related amino acids as well.

The preparation of the *N*-formyl esters of polyfunctional amino acids is accompanied by a number of side reactions (elimination of water, cyclization, etc.); these derivatives could not be obtained from lysine, histidine, tryptophan, and cysteine. The statement [4] that the *N*-formyl-α-amino acid methyl esters give mass spectra which are more indicative of the structure of the amino acid than are the spectra of the free esters is therefore somewhat difficult to rationalize. Nevertheless, these derivatives might be useful in certain cases as additional evidence to support conclusions drawn from the spectra of the more easily prepared free esters.

The mass spectra of amino esters therefore permit the identification of a known amino acid beyond any doubt by comparison with the spectrum of an authentic sample. Differentiation of diastereomers like threonine and allothreonine and hydroxyproline and its allo form requires careful comparison of spectra determined under identical conditions, because there the differences are only small variations in the peaks of otherwise identical mass (Sec. 3-2*D*).

The presence of the guanidino group in arginine reduces the volatility of even the ethyl ester so much that it cannot be introduced into a conventional inlet system. By conversion of the guanidino group, e.g., into a pyrimidine derivative, it is possible to obtain useful spectra.[5] The spectrum of free arginine has been determined (Sec. 7-3).

Consideration of the spectra shown in this section indicates that it is possible to recognize the individual amino acids present in a mixture from a single mass spectrum. The spectra are characterized by the presence of a few very intense peaks, which can easily be spotted in such a mixture. In this case it is of advantage to use a spectrum obtained with low-energy electrons (about 9.5 to 10 ev), as under these conditions the amine fragment is still very intense, while most other peaks are very small or have disappeared. This is illustrated particularly well by Fig. 7-14, the mass spectrum of methionine ester at 10 ev, in which the fragment of mass 61, the most intense one at 70 ev (Fig. 7-13), is now rather small, while the amine peak (m/e 104) is the most intense one. Unex-

[5] Unpublished experiments from the author's laboratory (by H. Vetter and W. Vetter).

pected or even new amino acids can be spotted from such a spectrum, and the presence of β-hydroxyaspartic acid [5] in the total hydrolyzate of duramycine and a methyltryptophan [6] in Telomycin were detected by this technique, because the spectra showed peaks at mass 132 and mass

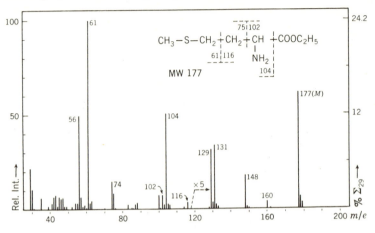

Fig. 7-13. Mass spectrum of methionine ethyl ester.

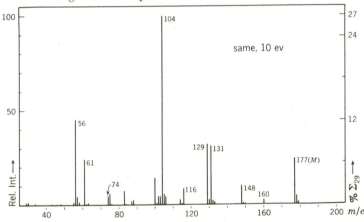

Fig. 7-14. Mass spectrum of methionine ethyl ester obtained with 10-volt electrons.

144, respectively, not accounted for by the presence of the amino acids previously reported in these antibiotics.

B. The Determination of the Structure of New Amino Acids

The structure of the first of the amino acids just mentioned was predicted on the basis of the intense peak at mass 132 in the product of esterification with ethanol of the acidic fraction of the amino acids of

[6] Determined on a sample kindly provided by J. C. Sheehan.

duramycine, which contains aspartic acid and glutamic acid. The mass difference between this new peak and the amine fragment of aspartic ester (m/e 116) suggested the presence of a related compound containing one oxygen atom more. The mass spectrum of a pure sample of this ester, isolated from the mixture by gas chromatography, was found to be identical with the spectrum of an authentic sample of erythro-β-hydroxyaspartic acid diethyl ester (8): [7]

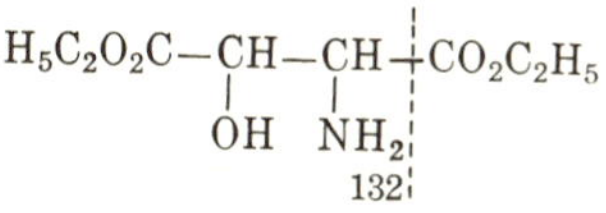

$$H_5C_2O_2C-\underset{\underset{OH}{|}}{CH}-\underset{\underset{NH_2}{|}}{CH}+CO_2C_2H_5$$

$$132$$

$$(8)$$

This amino acid had recently been found in a casein hydrolyzate.

Similarly, the basic hydrolyzate of Telomycine, which was known to contain tryptophan in addition to other common amino acids, showed an intense peak at mass 144 and a smaller one at mass 173, neither of which was expected in a spectrum containing only the esters of the amino acids known to occur in Telomycin. As both peaks are homologs of those found for tryptophan itself, it follows that the additional amino acid is a methyl-substituted tryptophan in which the additional group is located in the indole part of the molecule, or more probably on the carbon atom to which it is attached, but that it is not at C_α or N_α.

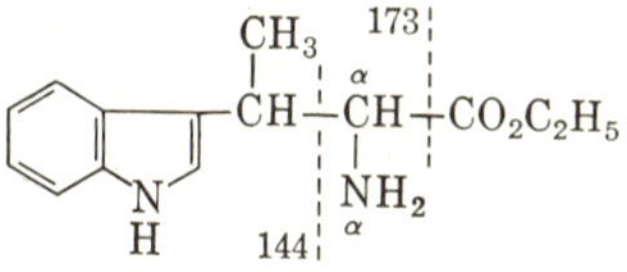

$$(9)$$

In another case it was possible to resolve the ambiguity concerning an amino acid which had been isolated from apples, for which both structures (10)[8] and (11)[9] had been suggested.

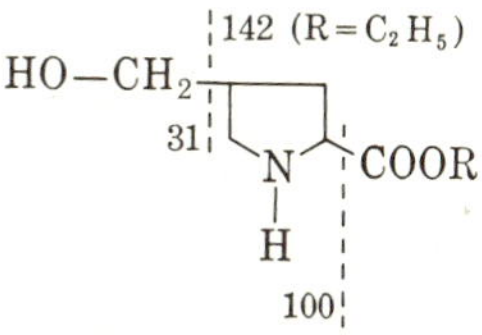

(10, R = H)
(12, R = C$_2$H$_5$)

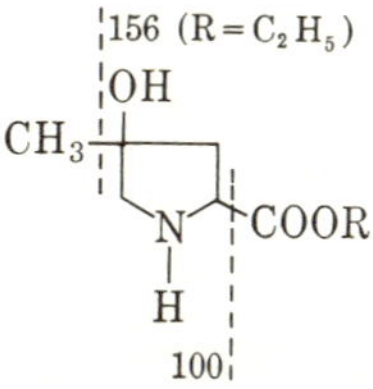

(11, R = H)
(13, R = C$_2$H$_5$)

[7] H. J. Sallach and M. L. Kornguth, *Biochim. et Biophys. Acta,* **34,** 582 (1959).
[8] G. Urbach, *Nature,* **175,** 170 (1955).
[9] A. C. Hulme and F. C. Steward, *Nature,* **175,** 171 (1955).

The mass spectrum [10] of the ethyl ester in fact exhibited the most intense peak at m/e 100, confirming the gross structure, and small ones at m/e 142 and 31, but no peak at all at m/e 156. The latter should be particularly abundant in the spectrum of (13), as it would result in a highly substituted Type-*B* ion. The correct structure of this amino acid is thus (10).

These examples dealt with new amino acids closely related to very common ones. A more complex example is the determination of the structure of an amino acid which had been isolated from the crown gall tissues of various plants.[11] By the usual analytical methods it had been shown

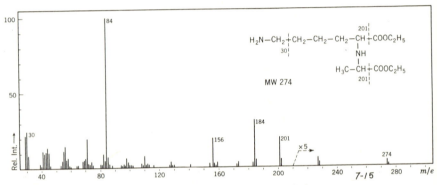

Fig. 7-15. Mass spectrum of lysopine ethyl ester.

not to be a primary α-amino acid; to contain half its nitrogen in an NH_2 group; to contain one $C—CH_3$, no $N—CH_3$, and no $O—CH_3$; and to be probably a diacid of the composition $C_9H_{18}N_2O_4$; but the elemental analysis was not conclusive, because the substance and all the derivatives tenaciously retained crystal solvent. The small amount of material available prevented a chemical determination of the structure of this compound.

Esterification of 0.4 mg of the amino acid and introduction of the free ester into the mass spectrometer by the technique discussed earlier gave the spectrum shown in Fig. 7-15. The small peak at mass 274 is due to the molecular ion, as the one at 275 showed the typical behavior of a "$M + 1$" peak. The other characteristic peaks in this spectrum are found at mass 201, 184, 156; the most intense peak is at mass 84. In addition,

[10] K. Biemann, G. G. J. Deffner, and F. C. Steward, *Nature*, **191**, 380 (1961).

[11] K. Biemann, C. Lioret, J. Asselineau, E. Lederer, and J. Polonsky, *Biochim. et Biophys. Acta*, **40**, 369 (1960); *Bull. soc. chim. biol.*, **42**, 979 (1960).

the metastable peaks found at mass 169 and mass 133 indicate that step-wise fragmentation occurs, namely, $201 \rightarrow 184 \rightarrow 156$.

The molecular weight of 274, an even number, indicates the presence of 0, 2, 4, etc., nitrogen atoms. Two is the most probable number, as an amino acid must contain nitrogen, and four or more nitrogens would not seem to give a spectrum of this type. The facile loss of 73 mass units ($COOC_2H_5$) is the process observed in all α-amino acids; but because there is no appreciable peak at mass 102, it would not be a primary amino acid. The formation of this fragment indicates part structure

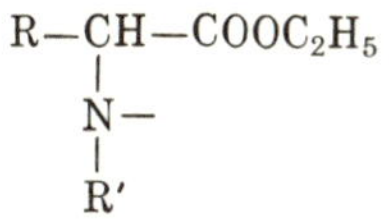

$$\begin{array}{c} R-CH-COOC_2H_5 \\ | \\ N- \\ | \\ R' \end{array}$$

The fragment of mass 201 loses 17 mass units to form the species of mass 184, a process indicating the elimination of NH_3. The compound must, therefore, contain a primary amino group:

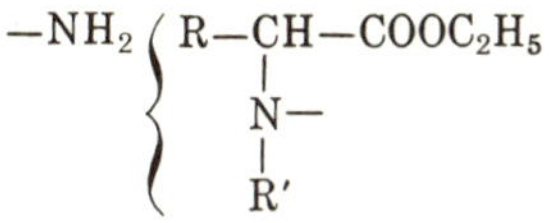

$$-NH_2 \left\{ \begin{array}{c} R-CH-COOC_2H_5 \\ | \\ N- \\ | \\ R' \end{array} \right.$$

The next step is the elimination of 28 mass units which could be either CO or C_2H_4. The latter process is reminiscent of the elimination of ethylene from the ester fragment (m/e 102) to give m/e 74 for most of the common amino esters (Sec. 7-1A) suggesting there is present a second carbethoxy group in addition to the one lost in the first step. Thus, one can write an extended part structure:

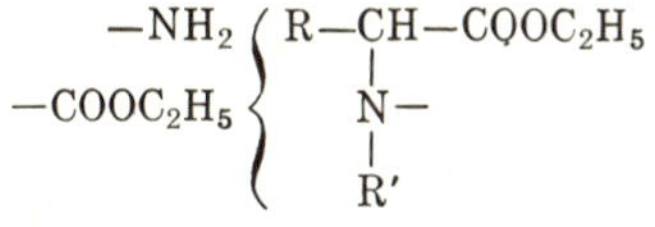

$$\begin{array}{c} -NH_2 \\ -COOC_2H_5 \end{array} \left\{ \begin{array}{c} R-CH-CQOC_2H_5 \\ | \\ N- \\ | \\ R' \end{array} \right.$$

The most intense peak in the spectrum is found at m/e 84, which is reminiscent of the similar peak ($C_5H_{10}N$) in lysine ester (Fig. 7-4) and suggests that possibly also in this compound the two nitrogen atoms are connected by a five-carbon bridge:

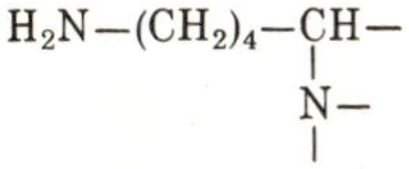

$$\begin{array}{c} H_2N-(CH_2)_4-CH- \\ | \\ N- \\ | \end{array}$$

One of the most plausible structures for this amino acid on the basis of these arguments is the following one:

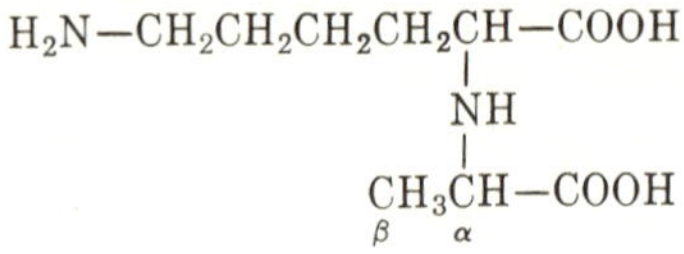

$$H_2N-CH_2CH_2CH_2CH_2CH-COOH$$
$$|$$
$$NH$$
$$|$$
$$CH_3CH-COOH$$
$$\beta \quad \alpha$$

(14)

Other possible isomers deserving brief consideration would be those in which the C_5 bridge is not an unbranched chain, or those in which the primary amino group is not on the terminal carbon atom, or the isomer in which the propionic acid moiety is substituted by nitrogen on the β carbon, rather than on C_α as shown above.

The last-mentioned possibility is excluded, because in that case one would expect loss of 87 mass units ($CH_2COOC_2H_5$) and there is no peak at m/e 187. Aside from the analogy of lysine, the presence of an unbranched chain and a terminal primary amino group is indicated by the absence of a peak at m/e 44, 58, 72, or 86 of higher intensity than the one at m/e 30. Finally, it was found that the free ester is of considerable thermal stability. All structures which would contain a carbethoxy group and an amino group in a relationship which could lead to a five- or six-membered lactam ring can therefore be excluded.

Although the stereochemistry of (14) could not, of course, be deduced from the mass spectrum (see Sec. 3-2D), it was found to be L in the lysine part and D in the alanine moiety on comparison of the natural acid with the synthetic specimen.[11] The substance was named "lysopine," as it is the lysine analog of octopine, which contains an arginine moiety.

The elucidation of the structure of such a relatively complex amino acid, on which no structural information aside from the usual analytical data had been obtained by conventional techniques, from only one mass spectrum outlines the potentialities of mass spectrometry in the investigation of such problems.

C. The Determination of N^{15} in Amino Acids

Comparison of Fig. 7-8a with Fig. 7-8b illustrates that the presence of heavy nitrogen in the amine fragment not only can be demonstrated but also can be quantitatively measured on the basis of the peak 1 mass unit above the amine fragment of the unlabeled acid. The ratio of the peaks at mass 116 and mass 117 (after correction for the carbon-isotope peak of the species of mass 116) in the spectrum shown in Fig. 7-8b permits the calculation of the ratio of N^{14}/N^{15} in this particular sample. The value of 58.7 per cent excess N^{15} was, in fact, obtained in this manner. To minimize the contributions from other fragments, it is of advantage to use spectra determined at about 9.5 to 10 ev, conditions under which the amine fragment still gives rise to an intense peak. Even a small excess of N^{15} (0.2 to 0.3 per cent) can be determined by an accurate measurement of the peak at mass 117 in the spectrum of aspartic ester, for example, and the same can be done for phenylalanine by measuring the intensity at mass 121. Not only is it thus possible to determine the concentration of heavy nitrogen in an amino acid without degradation of the molecule to nitrogen gas, as is generally done, but also, as is obvious from Fig. 7-8*b* and *d*, in a mixture of aspartic acid and phenylalanine the individual N^{15} content of each component can be determined from a single spectrum of the mixture, because the peaks to be measured for both components are not interfered with by other fragments.

This technique has been used to determine the isotope content of up to 11 components present in a mixture.[12] Advantage is taken, in the case of complex mixtures, of the different volatility of amino acid esters to minimize errors due to fragment peaks of other components which cannot be completely eliminated by the use of low-energy electrons. Since ionizing conditions are difficult to reproduce from sample to sample (see Sec. 5-2*B*), these contributions fluctuate too much to permit, for example, the accurate determination of the peaks at m/e 30 and m/e 31 due to glycine in the presence of a considerable amount of leucine ester, which also gives an abundant fragment of the composition CH_2NH_2 (see Fig. 7-1*b*). Similarly, the intense peak at mass 70 in the spectrum of aspartic ester (Fig. 7-8*a*) interferes even at 9.5 ev with the peak of the same mass from proline ester (Fig. 7-2), and as mass 70 of aspartic ester contains nitrogen (see Fig. 7-8*b*), its N^{15} content thus gives rise to an excessive peak at m/e 71 and would appear to be N^{15} in proline.

Fortunately the volatility of these compounds is sufficiently different to make it possible to obtain the mass spectrum of glycine ester free from leucine ester and proline ester free from aspartic ester, if the sample is fractionated into the instrument. This is accomplished by stepwise warming of the distillation tube to higher and higher temperatures, starting at 0° (see Sec. 2-5*B*). Up to four spectra containing different parts of the mixture may be obtained in this way, and the isotope content of the individual components is calculated from the corresponding amine peaks.

The accuracy of this method (±0.2 per cent of total nitrogen) is, of

[12] K. Biemann and G. G. J. Deffner, *Biochem. Biophys. Research Comm.*, **4**, 283 (1961).

course, much lower than that involving the degradation of a pure amino acid to nitrogen gas, the isotope content of which is then measured in a double-collector instrument (Sec. 1-2F), although the accuracy becomes comparable when one is working with samples of high N^{15} content (about 25 or 30 per cent). The advantage of the technique described here lies in the speed of the measurement, and it might be particularly useful for preliminary experiments or screening.

Furthermore, in compounds containing two nitrogen atoms their individual isotopic composition can be measured by the selection of suitable peaks in the mass spectrum. It is, for example, possible in tryptophan (15)

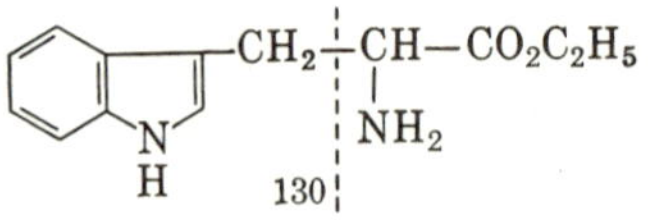

$$\text{indole ring}-CH_2 \!\mid\! CH-CO_2C_2H_5$$
$$\mid NH_2$$
$$130$$

(15)

to determine the extent of labeling in the indole-nitrogen from the peaks at m/e 130 and 131, while the molecular ion indicates the total N^{15} concentration in the molecule. Such a determination of the isotope content in the individual amino groups of a diamino acid is frequently of interest; this would require specific degradation of the molecule if an isotope-ratio instrument is to be used. The mass spectrum of the entire molecule makes such a degradation unnecessary if both parts of the molecule— each containing one of the two nitrogen atoms—give rise to specific intense peaks. This is unfortunately not the case for lysine ester, as the most intense peak of mass 84 (Fig. 7-4) is formed by elimination of either one of the amino groups (see page 265). Conversion to tetramethyllysine (16),

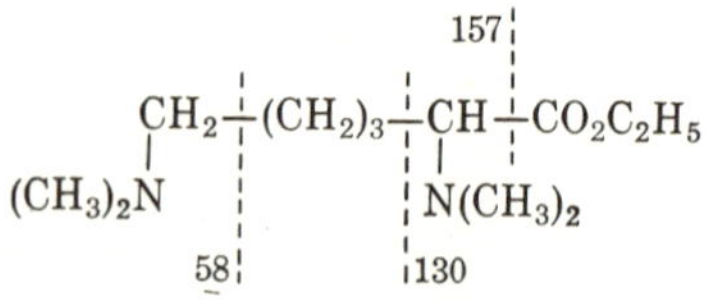

$$157$$
$$CH_2 \!\mid\! (CH_2)_3 \!\mid\! CH \!\mid\! CO_2C_2H_5$$
$$(CH_3)_2N \qquad \mid N(CH_3)_2$$
$$58 \qquad 130$$

(16)

using the reaction discussed in Sec. 4-5C, and esterification yields a molecule the mass spectrum of which does contain peaks which make it possible to determine the amount of heavy nitrogen present in the α- and ϵ-amino group separately.[13] The fragment of m/e 58 represents N_ϵ, the isotopic composition of which can be measured by using the ratio of

[13] Unpublished experiments from the author's laboratory (by A. L. Burlingame).

the peaks at m/e 58 to m/e 59. The ester peak, now at m/e 130, permits the determination of the isotope content of N_α. While this peak is a rather small one, either the amine peak or the molecular-ion peak can be used to measure the total isotope content in the molecule.

It has to be kept in mind that by measuring the intensity of the peak 1 mass unit above the amine peak in these amino esters, one actually determines the increase not only of N^{15} but also of C^{13} and of D in the unknown sample with respect to the standard, as has already been pointed out in Sec. 5-2B. In view of the possibility that an amino acid produced by a living cell may have a C^{13} content different from a synthetic specimen, one should always take care to use as standard an amino acid from the same source.

D. Quantitative Amino Acid Analysis

The mass spectra of various amino acid esters presented in this chapter (Figs. 7-1 to 7-9) indicate that these substances should lend themselves easily to quantitative determination, because all of them contain one or only a few very intense peaks, and most of these peaks fall at different mass numbers. The intensity of those peaks in a mass spectrum of a mixture of amino esters is thus a measure of the concentration of the individual components, and once a calibration spectrum has been obtained, such a mixture can be analyzed with the usual accuracy of mass spectrometric analysis.

We shall not discuss the necessary arithmetic to solve this problem but merely point out that the actual contributions of each individual amino ester to the mass at which its most intense or otherwise suitable peak is found can be calculated by subtracting from this peak the small contributions of all other amino acids present. This is most easily done by starting with the amino acid of which the "analytical" peak is at highest mass and therefore is not interfered with by other components. Subtracting the contributions of this component to all other peaks which will be needed for the further calculation eliminates the contributions of this amino acid. The next heaviest peak follows, and so on. Finally one may be left with a very few components which contribute appreciably to each other's analytical peaks, and these can be solved either by the use of simultaneous equations or successive approximations.

The major problem involved in this technique is therefore not one of mass spectrometry or arithmetic but the fact that the sample to be analyzed is composed originally of free amino acids which have to be esterified first and then introduced into the mass spectrometer without fractionation, in spite of the widely different boiling points of the components. Furthermore, it is most important to use a technique permitting a complete analysis with not more than 1 to 3 mg of the original mixture of free amino acids, because frequently not more than that can be spared. The procedure developed for the conversion of free amino acids into the esters on a small scale, as discussed earlier, satisfies all these requirements if particular care is taken in the handling of the sample.

The relative intensity of the analytical peaks is of course different for each amino ester. It has to be determined separately, most conveniently by adding a known amount of an internal standard, for example, aspartic acid, in the calibration experiment in order to determine these relative intensities.

Table 7-1. Results of Quantitative Amino Acid Analyses (From Ref. 14)

Amino acid	Analytical peak[a]	Mixture A		Mixture B		Mixture C		Mixture D	
		Calcd.	Found[b]	Calcd.	Found[c]	Calcd.	Found[d]	Calcd.	Found[d]
Glycine	30[e]	2.64[j]	2.63	2.16	2.09				
Alanine	44[e]	1.73	1.75	1.31	1.28				
α-Aminobutyric acid	58[e]	1.85	1.84						
Valine	72[e]	1.87	1.83					1.60	1.65
Leucine	44[f]	...	...	...	...	1.41	1.38		
Isoleucine	69[f]	...	...	...	...	1.66	1.68		
Proline	70[e]	1.30	1.32	...	...	1.18	1.17		
Serine	60[e]	...	...	1.44	1.42				
Threonine	74[e]	...	...	0.98	0.98				
Oxyproline ...	86[e]	1.40	1.41	1.01	1.00				
Methionine ...	61[g]	...	...	...	...	1.43	1.44		
Phenylalanine .	120[e]	1.00	1.00	...	...	...	...	1.00	1.03
Tyrosine	107[h]	...	...	...	...	...	...	0.80	0.76
Aspartic acid..	116[e]	1.03	1.05	1.00	1.00	1.00	1.02	1.19	1.21
Glutamic acid .	84[f]	1.40	1.41						
Ornithine	69[i]	3.10	3.27						

[a] m/e of peak used for calculation.
[b] Average of 2 determinations.
[c] Average of 4 determinations.
[d] Average of 3 determinations.
[e] "Amine fragment."
[f] Originates through further decomposition of the amine fragment.
[g] $(CH_3 - S - CH_2)^+$.
[h] $(HO - C_7H_6)^+$.
[i] Fragment of orn-lactam.
[j] Values represent molar ratios.

Table 7-1 shows the results of such analyses on a few synthetic mixtures of amino acids.[14] While this technique is probably not more accurate than the conventional method which uses ion-exchange chromatography and automatic colorimetry of the effluent,[15] it has the advantage of being very fast, at least with respect to instrument time. While it takes 24 hr to analyze an amino acid mixture by the ion-exchange technique, only 30 to 40 min of instrument time is required for the mass spectrometric determination; the pretreatment of samples can be done in larger groups. Considering the relatively elaborate instrumentation involved in the mass spectrometric amino acid analysis, one will use this technique only if a problem really requires a very large number of quantitative analyses, and even in this area it is possible that one of the various gas chromatographic techniques will eventually be more successful.

7-2. THE DETERMINATION OF THE AMINO ACID SEQUENCE IN PEPTIDES

Just as it is possible to deduce the structure of an amino acid from the mass spectrum of a derivative, it has also been shown that the amino acid sequence in small peptides can be deduced from the mass spectrum of a suitable derivative.[2,16] Such determinations are an important problem in the elucidation of the structure of polypeptides and proteins which require this information for a very large number of small peptides obtained by degradation of the larger molecule either by acidic, basic, or enzymatic hydrolysis. Conventional techniques involve separation of these small peptides into the individual components, marking of the end groups, complete hydrolysis, and complete identification of the products by paper chromatography, or similar techniques. These procedures have been used with great success in the recent past for the solution of structural problems in this area, ranging from the determination of the structure of insulin to that of hemoglobin.

The mass spectrometric technique may be an addition, making such work less time-consuming. It may perhaps also add confidence by providing a completely different approach for checking the results. Again the foremost problem is the conversion of the rather nonvolatile peptide into a derivative of sufficient vapor pressure to yield useful mass spectra although free peptides have also been used (see Sec. 7-3). Two basically

[14] K. Biemann and W. Vetter, *Biochem. Biophys. Research Comm.*, **2**, 93 (1960).
[15] D. H. Spackman, W. H. Stein, and S. Moore, *Anal. Chem.*, **30**, 1190 (1958).
[16] K. Biemann, F. Gapp, and J. Seibl, *J. Am. Chem. Soc.*, **81**, 2274 (1959).

different approaches have been used: The methyl esters of N-trifluoro-
acetyl peptides (17)

$$F_3CCO-NH-\underset{\underset{(17)}{|}}{\overset{\overset{R_1}{|}}{CH}}-CO-NH-\underset{\overset{|}{R_2}}{\overset{\overset{R_2}{|}}{CH}}-CO-NH-\underset{\overset{|}{R_3}}{\overset{\overset{R_3}{|}}{CH}}-COOCH_3$$

are sufficiently volatile for mass spectrometry [2] provided that they contain not more than two or three amino acids. The other techriique [16] involves the reduction of the peptide (18) to a polyamino alcohol (19) by
the action of lithium aluminum hydride:

$$H_2N-\overset{\overset{R_1}{|}}{CH}-CO-NH-\overset{\overset{R_2}{|}}{CH}-CO-NH-\overset{\overset{R_3}{|}}{CH}-COOH$$

(18)

$$\downarrow LiAlH_4$$

$$H_2N-\overset{\overset{R_1}{|}}{CH}-CH_2-NH-\overset{\overset{R_2}{|}}{CH}-CH_2-NH-\overset{\overset{R_3\cdot}{|}}{CH}-CH_2OH$$

(19)

The conversion of the amide groups, the polar nature of which considerably contributes to the low volatility of these compounds, to amino
groups and of the carboxyl groups to alcohol groups makes a wide variety
of peptides sufficiently volatile; compounds as large as pentapeptides have
been investigated by this technique. A further advantage of the reduction of the peptide linkages to amino groups is the formation of a poly-
ethylene-diamine backbone in the reduction product containing a number of carbon-carbon bonds substituted on each side by a basic amino
group. Fragmentation of Type B is thus greatly facilitated and gives rise
to intense and characteristic peaks which can be used to deduce the
amino acid sequence in such a molecule. This has been shown to be the
case on the basis of the mass spectra of a considerable number of such
peptide derivatives, and it should therefore be possible to deduce the
amino acid sequence of any small peptide if the corresponding polyamino
alcohol (or polyamine—see below) is of the volatility required to give a
good mass spectrum. The interpretation is facilitated if it is known that
the peptide chain consists only of α-peptide linkages and of amino acids
of known structure, because if this is the case, one already knows that the
backbone of the molecule consists of repeating CH_2—NH—CH units; also
the structures of the side chains which can possibly be attached to the CH

groups of the backbone are in general known from the qualitative amino acid composition of the entire peptide or protein.

Fragmentation of the ethylene-diamine bonds gives rise, in fact, to the most prominent peaks in the mass spectra of such polyamino alcohols as shown in the illustrations in this section.

In these studies N-acetyl peptides have been used, because these model compounds are easier to synthesize and both the acetyl derivatives and the N-ethylpolyaminoalcohols (20)

$$CH_3CH_2NH\overset{\overset{\displaystyle R_1}{|}}{C}HCH_2NH\overset{\overset{\displaystyle R_2}{|}}{C}H-----CH_2NH\overset{\overset{\displaystyle R_{n-1}}{|}}{C}HCH_2NH\overset{\overset{\displaystyle R_n}{|}}{C}HCH_2OH$$

(20)

derived from them are somewhat more suitable for this procedure owing to their more favorable solubility properties.

The most intense peak is always due to the fragment

$$CH_3CH_2NH\overset{\overset{\displaystyle R_1}{|}}{C}H^+$$

because the positive charge is retained at a tertiary carbon atom and it is the smallest fragment of this type that can be formed. The size of the side chain (R_1 and therefore the nature of the N-terminal amino acid) is obtained by subtraction of 57 mass units (CH_3CH_2NHCH) from the mass of this fragment.

The next peak of this series will be found $42 + R_2$ mass units higher, because this species is obtained if the second rather than the first ethylene-diamine bond is broken and if the charge is retained on the tertiary carbon atom:

$$CH_3CH_2NH\overset{\overset{\displaystyle R_1}{|}}{C}HCH_2NH\overset{\overset{\displaystyle R_2}{|}}{C}H^+$$

The mass of this fragment must be $98 + R_1 + R_2$, and since R_1 was determined in the first step, R_2 follows. This periodicity of peaks continues, and the next peak is again found $42 + R_3$ mass units higher. The intensity of these peaks becomes progressively lower, as is always the case in aliphatic compounds (e.g., Figs. 3-9 and 3-10).

It is thus possible to follow the amino acid sequence in such a peptide derivative from the N-terminal to the C-terminal amino acid.

Although the positive charge is preferentially retained at the more substituted carbon atom, it may still, but less frequently, be retained at the CH_2 group, and these spectra therefore exhibit somewhat less intense peaks for the corresponding fragments containing the C terminal. The masses of these fragments are 31, $73 + R_n$, $115 + R_{n-1} + R_n$, etc.:

$$^+CH_2OH \qquad m/e\ 31$$

$$\overset{R_n}{\underset{|}{^+CH_2HNCHCH_2OH}} \qquad m/e\ 73 + R_n$$

$$\overset{R_{n-1}}{\underset{|}{^+CH_2HNCHCH_2}}\overset{R_n}{\underset{|}{NHCHCH_2OH}} \qquad m/e\ 115 + R_{n-1} + R_n$$

These peaks may be used to check the sequence found above.

In addition to the fragments obtained on cleavage of the ethylene-diamine bond, there are also other characteristic peaks present in the spectrum which arise from the loss of any one of the R groups from the molecule, because the resulting ion formed is also of Type B. In accordance with the discussion in Sec. 3-2A, such fragments will be formed more easily if the radical lost is of the benzyl type (e.g., from phenylalanine) or a more highly substituted one (e.g., from valine or isoleucine).

A number of rearrangement peaks of Type F or G can be observed in these spectra but are in general of much lower intensity. The peak at m/e 58 (60 in deuterated compounds obtained with $LiAlD_4$) is formed by elimination of R_1 as an olefin from the N-terminal fragment, e.g.,

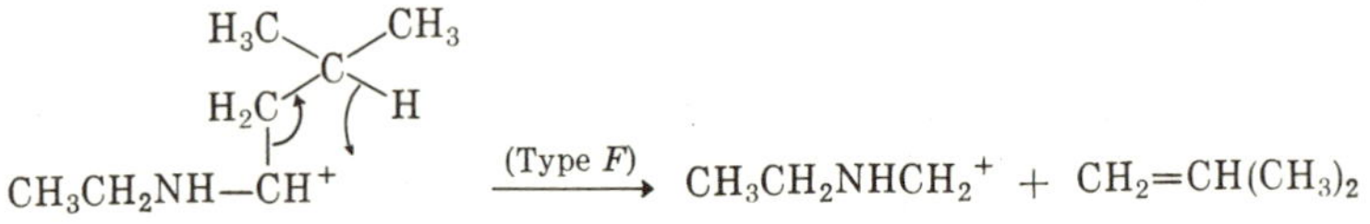

$$CH_3CH_2NH{-}CH^+ \xrightarrow{\text{(Type } F)} CH_3CH_2NHCH_2^+ + CH_2{=}CH(CH_3)_2$$
$$\qquad m/e\ 114 \qquad\qquad\qquad\qquad m/e\ 58$$

An interesting and sometimes helpful peak is found at $43 + R_n$ and can be used to confirm a C-terminal amino acid. It may be formed by one of the following processes:

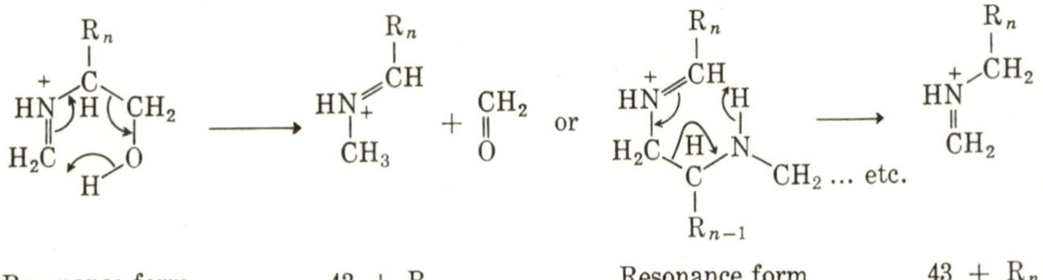

Resonance form $43 + R_n$ Resonance form $43 + R_n$
of mass $73 + R_n$ of mass M-31

It may be noted from some of the figures that peaks due to fragmentation of the molecule at a point of attachment of an aromatic amino acid are exceptionally intense and that cyclic amino acids such as proline also facilitate charge retention. In contrast, fragmentation at the part which was originally a glycine moiety leads to only weak peaks because of the lack of a substituent at that carbon atom. Finally, the peak at mass 31, $(CH_2OH)^+$, is also of low intensity because of the successfully competing nitrogen-containing fragment (see page 87).

The determination of the molecular weight of such a polyamino alcohol is of course helpful, since it permits the determination of the sum of all R groups present. The molecular ions of these compounds have a high tendency to fragment, and the abundance of such ions is very low (see Sec. 3-1A). The protonated form is, however, a much more stable entity, and these molecules give rise to an appreciable "$M + 1$" peak, which can be used to deduce the molecular weight of the polyamino alcohol. A small peak at $M + 11$ was found in the spectra of many such compounds, and although its origin is not yet clear, it may be used to confirm the molecular weight.

The correctness of the assignment of the peaks in the mass spectra of polyamino alcohols has been corroborated in many instances by the mass spectra of the corresponding deuterated products obtained by reducing the peptide ester with lithium aluminum deuteride. Comparison of Figs. 7-16a and b shows that the peaks are shifted in agreement with the fact that now each one of the former carbonyl groups has become CD_2 instead of CH_2. It is also obvious how advantageous the use of lithium aluminum deuteride is in this particular case, as it eliminates the coincidence of the mass of the N-terminal leucine fragment and the C-terminal proline (both at m/e 114) in the LiAlH$_4$-reduction products of N-acetyl peptide esters.

The fact that these reductions can be performed on about 1 mg of the peptide brings this technique within the range that is tolerable in the work on the amino acid sequence of large peptides. In this field one is usually confronted with a mixture of many small peptides obtained by partial hydrolysis of a larger one, and the separation problem is therefore formidable. The production of a volatile derivative for mass spectrometric investigation makes it possible to use gas chromatography in the separation of the mixture of polyamino alcohols obtained on reduction with lithium aluminum hydride of a previously acetylated peptide mixture.[17] Figure 7-17 shows a gas chromatogram of such a mixture. The individual fractions may be collected in capillaries (Sec. 2-5D) and their mass spectra determined.

[17] K. Biemann and W. Vetter, *Biochem. Biophys. Research Comm.*, 3, 578 (1960).

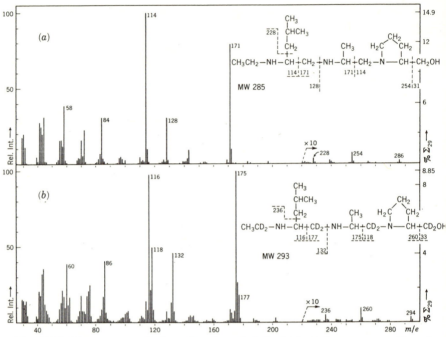

Fig. 7-16. Mass spectra of the polyamino alcohol obtained from an acetyl-leucyl-alanyl-proline upon reduction with (a) lithium aluminum hydride and (b) lithium aluminum deuteride.

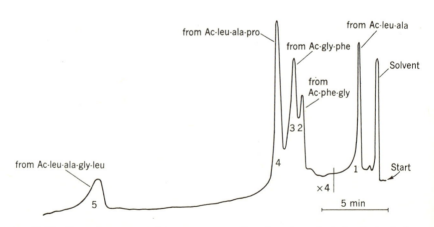

Fig. 7-17. Gas chromatographic separation of polyamino alcohols derived from peptides (2-m column; 8 per cent Apiezon L; 260°).

In order to extend the range of applicability of this separation technique and also of the mass spectrometric sequence determination, a further reduction of the polyamino alcohols to polyamines is suggested, if polyfunctional amino acids, such as glutamic acid, aspartic acid, serine, threonine, or hydroxyproline are present in the peptide, in which case the polyamino alcohol would have more than one hydroxyl group. Although such polyamino diols still give useful mass spectra, their separation by gas chromatography is more difficult, while the corresponding amines are very well separated (Fig. 7-18).

Replacement of the hydroxyl group by chlorine followed by reduction with lithium aluminum hydride is used for this purpose: [17]

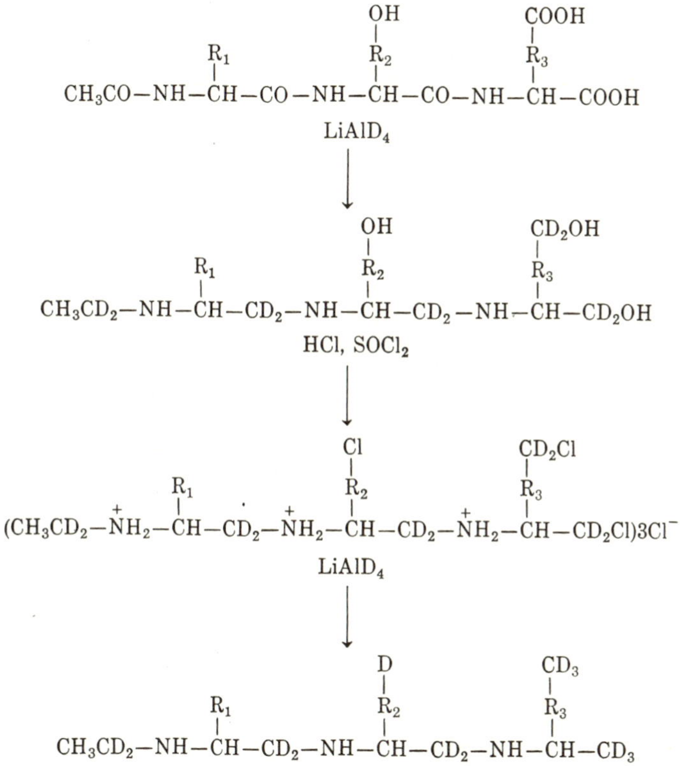

$$CH_3CO-NH-\underset{\underset{R_1}{|}}{CH}-CO-NH-\underset{\underset{R_2}{\overset{\overset{OH}{|}}{|}}}{CH}-CO-NH-\underset{\underset{R_3}{\overset{\overset{COOH}{|}}{|}}}{CH}-COOH$$

LiAlD$_4$

$$CH_3CD_2-NH-\underset{\underset{R_1}{|}}{CH}-CD_2-NH-\underset{\underset{R_2}{\overset{\overset{OH}{|}}{|}}}{CH}-CD_2-NH-\underset{\underset{R_3}{\overset{\overset{CD_2OH}{|}}{|}}}{CH}-CD_2OH$$

HCl, SOCl$_2$

$$(CH_3CD_2-\overset{+}{N}H_2-\underset{\underset{R_1}{|}}{CH}-CD_2-\overset{+}{N}H_2-\underset{\underset{R_2}{\overset{\overset{Cl}{|}}{|}}}{CH}-CD_2-\overset{+}{N}H_2-\underset{\underset{R_3}{\overset{\overset{CD_2Cl}{|}}{|}}}{CH}-CD_2Cl)3Cl^-$$

LiAlD$_4$

$$CH_3CD_2-NH-\underset{\underset{R_1}{|}}{\overset{\overset{D}{|}}{CH}}-CD_2-NH-\underset{\underset{R_2}{|}}{\overset{\overset{D}{|}}{CH}}-CD_2-NH-\underset{\underset{R_3}{|}}{\overset{\overset{CD_3}{|}}{CH}}-CD_3$$

In this case, it is imperative to use lithium aluminum deuteride to make possible a differentiation between an alkyl group originally present and one formed during this reaction from a side chain which was originally oxygenated. The ethyl group of "reduced" threonine becomes $CHDCH_3$, while aspartic acid gives CH_2CD_3. In the mass spectrum these ethyl groups therefore behave as different groups and are recognized as such (see Fig. 7-19).

The fragmentation pattern of such polyamines (Fig. 7-20) follows the same rules as the polyamino alcohols except that they seem to consist to an ever greater extent of only those peaks due to cleavage of the ethylene-diamine bond, thus facilitating the interpretation.[17]

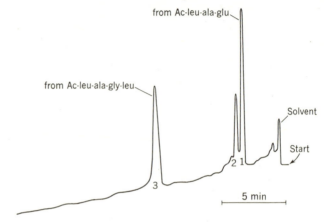

Fig. 7-18. Gas chromatographic separation of polyamines derived from peptides (2-m column; 8 per cent Apiezon *L*; 260°).

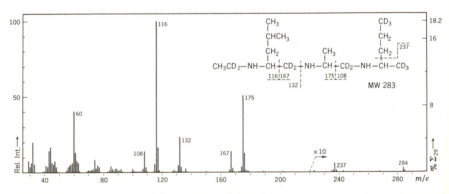

Fig. 7-19. Mass spectrum of the triamine obtained from acetyl-leucyl-alanyl-glutamic acid upon reduction with lithium aluminum deuteride.

The polyamines are highly suitable for gas chromatographic separation, and comparison of peak 5 in Fig. 7-17 and peak 3 in Fig. 7-18 shows the retarding effect of one hydroxyl group.

It is of course not possible to distinguish between isomeric amino acids, such as leucine and isoleucine, on the basis of the mass of the fragments discussed on page 285; the only difference expected between such spectra would be a higher intensity for the peak due to the loss of the side chain of isoleucine. Since this cannot be predicted, it is not possible a priori to interpret a mass spectrum of a polyamino alcohol or a polyamine in terms of the presence of either leucine or isoleucine. If such a decision has to be made, it will be necessary to synthesize this peptide and determine the mass spectrum of the authentic amino alcohol. The differences in the intensity of the $M - 57$ peaks can then be related to these amino acids. In most cases a simple di- or tripeptide containing this amino acid will be found that can easily be synthesized.

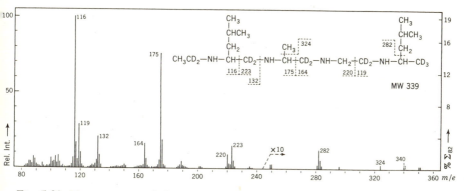

Fig. 7-20. Mass spectrum of the tetramine obtained from acetyl-leucyl-alanyl-glycyl-leucine upon reduction with lithium aluminum deuteride.

The mass spectrometric technique for determining the amino sequence in small peptides is obviously most suitable for investigating the less polar compounds of this type. Since it is these which are less easily separated and characterized by conventional techniques, it is conceivable that a combination of the mass spectrometric and the "wet" techniques for sequence determination may turn out to be the most speedy and facile approach for the work on larger peptides or proteins.

At the outset it was mentioned that the N-trifluoroacetylpeptide esters too have appreciable volatility, and the mass spectra of a number of these has been obtained (Figs. 7-21 and 7-22).[2] Their fragmentation is somewhat more complex than that obtained with the polyamino alcohols, but valuable information concerning the sequence is contained in these spectra too. The N-terminal amino acid residue appears as

$$CF_3-\underset{\underset{O}{\|}}{C}-NH-\overset{\overset{R_1}{|}}{CH^+}$$

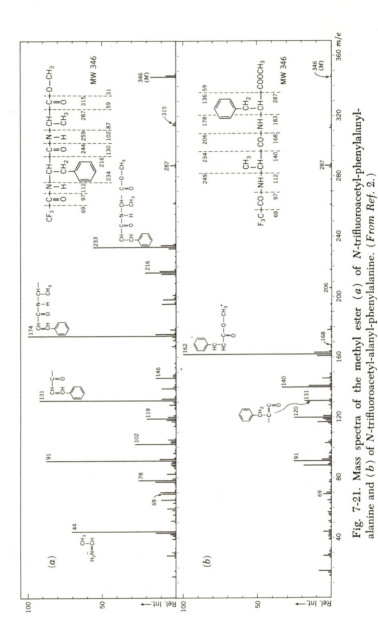

Fig. 7-21. Mass spectra of the methyl ester (a) of N-trifluoroacetyl-phenylalanyl-alanine and (b) of N-trifluoroacetyl-alanyl-phenylalanine. (*From Ref. 2.*)

292

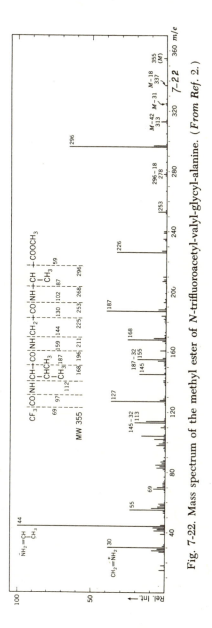

Fig. 7-22. Mass spectrum of the methyl ester of N-trifluoroacetyl-valyl-glycyl-alanine. (*From Ref. 2.*)

The C-terminal group gives rise to peaks of varying intensity of mass

$$\overset{\displaystyle R_n}{\underset{\displaystyle ^+NH-CH-CO_2CH_3}{|}}$$

and also to "amine peaks" $(H_2N-CH-R)^+$ as does the central amino acid (Fig. 7-22). The mode of fragmentation of these molecules and therefore the spectra is much more complex than that of the polyamino alcohols or polyamines, and more spectra of peptides containing three or more amino acids have to be available before the applicability of this technique to sequence determination can be fully judged.

7-3. MASS SPECTRA OF FREE AMINO ACIDS AND PEPTIDES

Conversion of the compound to more volatile derivatives was always employed in the investigations discussed earlier in this chapter, because the extremely low vapor pressure of free amino acids and peptides makes the conventional determination of their mass spectra impossible. Furthermore, a spectrum of the highest quality is desirable for the interpretation of the data.

Disadvantages of chemical pretreatment are the necessity of using a larger sample and the manipulations involved in the chemical conversion.

The vapor pressure of these substances is, however, sufficient to yield a usable mass spectrum if the sample is introduced directly into the ion source of a time-of-flight mass spectrometer (Sec. 1-2G).[18] A spectrum obtained with about 10 μg of methionine is shown in Fig. 7-23. The molecular weight (149) is clearly indicated, and the entire spectrum is very similar to the one of the ethyl ester (Fig. 7-13). Differences of 28 mass units are observed in the mass of those fragments containing now a carboxyl rather than a carbethoxy group (for example, m/e 74 replaces the "ester fragment" of mass 102). Rearrangement of Type H (m/e 75) is more pronounced in the spectra of the free acids than of the esters if fulfilling the structural requirements. This is attributed to decreased availability of the free electron pair on nitrogen owing to hydrogen bonding with the carboxyl group.

The spectra of many other free amino acids and even of arginine have been obtained, and all are in perfect agreement with the corresponding ester spectra[3] discussed in Sec. 7-1A. Hydrochlorides of amino acids

---

[18] K. Biemann and J. A. McCloskey, *J. Am. Chem. Soc.*, **84**, 3192 (1962).

are suitable too, as they dissociate upon heating under very low pressure and give rise to the spectrum of the free amino acid with the peaks (at m/e 35 to 38) of HCl superimposed.[18]

Such spectra of free amino acids may thus be used for the identification and structure determination of this class of compounds. As their

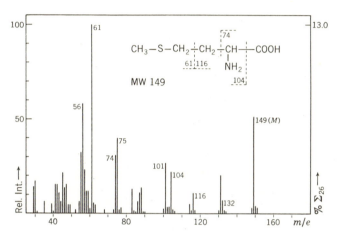

Fig. 7-23. Mass spectrum of free methionine.

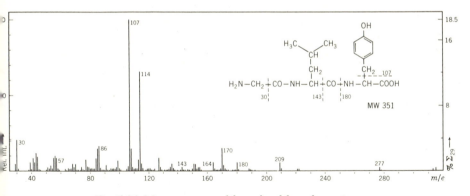

Fig. 7-24. Mass spectrum of free glycyl-leucyl-tyrosine.

molecular weights are low, the resolution of the presently available time-of-flight mass spectrometer suffices for this purpose.

Even spectra of small peptides, such as the one shown in Fig. 7-24, can be obtained in this manner and may be used for the determination of the amino acid sequence. The fragmentation of such molecules is quite different from the cleavage their reduction products (Sec. 7-2) undergo, because amide groups are present rather than ethylenediamine moieties. Rearrangements are much more abundant in the peptide spectra, and some of them are due to the presence of the carbonyl group, e.g., the elimination (Type H) of amide. groups from the molecular ion or fragments:

$$
\begin{array}{cc}
\text{H}_3\text{C} \diagdown \diagup \text{CH}_3 & \\
\qquad \text{CH} & \text{C}_6\text{H}_4\text{OH} \\
\quad \text{H} \; | & | \\
\text{O} \leftarrow \text{CH} & \text{CH}_2 \\
\quad \| \qquad | & | \\
\text{CH} - \text{C} \diagdown \quad \diagup \text{CH} - \text{CO} - \text{NH} - \text{CH} - \text{COOH} \\
\quad | \qquad \text{N} & \\
\text{NH}_2 \quad \text{H} &
\end{array}
\longrightarrow
\begin{array}{cc}
\text{H}_3\text{C} \diagdown \diagup \text{CH}_3 & \\
\qquad \text{CH} & \text{C}_6\text{H}_4\text{OH} \\
\qquad | & | \\
\qquad \text{CH} & \text{CH}_2 \\
\qquad \| & | \\
\qquad \text{CH} - \text{CO} - \text{NH} - \text{CHCOOH} \\
& m/e \; 277
\end{array}
$$

The peak at m/e 164 may arise in an analogous fashion (elimination of glycylleucine amide).

Elimination of $\text{H}_2\text{N}-\text{R}$ via Type E_1 gives rise to aminoketene ions:

$$
\begin{array}{ccc}
\text{R}_1 & \text{R}_2 & \text{R}_3 \\
| & | & | \\
\text{H}_2\text{N}-\text{CH}-\text{CO}-\text{NH}-\text{CH}-\text{CO}-\text{NH}-\text{CH}-\text{COOH} \longrightarrow
\end{array}
$$

$$
\begin{array}{cc}
\text{R}_1 & \text{R}_2 \\
| & | \\
\text{H}_2\text{N}-\text{CH}-\text{CO}-\text{NH}-\text{C}{=}\text{C}{=}\text{O}
\end{array}
$$

$$(m/e \; 170 \; \text{if} \; \text{R}_1 = \text{H}, \; \text{R}_2 = \text{C}_4\text{H}_9)$$

Finally, the resonance form of the "amine fragments" may decompose further by a process similar to the one leading to the $\text{R}_n + 43$ peak in polyamino alcohols (page 286); for example,

$$
\begin{array}{cc}
\text{H}_3\text{C} \diagdown \diagup \text{CH}_3 & \\
\qquad \text{CH} & \\
\qquad | & \\
\qquad \text{CH}_2 & \\
\qquad + \; | & \\
\qquad \text{NH}{=}\text{CH} & \\
\text{O}{=}\text{C} \diagdown \quad \diagup \text{H} & \\
\qquad \text{CH}_2{-}\text{NH} &
\end{array}
\longrightarrow
\begin{array}{c}
\text{H}_3\text{C} \diagdown \diagup \text{CH}_3 \\
\qquad \text{CH} \\
\qquad | \\
\qquad \text{CH}_2 \\
\qquad + \; | \\
\text{HN}-\text{CH}_2 \\
\text{O}{=}\text{C} \diagup\!\!\diagup
\end{array}
$$

$$m/e \; 143 \qquad\qquad\qquad m/e \; 114$$

The presence of the amino acids leucine and, particularly, tyrosine can be recognized from the peaks at m/e 57 and 107.

It seems that a considerable amount of structural information can be obtained in this way using an extremely small amount of material.

8. Alkaloids

For over a century chemists have been interested in the determination of the structure of alkaloids because of their complex constitution and their frequently remarkable biological activity, and because of a desire to learn how plants are able to produce such a variety of molecules. The classical methods of chemical degradation are tedious and time-consuming, requiring relatively large amounts of material. The advent of spectroscopic techniques has greatly aided work in this field, and very recent investigations indicate that mass spectrometry is a particularly useful technique. At present in fact, it seems that alkaloids represent the largest single group of natural products of which the structures have been determined in part or entirely by mass spectrometry. The extreme sensitivity of the mass spectrometer, which permits the investigation of traces of material, such as the minor components of complex alkaloid mixtures, is one of the many factors contributing to its usefulness. For the determination of the structure of some of the compounds discussed here, far less material was used than would have been needed for a single elemental analysis. In addition, the specificity of information obtained is very helpful for the correlation of related compounds, e.g., alkaloids of the same structural group.

The determination of alkaloid structure by mass spectrometry will be discussed in this chapter, beginning (Sec. 8-1) with the techniques used for the identification of the more commonly encountered types of degradation products, which may sometimes still be necessary. In Sec. 8-2 the more direct approach of making use of the mass spectrum of the undegraded molecule and comparing it in simple cases with the spectra of more or less closely related ones, is considered. Finally it will be shown in Sec. 8-3 that, by a detailed interpretation of the spectrum, the structure of a new system can be deduced.

8-1. IDENTIFICATION OF DEGRADATION PRODUCTS

The identification of the products resulting from drastic degradation of alkaloids is frequently necessary to obtain information about the gross structure of these molecules. Direct pyrolysis, distillation with zinc dust, or dehydrogenation with palladium or selenium are most often used. The relatively low yield by which those products are generally formed and the complexity of the mixtures obtained often make it difficult to identify all the products. For this reason such degradations are usually done with a considerable amount of material, up to a few grams. A rather complete investigation of all the products formed is desirable to avoid misinterpretations due to the isolation of a minor component formed under drastic rearrangement, while a major product, more closely related to the structure of the starting material, escapes identification because of higher solubility or too high or too low volatility.

Employing mass spectrometry for the identification of such products permits the use of a much smaller amount of the original alkaloid and facilitates the identification of both major and minor products. The individual components of incompletely separated fractions can be recognized in most cases, and gas chromatography may be used for further separation.

For preliminary experiments the degradation reaction is best produced in a sealed evacuated ampoule, and the volatile products are introduced into the mass spectrometer by the technique discussed in Sec. 2-4. Most of the compounds formed, however, will not have sufficient vapor pressure at room temperature, and both ampoule and adapter will have to be heated. For this purpose the ampoule containing the pyrolyzed material is sealed in an all-glass adapter (Fig. 8-1) along with an iron bar, permitting the breaking of the ampoule tip after evacuation of the adapter. The entire unit is then brought to the desired temperature simply by wrapping it with electric heating tape. A considerable degree of fractionation of the products is achieved by introducing the sample in several steps at consecutively higher temperatures. By this technique, for example, it was possible to detect the formation of at least three alkyl pyridines and four alkyl indoles in the zinc dust distillation of quebrachamine (1), using as little as 3 mg of the alkaloid.[1] The handling of the pyrolysis products and

[1] K. Biemann and G. Spiteller, *Tetrahedron Letters*, no. 9, p. 299, 1961.

therefore any loss of material are minimized by this technique, and the qualitative and semiquantitative results obtained give a representative picture of the products of this reaction with the possible exception of compounds not sufficiently volatile to enter the mass spectrometer.

For the final and definite identification of the individual components of such complex mixtures, however, it is advisable to obtain the mass spectra of each compound in pure form, and gas chromatography is certainly the most suitable technique for their separation and purification.

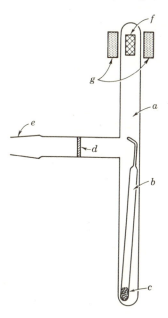

Fig. 8-1. Adapter for direct sampling of volatile products of a pyrolytic reaction performed in an ampoule. (*a*) Adapter; (*b*) ampoule; (*c*) nonvolatile residue; (*d*) sintered-glass disk; (*e*) tapered joint (12/30); (*f*) iron bar; (*g*) magnet.

Here again the actual reaction may be produced in a sealed ampoule, part of which is kept at room temperature to permit condensation of the products. These are then injected into a suitable gas chromatographic column and the individual fractions collected as described in Sec. 2-5*D*.

Figure 8-2 shows the gas chromatogram of the pyridine fraction obtained from 13 mg of quebrachamine (1): [1]

(1)

The mass spectrum of the major component indicated a mol. wt 107, corresponding to a C_2 pyridine, and the very intense peak at m/e 92 (loss of CH_3) pointed to 3-ethylpyridine rather than any other isomer (see Fig. 3-26). Of the minor components, fractions B and C had mol. wt 121 and D had 135, corresponding to C_3 and C_4 pyridines, respectively.

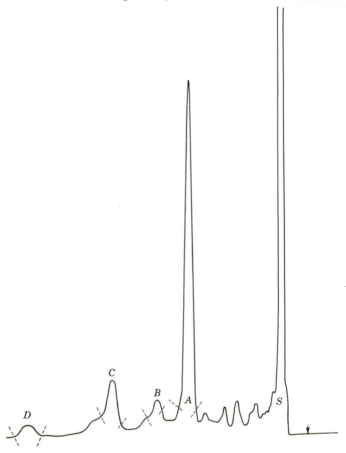

Fig. 8-2. Gas chromatogram of the pyridine fraction of a zinc dust "distillation."

All the spectra showed intense peaks due to the loss of 15 mass units, indicating the presence of an ethyl group in position 3. In addition, the absence of rearrangement peaks indicating the loss of an olefin molecule (fragmentation Type H) eliminated the possibility that an alkyl chain longer than two carbon atoms[2] could be present. The fractions were then identified as 3-ethyl-5-methylpyridine (B), 3-ethyl-4-methylpyridine (C), and 3,5-diethylpyridine (D).

[2] K. Biemann and G. Spiteller. (To be published.)

During an earlier investigation, which had employed conventional techniques for the identification of the products, only a mixture of 3,5-diethylpyridine and 3-methyl-5-ethylpyridine had been isolated in the form of a picrate, although 2.5 gm of the alkaloid were degraded.[3] The major component, 3-ethylpyridine, probably escaped detection because of the high solubility of its picrate.

At higher temperatures the gas chromatographic separation of indoles, carbazoles, and more complex molecules, such as unreacted starting material, is possible, and the fractions can be identified by mass spectrometry. Such a thorough investigation of drastic-degradation reactions is of considerable help, but one must keep in mind the frequent occurrence of alkyl migration at these elevated temperatures. More significance must be attached to the major components, while the minor products should be considered cautiously.

The nature of the aromatic ring system present in these degradation products may be deduced from the molecular weight of the compound, assuming that the substituents are saturated alkyl groups. The more common of these fall into the following homologous series ($n =$ total number of carbon atoms in side chains):

$68 + 14n$ furanes
$78 + 14n$ benzenes
$79 + 14n$ pyridines
$80 + 14n$ pyrazines, pyrimidines, pyridazines
$84 + 14n$ thiophenes
$117 + 14n$ indoles
$128 + 14n$ naphthalenes, azulenes
$129 + 14n$ quinolines, isoquinolines
$167 + 14n$ carbazoles
$168 + 14n$ carbolines

The UV spectrum of the material should be taken whenever the type of the aromatic system is in doubt, and it is of particular help in locating the alkyl side chains. Although the position of an alkyl group larger than methyl can be deduced from the mass spectrum in the case of substituted pyridines, as was shown above, it is more difficult to distinguish α-substituted indoles from β-substituted ones, and the same holds true for more complex aromatic systems.

In most cases, however, the size and structure of an alkyl side chain attached to an aromatic nucleus can be established by mass spectrometry. As an illustration, the mass spectra of three β-carbolines will be discussed.

[3] B. Witkop, *J. Am. Chem. Soc.*, **79**, 3193 (1957).

The molecular weight of the compound, the spectrum of which is shown in Fig. 8-3a, points to a β-carboline substituted with three carbon atoms [$168 + (14 \times 3)$]. The most intense peak at m/e 195 corresponds to the loss of a methyl group from a carbon atom attached to the aromatic system (cleavage of Type A_4). The peak at m/e 182 corresponds to the loss of 28 mass units and could be interpreted as the loss of ethylene via a rearrangement of Type H. Such an elimination would imply the presence of an n-propyl group, making it difficult to understand the facile loss of a methyl group. An alternative explanation for the fragmentation process leading to mass 182 is the loss of 27 mass units from the fragment of mass 209. The loss of HCN, a particle of low energy content, is frequently observed in the spectra of nitrogen-containing heterocyclics such as indoles;[4] pyridine (mol. wt 79) too exhibits such a peak at m/e 52. Such a two-step process for the formation of mass 182, loss of hydrogen followed by loss of HCN, is corroborated by the presence of a pronounced metastable peak, the maximum of which is found at m/e 159; it is expected at m/e 158.5 for the decomposition of mass 209 to 182, while it would have to be at 157.7 for the loss of 28 mass units from mass 210 (Sec. 3-3). Correct mass measurement (Sec. 4-6) would also indicate whether one or two nitrogen atoms are still present in the fragment of mass 182.

This interpretation of the spectrum shown in Fig. 8-3a is in agreement with an isopropyl β-carboline, such as (2):

$$(2) \quad R = -\overset{\displaystyle CH_3}{\underset{\displaystyle CH_3}{CH}}$$

$$(3) \quad R = -CH_2-CH_2-\underset{\displaystyle CH_3}{CH}-CH_2-CH_3$$

$$(4) \quad R = -\underset{\displaystyle \underset{\displaystyle CH_3}{\underset{\displaystyle |}{CH_2}}}{\overset{\displaystyle |}{CH}}-\overset{\displaystyle CH_3}{\underset{\displaystyle CH_3}{CH}}$$

While this is indeed the compound from which the spectrum was obtained, a conclusive identification would require comparison with an authentic sample, because those fragments could be obtained also from a methyl ethyl β-carboline and perhaps even from a trimethyl β-carboline,

[4] J. H. Beynon and A. E. Williams, *Appl. Spectroscopy*, **13**, 101 (1959).

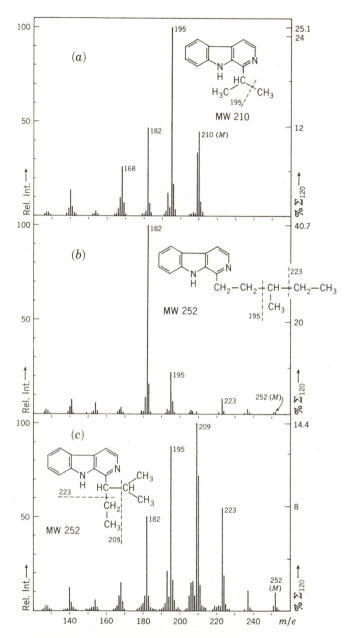

Fig. 8-3. Mass spectra of three alkyl β-carbolines.

which in analogy to polymethyl benzenes may lose a methyl group to a considerable extent, although one would expect the peak at mass 195 to be much lower in the trimethyl derivative. The UV spectrum would be of considerable help in establishing both the number and the position of the alkyl substituents present, and so would the NMR spectrum, but frequently not enough material can be obtained in such degradation reactions to obtain a sufficiently intense NMR spectrum.

The mass spectra of two isomeric β-carbolines containing more complex side chains are shown in Fig. 8-3b and c. Both are of mol. wt 252, indicating six carbon atoms in addition to the basic carbon skeleton of the aromatic system. One of them exhibits a strong peak at m/e 182, corresponding to the loss of C_5H_{10}, indicative of the elimination of five carbon atoms as an olefin via a rearrangement of Type H. It follows that the carbon atom directly attached to the aromatic system bears two hydrogen atoms. The very low intensity of the peak at m/e 209 implies that three carbon atoms cannot be lost as easily as other alkyl groups, and it is best interpreted by assuming a 3-methylpentyl side chain, as in (3).

The mass spectrum of the isomer (4) (Fig. 8-3c) seems to consist of many intense peaks, but consideration of their intensity in terms of total ionization (right-hand ordinate) shows that the average absolute intensity of these peaks is much lower than that of the fragment of mass 182 in isomer (3). The peaks at m/e 223 and 209 are due to the loss of either one of the two alkyl substituents at C_α by simple cleavage, facilitated by the higher substitution at C_α. Elimination of these substituents (via Type H), on the other hand, gives rise to the peaks at m/e 224 and 210. The fragment of mass 195 seems to be due to the loss of 15 mass units from 210:

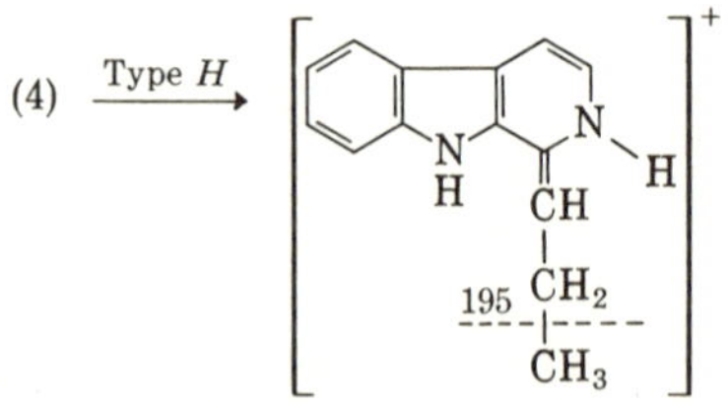

$$(4) \xrightarrow{\text{Type } H}$$

m/e 210

Mass 182 appears to be due to the loss of HCN from mass 209, as indicated by a metastable peak, the maximum of which is found at m/e 159 (calcd. 158.5).

These three examples illustrate how the complexity of the mass spectrum of such compounds increases with increasing branching in the alkyl substituent. In more complex cases, particular care must be taken to use a pure sample uncontaminated by isomers or lower homologs. If spectra are obtained with an electron energy of about 10 volts, the detection of such impurities is facilitated. The contributions of lower homologs could be taken as an indication of a rearrangement ion of Type *H* formed from a molecular ion containing two or more carbon atoms more. It must be kept in mind, however, that these rearrangement ions are still rather pronounced at low ionizing voltage in contrast to simple cleavage of the C_α—C_β bond, as has been pointed out on page 85. The mass spectrum of compound (4) determined with low-energy electrons thus exhibits only very small peaks at m/e 195, 209, and 223.

8-2. THE CORRELATION OF RELATED ALKALOIDS WITH IDENTICAL CARBON SKELETON

A. Alkaloids Differing in the Substitution of the Aromatic Moiety

The UV spectrum of an alkaloid is indicative of the aromatic system present, and therefore in general it is not difficult to recognize the type of aromatic or heterocyclic ring system and to detect the kind and position of substituents attached to it. It is a much more formidable task to recognize or correlate the nonaromatic part of such a molecule, which commonly requires chemical degradation or conversion to a compound of known structure. This can now be achieved by means of the mass spectra of such compounds, because they reflect the type and arrangement of the bonds in the molecule which are easily broken. Such spectra are thus indicative of the arrangement of the aliphatic or alicyclic bonds rather than of the aromatic ones.

Mass Spectrometric Shift Technique. To have such a method available is of particular value for correlating various alkaloids from the same plant or botanical family, because frequently those compounds contain the same basic carbon skeleton and vary in the type of substitution in the aromatic ring system. For such a molecule, represented schematically by expression (5),

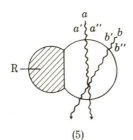

(5)

in which the shaded part denotes the aromatic moiety of the molecule while the light circle indicates the alicyclic system attached to it, one may schematically picture the fragmentation processes which the molecular ion undergoes by the lines a and b. Such a fragmentation leads to two particles, one of which retains the positive charge and is therefore recorded in the mass spectrum. This charge distribution will, of course, depend on the extent of stabilization provided for the positive charge at one of the two particles and the stabilization of the remaining electron as a radical on the other part. If fragmentation takes place at a and the positive charge is retained at fragment a'', a peak corresponding to the mass-to-charge ratio of fragment a'' will be observed in the spectrum regardless of the size of the substituent R attached to the aromatic ring. If, however, the charge is better stablized on fragment a', this particle is recorded in the spectrum, and its mass of course includes the substituent R. Similarly, if fragmentation takes place at b, the particle recorded will correspond either to the mass of b'' or to that of b', and only in the latter case will the substituent R have any influence with respect to the mass of this peak.

In summary, the mass spectrum of a complex molecule containing an aromatic and an alicyclic moiety consists of two groups of peaks, those representing particles which contain the aromatic system and another group which does not. The mass spectrum of another compound which has the same alicyclic carbon skeleton attached to the same aromatic system but with an additional substituent will exhibit peaks at exactly the same mass and similar intensity belonging to the group of peaks not related to the aromatic part of the molecule. The second group of peaks, however, will be shifted to higher masses for the exact mass difference due to the additional substituent. If this is the case, the carbon skeleton of the two compounds can be considered to be identical.

The compounds to be compared must fulfill a few basic requirements in order that this technique may be applied successfully and without error.

First, in the model discussed above it was assumed that the substituent R will not influence the mode of fragmentation taking place in the alicyclic part of the system. This assumption will not hold if the substituent prevents the splitting of any bond involved in fragmentation a or fragmentation b or, on the other hand, greatly facilitates the cleavage of another bond, thus giving rise to a new mode of fragmentation. If such were the case, the mass spectrum of the substituted and unsubstituted compound would greatly differ, and the identity of the basic skeleton of the molecules would not be recognized. Second, the substituent may by resonance stabilize or destabilize the positive charge on particle a' or b' and thus appreciably increase or decrease the intensity of the corresponding peak, which in extreme cases would again lead to spectra of very different appearance.

Examples of these two situations are shown in Fig. 8-4, which presents the mass spectra of three methyl phenylacetates.[5] The *o*-methoxy derivative gives a spectrum which cannot be resolved clearly into two groups—one present as such in the mass spectrum of the unsubstituted ester and the other shifted 30 mass units. The ortho substituent is so close to that area of the molecule which undergoes fragmentation as to change the spectral pattern considerably. Loss of the methoxyl group from the primary fragment of mass 121 is facilitated, giving rise to two intense peaks at m/e 121 and at m/e 91. The spectrum of the *p*-methoxy ester, on the other hand, is much more similar to the one of unsubstituted phenylacetate, as its C_7H_7 fragment of mass 91 is almost exclusively displaced to mass 121 (C_8H_9O). The intensity of this peak is higher (44.6 per cent Σ_{25}) than the corresponding one in the spectrum (not shown) of the *m*-methoxy analog (m/e 121 = 28.1 per cent Σ_{25}) because of the increased stabilization of the positive charge due to the *p*-methoxy group in the former.

A third assumption implicit in the model presented earlier in this section is that the additional substituent R should not be a group containing a bond or bonds which are easily fragmented. If such is the case, the mass spectrum of the derivative containing such a group would consist of three parts: the two groups discussed above and a third group of peaks which arise by fragmentation of a bond at R. If this is important only for the molecular ion, then it is no serious limitation. If, however, this cleavage also occurs in fragments, the picture may be rather confused. Fortunately the additional substituents which lead to the sometimes wide variety of structures within a given group of alkaloids are, in general, small groups such as methyl, methoxyl, methylenedioxy, formyl, or acetyl. Sometimes larger substituents are present, but they are frequently attached via an ester or amide linkage and therefore can be easily removed before the spectrum is taken. This third assumption is thus correct for most practical cases, and it will be illustrated later that groups like acetyl or ethyl, which contain a bond easily cleaved, do not introduce serious difficulties. Such groups merely give rise to additional peaks at m/e 43, M − 43, and M − 15 (in case of acetyl) or M − 15 (in case of

[5] Unpublished experiments from the author's laboratory (by H. K. Schnoes).

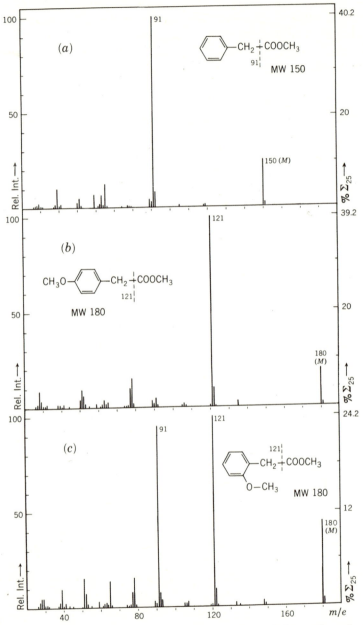

Fig. 8-4. Mass spectra of (a) methyl phenylacetate, (b) methyl p-methoxyphenylace-tate, and (c) the ortho isomer.

ethyl). Furthermore, acetyl groups at aromatic hydroxyl or amino groups may be eliminated as ketene (Type E_1), giving rise to peaks 42 mass units lower than expected (see, for example, m/e 150 and 174 in Fig. 8-8*d*).

This approach in the determination of the structure of alkaloids has, as yet, been used almost exclusively on indole and dihydroindole alkaloids of type (6) and (7), respectively:

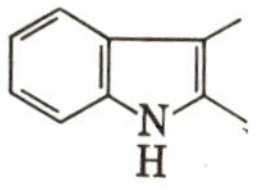

(6) 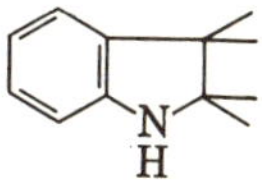   (7)

The various derivatives of these alkaloids frequently occur in nature with substitution of methoxyl or free hydroxyl groups in the benzene ring and substitution of methyl or acyl groups on the nitrogen atom. Such substituents do not seem to influence the fragmentation of the alicyclic ring system attached to the indole or dihydroindole moiety to any appreciable extent. These groups of alkaloids are therefore particularly suitable for structure determination by this "mass spectrometric shift technique," once a single representative of the particular group is available and its structure has been established.

(8)   (9)

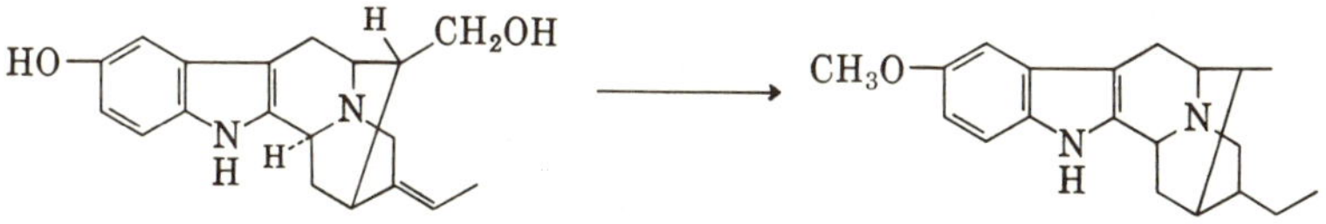

(10)   (11)

The first successful correlation of this type related the structure of a degradation product (9) of ajmaline (8)[6] with a conversion product (11) of sarpagine (10). The mass spectra of the two compounds were very similar, but the one of (11) was shifted 16 mass units, because the net difference between the two molecules (9) and (11) amounts to one oxygen atom, that is, 16 mass units.[7]

[6] R. B. Woodward, *Angew. Chem.*, **68**, 13 (1956).

[7] K. Biemann, *Tetrahedron Letters*, no. 15, p. 9, 1960; *J. Am. Chem. Soc.*, **83**, 4801 (1961).

A large group of related alkaloids is represented by the alkaloids of *Tabernanthe iboga,* which occur in nature in various degrees of methoxylation:

(12) $R_1 = R_2 = H$
(13) $R_1 = OCH_3$, $R_2 = H$
(14) $R_1 = H$, $R_2 = OCH_3$
(15) $R_1 = R_2 = OCH_3$

In Fig. 8-5 the mass spectra of ibogamine (12), ibogaine (13), tabernanthine (14), and ibogaline (15) are compared.[8] They clearly exhibit a group of peaks in the lower part of the spectrum (e.g., m/e 122, 124, 135, 136, and 149) which are present in all four spectra and are of about the same intensity. Obviously these peaks are due to fragments of the molecule originating from a part that does not contain the additional substituents in the benzene ring. The second group of peaks, on the other hand, which fall in ibogamine at m/e 156, 195, 251, 265, and 280, appear with almost the same intensity but 30 mass units higher in ibogaine and tabernanthine and 60 mass units higher in ibogaline. They therefore contain the benzene ring, which is substituted differently in these molecules. It is of interest to note that the mass spectra of tabernanthine and ibogaine are identical except for small differences in intensities, which indicates that the position of the methoxyl group is of little consequence to the fragmentation far away at the alicyclic moiety of these molecules, in agreement with the discussion at the beginning of this section.

In contrast to the other three alkaloids [9] the structure of ibogaline had not been established by chemical correlation or degradation, but its mass spectrum [8] combined with the UV and IR data, which indicated the presence of a 5,6-dimethoxyindole derivative,[10] definitely prove it to be 12,13-dimethoxyibogamine, a structure which had already been suggested on biogenetic grounds.[10] The chemical correlation with a degradation product of ibogaine was impossible at that time, because sufficient amounts of this minor alkaloid were not available.

In the illustrations in this chapter, the low-mass part of the spectra is generally omitted to save space. In that region of the spectra of the compounds discussed here, the peaks are of quite low intensity and are rather unimportant because the mass of the substituted aromatic ring alone is above 100 and because smaller parts of the alicyclic system are no longer

[8] K. Biemann and M. Friedmann-Spiteller, *J. Am. Chem. Soc.,* **83**, 4805 (1961).

[9] M. F. Bartlett, D. F. Dickel, and W. I. Taylor, *J. Am. Chem. Soc.,* **80**, 126 (1958); G. Arai, J. Coppola, and G. A. Jeffrey, *Acta Cryst.,* **13**, 553 (1960).

[10] N. Neuss, *J. Org. Chem.,* **24**, 2047 (1959).

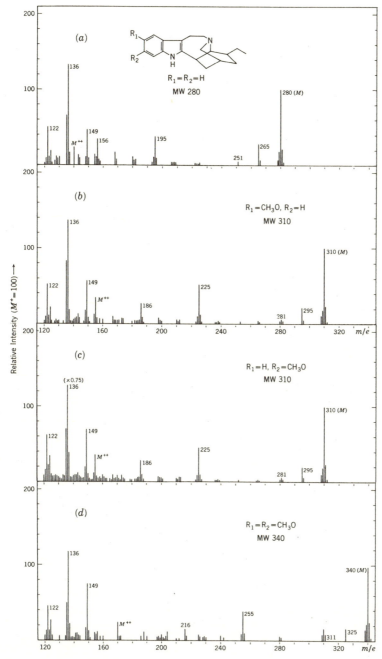

Fig. 8-5. Mass spectra of (a) ibogamine, (b) ibogaine, (c) tabernanthine, and (d) ibogaline.

311

characteristic for a particular carbon skeleton. As an example, a complete spectrum is shown in Fig. 8-7. The acetyl group is one of the few substituents giving rise to intense peaks at low mass (m/e 43), particularly at the dihydroindole nitrogen or on oxygen.

The technique outlined above has also been employed to establish the structure of quebrachamine (1) by comparison of its mass spectrum with that of a compound (16) with an identical carbon skeleton but containing an additional methoxyl group: [1]

(16)

This compound was chosen because it could be synthesized from deacetylaspidospermine (17c). The structure of a considerable number of alkaloids related to (17c) have been determined [11] by such a correlation of their mass spectra.

Interpretation of the Spectra. This direct matching of mass spectra is successful in all those cases where the spectra turn out indeed to be very closely related and where it is established by other techniques (e.g., UV spectra) that the additional substituents are attached directly to the aromatic ring. However, a more detailed knowledge of the fragmentation processes which such molecules undergo considerably broadens the area of possible application of this approach, as it would aid in elucidating structures of similar molecules modified in the alicyclic sections.

Such detailed interpretations of the mass spectra of the compounds discussed above have been presented,[5,7,8,11] and only a few of the more interesting and more important fragmentation processes will be discussed here.

Iboga Alkaloids. Because of the polycyclic nature of these compounds most of the fragmentation processes involve the cleavage of two or more bonds, which must be broken in an energetically favorable way in order to lead to fragments of considerable abundance. The fragments formed by loss of the ethyl or methyl group of the iboga alkaloids have been discussed earlier (Sec. 5-3B), and the stereochemical implications of the preferred loss of the methyl group have been pointed out in Sec. 3-2C. The fragment of mass 225 in the spectrum of ibogaine seems to contain

[11] K. Biemann, M. Friedmann-Spiteller, and G. Spiteller, *Tetrahedron Letters,* no. 14, p. 485, 1961.

ring *C* in addition to the indole moiety, and the following fragmentation is suggested:

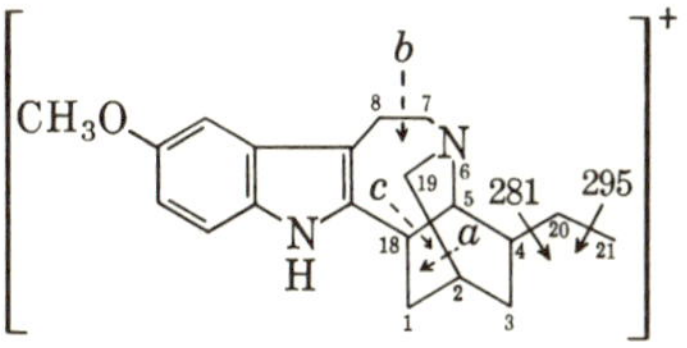

(13)

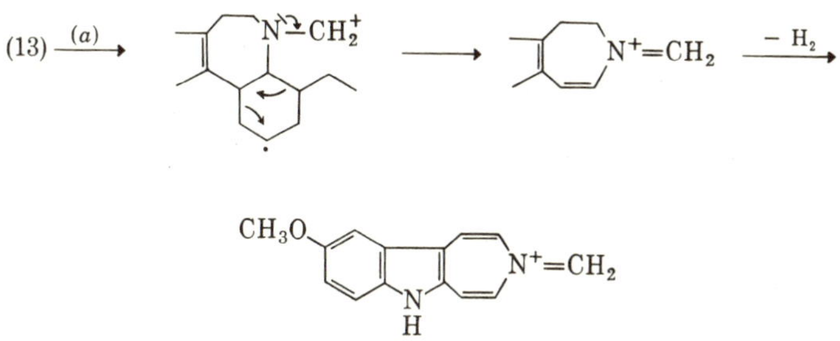

(13) $\xrightarrow{(a)}$

225

The first step is the cleavage of a carbon-carbon bond (a) with retention of the positive charge at C-19. Elimination of ring *D* and a molecule of hydrogen lead to a highly conjugated ion which can be viewed as an indoloazaheptafulvene. In agreement with this fragmentation is the fact that the deuterated ibogaine molecule (see Sec. 5-3*B*) containing deuterium at C-20 also exhibits the peak at m/e 225 rather than 226. In Fig. 8-6 the partial spectra of a few specifically deuterated ibogaine molecules are compared with the nondeuterated species.

The deuterium atom at C-20 is retained, however, in the fragment of mass 122, which arises via the following path:

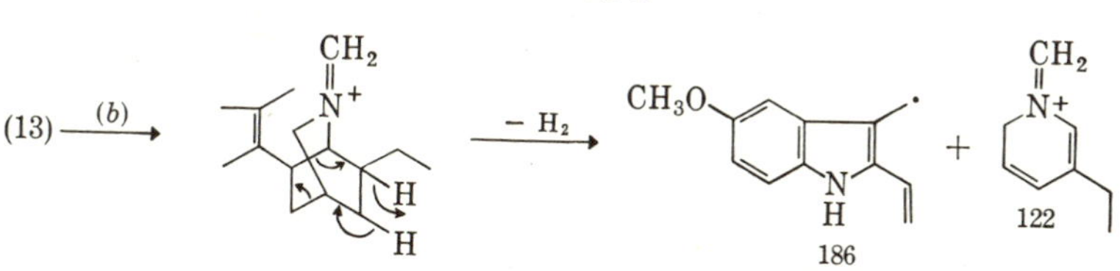

(13) $\xrightarrow{(b)}$

186

122

Fragmentation of the C-7,C-8 bond and retention of the positive charge at C-7, where it is stabilized by the free electron pair on N-6, lead to a species which is still of the same mass as the molecular ion but which fragments by a concerted shift of four electron pairs into a radical of mass 186, a cation of mass 122, and a hydrogen molecule. In the charged

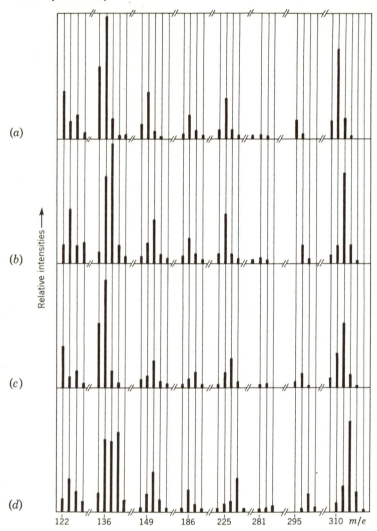

Fig. 8-6. Partial mass spectra of (*a*) ibogaine and of ibogaines (*b*) deuterated at C-20, (*c*) deuterated at C-18, and (*d*) dideuterated at C-19. (Intensities normalized in terms of the sum of the molecular ions.)

fragment an aza-polyene system is again present. If in the first step the remaining electron is retained at C-8 rather than C-7, the fragment of mass 186 is recorded in the spectrum.

The value of deuterium labeling for the elucidation of fragmentation mechanisms is borne out by a consideration of the formation of a fragment of mass 136. Deuterium at C-18 is not retained in this fragment, but the spectrum of ibogaine dideuterated at C-19 shows that the corresponding fragment now has mass 137 and 138. It therefore does not contain C-18 but does contain C-19, and the one hydrogen atom at C-19 may be lost in this fragmentation. The following mechanism is in agreement with these findings, particularly since in the last step hydrogen atoms at C-3 and C-19 become equivalent with respect to their possible elimination:

$$(13) \xrightarrow{(c)} \quad \longrightarrow \quad \longrightarrow \quad 136$$

The peaks at m/e 124 and m/e 149 are due to related fragmentation processes.[8]

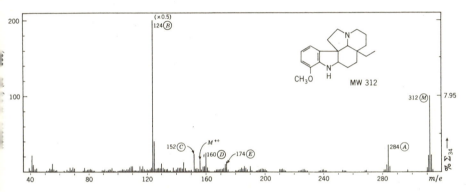

Fig. 8-7. Mass spectrum of deacetylaspidospermine (17c); the encircled letters refer to the fragmentation scheme on page 316. The peak at m/e 124 is twice as intense as shown.

Aspidospermine-like Alkaloids. A rather different type of carbon skeleton is represented by aspidospermine (17e), a dihydroindole alkaloid the structure of which had been determined by X-ray crystallography[12] and by chemical degradation.[13] A number of derivatives thereof have recently been found in nature. The mass spectrum of deacetylaspidospermine (17c), shown in Fig. 8-7, is very characteristic, and the two most significant features are the intense peak at m/e 124 and the loss of 28 mass units from the molecular ion giving rise to a peak at m/e 284, accompanied by a striking metastable peak (found at m/e 259, calcd. 258.5). The peak at mass 124 is surprisingly intense compared with the mass

[12] J. F. D. Mills and S. C. Nyburg, *Tetrahedron Leters*, no. 11, p. 1, 1959.
[13] H. Conroy, P. R. Brook, and Y. Amiel, *Tetrahedron Letters*, no. 11, p. 4, 1959.

spectra of the alkaloids discussed above and indicates that this fragment is formed by a particularly favorable decomposition process.

The following scheme [11] is in agreement with such a spectrum and derives its driving force from the aromatization of ring B and the elimination of a neutral molecule, ethylene:

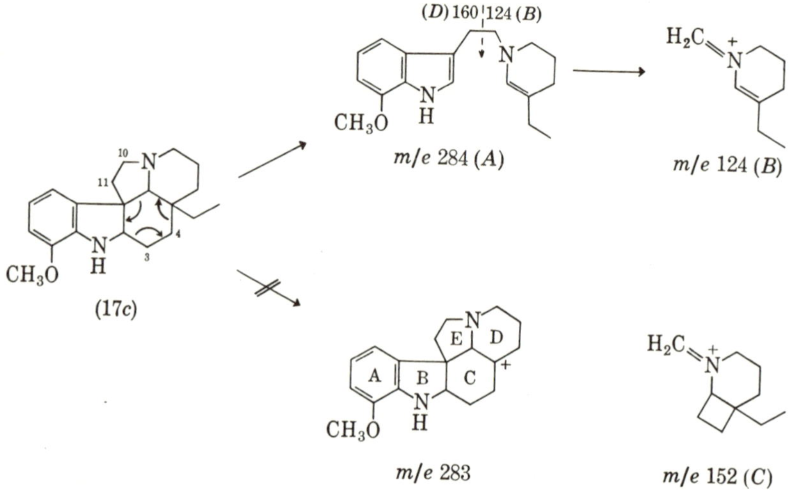

In fragment A of mass 284 the indole system and ring D are attached to each other only by a two-carbon bridge. Fragmentation of the C-10—C-11 bond and retention of the positive charge at C-10 give rise to the conjugated ion B of mass 124 and an indolylmethyl radical. If the positive charge is retained at C-11 rather than C-10, fragment D of mass 160 is recorded in the spectrum. The fragment of mass 152 seems to correspond to the one of mass 124 but has retained C-3 and C-4, possibly forming the bicyclic ion C shown in the scheme above. Mass 174 (E) must be a homolog of 160, which has retained C-10. The correctness of this interpretation is corroborated by the mass spectrum of a sample of deacetylaspidospermine containing deuterium at C-2, in which these peaks are found at mass 124, 152, 161, 175, 285, and 313, and of a sample of the related ketone $(20a)$ deuterated at C-3 (see Fig. 8-9c). It is of interest to note that the angular ethyl group, although attached to a tertiary carbon atom, is not lost easily; this is borne out by only a very small peak at m/e 283 $(M - 29)$. Such an ion is not favored, as it would be located on a bridge head.

A change in substitution at rings A and B, or at C-11, will thus give rise to a change in the mass of ions D, A, and M, which are of mass 160, 284, and 312 in deacetylaspidospermine $(17c)$, while the strong peak at m/e 124 (B) and at m/e 152 (C) will remain. In principle, additional substituents attached to C-3 and C-4 or to ring D, C-10, C-14, and C-15 can also be located in these parts of the molecule unless their presence would change the fragmentation mode of the entire molecule (see Sec. 8-2*B*).

(a) $R_1 = R_2 = R_3 = H$
(b) $R_1 = CH_3$, $R_2 = R_3 = H$
(c) $R_1 = R_3 = H$, $R_2 = CH_3O$
(d) $R_1 = CH_3$, $R_2 = CH_3O$, $R_3 = H$
(e) $R_1 = CH_3CO$, $R_2 = CH_3O$, $R_3 = H$
(f) $R_1 = CH_3CO$, $R_2 = R_3 = CH_3O$
(g) $R_1 = C_2H_5$, $R_2 = CH_3O$, $R_3 = H$

(17)

On the basis of this interpretation, the structure of a number of alkaloids isolated from *Aspidosperma quebracho blanco* have recently been determined.[11] One of them was the unsubstituted analog (17*a*) of aspidospermine, while all others contained methyl, methoxyl, or acetyl groups in ring A or B. The spectra of these substances (17*a* to *f*), shown in Fig. 8-8, exhibited the characteristically intense peak (note the reduction factor) at mass 124 in their spectra, while the molecular weight indicated the number and kind of substituents present. They all showed the characteristic loss of 28 mass units from the molecular ion.

The presence of the acetyl group at N-1 is indicated by a more intense peak at $M - 15$ and one at $M - 43$; the "indole peaks" have lost the acetyl group as ketene (C_2H_2O) through a rearrangement of Type *E*, and appear at the same mass as in the unacetylated molecule (160 and 174, and 190 and 204, respectively). Similarly, *N*-ethyldeacetylaspidospermine (17*g*), which also contains an easily split C—C bond (next to nitrogen) in the additional substituent, gives a mass spectrum which clearly exhibits the pattern of this type of alkaloid with the exception only of a much higher $M - 15$ peak. Once this bond is broken, no further fragmentation of the resulting ion seems to occur. Another alkaloid, pyrifolidine, isolated from various *Aspidosperma* species, was found to be the optical antipode of (17*f*) by mass-spectrometric correlation with (17*c*).[14]

It is of interest to note that the unacetylated derivatives exhibit a rather intense peak for the doubly charged molecular ion while this is not the case for the acetylated alkaloids of this type, which instead show an intense fragment corresponding to $(M - 42)^{++}$.

Some of these compounds are minor alkaloids of the plant that are present in the crude mixture of total alkaloids to an extent of less than 1 per cent. Nevertheless, with the aid of aluminum oxide and high-temperature gas chromatography it was possible to isolate pure samples

[14] C. Djerassi, B. Gilbert, J. N. Shoolery, L. F. Johnson, and K. Biemann, *Experentia*, **17**, 162 (1961).

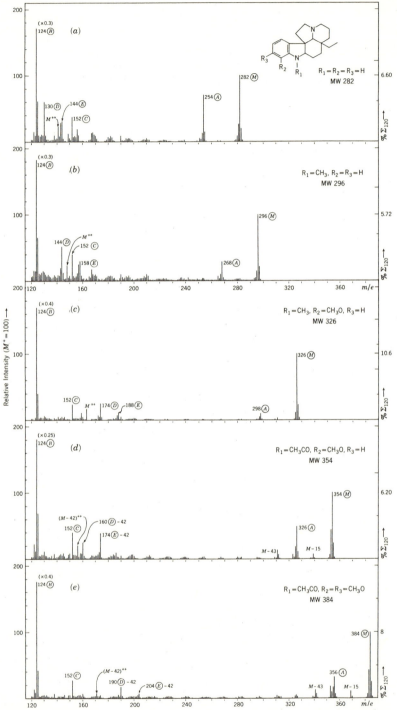

Fig. 8-8. Mass spectra of various alkaloids of the aspidospermine type (17*a*,*b*,*d* to *f*); the encircled letters refer to the fragmentation scheme on page 316.

in an amount sufficient for a mass spectrum from which the structure of the compound could then be deduced.

B. *Alkaloids Differing in the Substitution of the Alicyclic Moiety*

Recognition of the fragmentation processes giving rise to a typical mass spectral pattern exhibited by a partly aromatic polycyclic system permits drawing conclusions beyond the correlation of compounds differing only in the substitution of the aromatic moiety. While changes at the alicyclic part could, in principle, also lead merely to a shift in mass of certain peaks, namely, those containing the additional substituents, one has to keep in mind that such additional substituents are now present at the site of fragmentation, which may then take a different path.

Both these extreme situations can be encountered, as are intermediate ones, depending on the group(s) introduced. These groups may be of three types.

1. Substituents such as methyl or carbonyl groups, which neither appreciably change the fragmentation mode exhibited by the unsubstituted system nor contain bonds cleaved with great facility. Such derivatives will exhibit spectra in which some of the peaks are shifted for the mass of the additional substituents. The relative intensity of the peaks may vary more than in the cases discussed in the previous section.

2. Substituents such as hydroxy, acetoxy, carbomethoxy groups, or double bonds in place of certain single bonds, lead again to displacement to a correspondingly differing mass of the peaks due to fragments containing these substituents; in such a case the relative intensities may change appreciably. In addition, there will be new peaks superimposed on the basic spectrum, owing to the presence or creation of additional bonds prone to cleavage.

3. The introduction of certain groups which strongly interfere with the fragmentation mode exhibited by the plain carbon skeleton results in an entirely different spectrum. In this category belong double bonds (if located so as to prevent the necessary cleavage of a given bond) or additional rings at positions where they link two parts of the molecule which are to separate in a given fragmentation.

The wide variety of consequences of such substitutions is best outlined by a few typical examples. These show that the similarity in appearance of the spectra of closely related compounds (see, for example, Fig. 8-5 or 8-8) decreases with increasing complexity of the substitution pattern. Nevertheless, it is possible to recognize a certain fragmentation mode, even in spectra which appear to be quite different from the one of the unsubstituted model.

Such a trend is borne out by the mass spectra (Fig. 8-9) of vindoline (18) and dihydrovindoline (19) and of a degradation product (20a) of the latter.[15]

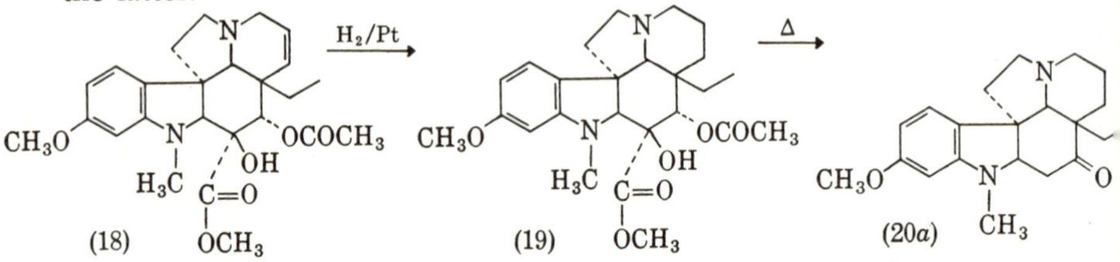

(18)   (19)   (20a)

The ketone (20a) exhibits a spectrum (Fig. 8-9c) clearly reminiscent of an aspidospermine derivative (see Fig. 8-8, especially part c) with methoxy and methyl in the aromatic portion of the molecule. The carbonyl

[15] M. Gorman, N. Neuss, and K. Biemann, *J. Chem. Soc.*, 84, 1058 (1962).

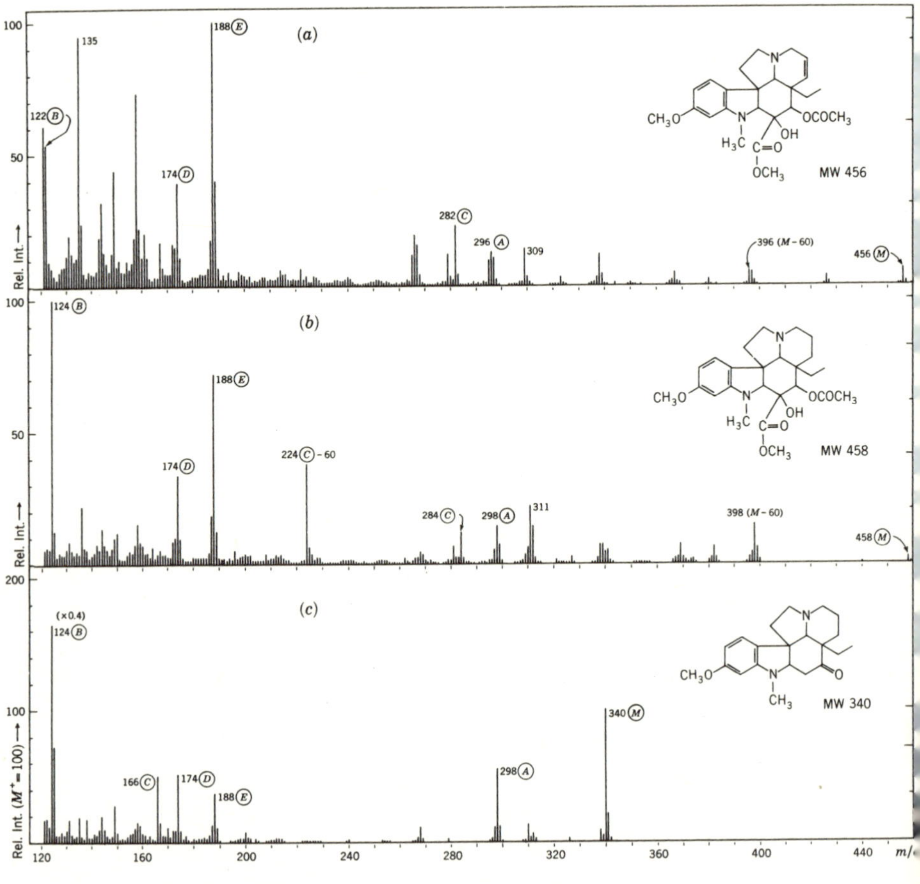

Fig. 8-9. Mass spectra of (a) vindoline (18), (b) dihydrovindoline (19), and (c) compound (20a). (For the significance of arrows and encircled letters, see text.)

group (the presence of which was borne out by the IR spectrum) must be at C-3 or C-4, because the peak at m/e 298 indicates the loss of 42 (C_2H_2O) instead of 28 (C_2H_4) mass units in the formation of fragment A of the scheme on page 316. Deuterium exchange of the α hydrogens (see Sec. 5-3A) leads to the incorporation of two deuterium atoms, resulting in a molecular weight of 342. This is only possible if the carbonyl group is at C-4. Fragments D and E remained unchanged while C was displaced for 2 mass units, which is further proof for the fragmentation scheme outlined earlier. In particular, it shows that fragment E does in fact retain C-10 and C-11 and not C-3 and C-11.

Subtle differences in type or location of functional groups can sometimes lead to drastic changes in the spectrum. As outlined above, the introduction of a carbonyl group at position 4 of the aspidospermine skeleton does not change the mode of fragmentation. However, the presence of a carbonyl group at position 3 in the oxidation product ($20b$) of spegazzinine methyl ether ($20c$) seems to alter the fragmentation of ring C, as this compound is reported [16] to have its most intense peak at m/e 138 rather than at 124. Such a difference may be readily explained by a loss of carbon monoxide after cleavage of the C-2–C-3 bond, possible in this molecule because the carbonyl group is now at the terminal of a chain where it may be lost easily (some general examples of this variation of Type A_2 are discussed on pages 82 and 105):

(20b) R = O
(20c) R = H, OH

m/e 138

In the same step, a CH_2 group is at the terminal in the case of the isomer ($20a$). As carbene is of much higher energy content than carbon monoxide, CH_2CO rather than CH_2 is expelled, leading to fragment B of m/e 124 in strict analogy to the scheme discussed on page 316. Retention of C-2 and C-3 produces fragment C of mass 166.

Dihydrovindoline (19) is substituted by acetoxy, hydroxy, and carbomethoxy groups in the alicyclic part of the aspidospermine skeleton, which is nevertheless still recognizable in the spectrum (Fig. 8-9b). Peaks

[16] C. Djerassi, H. W. Brewer, H. Budzikiewicz, O. O. Orazi, and R. A. Corral, *Experientia*, 18, 113 (1962).

at m/e 124, 174, 188, and 298 correspond to the ones in Fig. 8-8c, because N-methyldeacetylaspidospermine (17d) has the same substituents in the aromatic moiety, aside from the difference in the position of the methoxyl group, which influences the spectrum only slightly (see ibogaine and tabernanthine in Fig. 8-5).

The presence of the other groups in the alicyclic system leads to a shift of certain peaks by 16 (OH versus H) or 58 (COOCH$_3$ or OCOCH$_3$ versus H) mass units. Fragment C is now found at m/e 284 rather than at 152, because it contains all three of these groups. Superimposed are various fragments involving the elimination of CH$_3$COOH (mass 60), which gives rise to the peaks at, for example, m/e 224 and 398. As there is no hydrogen at C-3 or C-5, cyclization (see Sec. 3-2B), possibly involving the side chain, must take place.

The peak at m/e 311, however, does not fit into the normal aspidospermine scheme and must be due to participation of one of the additional groups in a new fragmentation process, possibly

The presence of one more functional group, a double bond, in vindoline (18) further complicates the spectrum (Fig. 8-9a). Many of the peaks in Fig. 8-9b are displaced to lower masses by two units. The relative intensities vary considerably, and some peaks, such as the equivalent of m/e 224 in Fig. 8-9b, are absent. While it is possible to recognize the compound as a dehydro derivative of (19), it is more difficult to spot the presence of the aspidospermine skeleton.

These three spectra are good examples of the varying influence of functional groups on the basic fragmentation pattern of a polycyclic system. They also show that simplification of the molecule by stepwise removal of such functional groups, for example, (18) → (19) → (20a), may greatly aid in the structure determination of a compound of such complexity. In fact, the mass spectrum of the degradation product (20a) was the first and only conclusive evidence of the presence of the aspidospermine carbon skeleton in vindoline, an alkaloid isolated from *Vinca rosea*. The area of attachment (C-3 and C-4) of the three functional groups was indicated by the spectrum of (19), because they are not retained in fragments *A*, *B*, and *E* (Fig. 8-9b).

The elucidation of the structure of vindoline is a good example of the successful combination of mass spectrometry with UV, IR, and NMR spectra. The latter, in particular, contributed evidence of the position of the methoxyl group, the presence of an *N*-methyl group and of a *cis* double bond and its substitution pattern.[15]

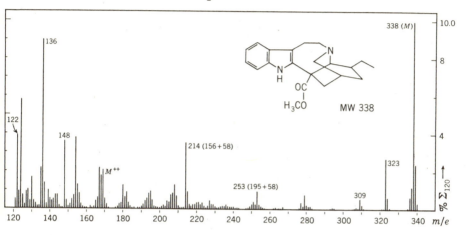

Fig. 8-10. Mass spectrum of coronaridine (21).

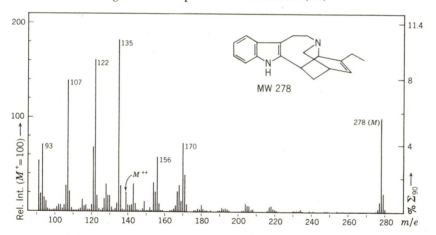

Fig. 8-11. Mass spectrum of decarbomethoxycatharanthine (22).

Further illustrations of the widely varying influence additional functional groups may exert on the fragmentation of a molecule are represented by the spectra of coronaridine [(21), Fig. 8-10], decarbomethoxycatharanthine [(22), Fig. 8-11], and 1,2-dehydrodeacetylaspidospermine [1] [(23), Fig. 8-12].

The structural difference between (21) and ibogamine (12) rests on the carbomethoxy group at C-18 in coronaridine (21).[17] Consequently, their spectra (Figs. 8-5a and 8-10) are rather analogous, because those peaks of ibogamine which contain the aromatic nucleus and C-18 (m/e 156, 195, 251, 265, and 280) are found 58 mass units higher in Fig. 8-10. The typical iboga pattern of between mass 120 and 150 is, however, retained without shift. A similar relationship exists between the spectra of ibogaine (13) and voacangine (18-carbomethoxyibogaine).

Decarbomethoxycatharanthine (22), a 3,4-dehydroibogamine,[18] exhibits a spectrum (Fig. 8-11) less similar to Fig. 8-5a. Loss of 15 or 29 mass units is insignificant because C-20 is no longer close to N-6, which

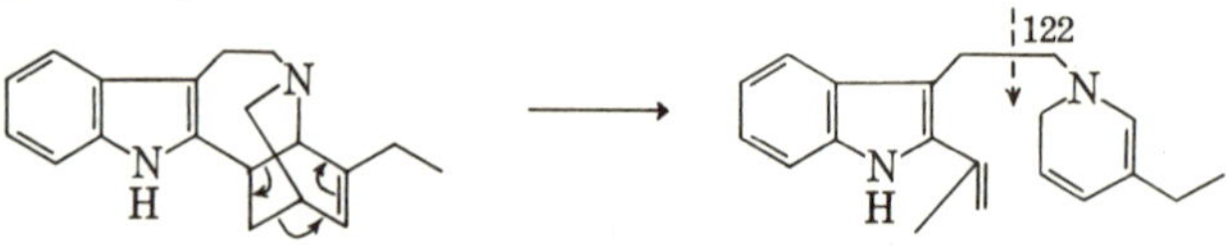

(22)   (22a)

stabilizes the positive charge in the saturated molecules [see (72), Chap. 3]. The ethyl group is also not lost, because it is now attached to a double bond. Furthermore, this bond facilitates cleavage of Type D, the product (22a) of which directly yields m/e 122 or, under hydrogen rearrangement, m/e 135. It should be noted that fragment A of mass 296 from vindoline (18), which also exhibits an intense peak at m/e 135, contains a moiety similar to (22a) (a dihydropyridine ring attached to the β position of an indole via a C_2 bridge).

That such a small change as a double bond in place of a single bond can, however, drastically change the fragmentation of a molecule is shown by a comparison of the spectrum of deacetylaspidospermine [(17c), Fig. 8-7] and its 1,2-dehydro derivative [(23), Fig. 8-12]. A double bond in this particular position makes cyclic fragmentation [the first step in the case of (17c)] impossible, because it would require the formation of an allene system in a five-membered ring.

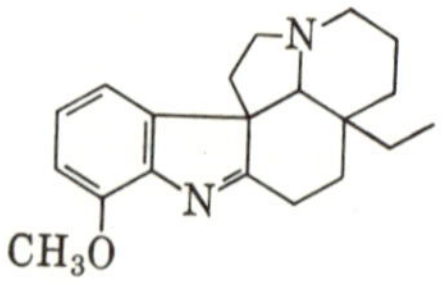

(23)

[17] M. Gorman, N. Neuss, N. J. Cone, and J. A. Deyrup, *J. Am. Chem. Soc.,* 82, 1142 (1960).

[18] N. Neuss and M. Gorman, *Tetrahedron Letters,* no. 6, p. 206, 1961.

Modification of the functional groups by chemical means, possibly accompanied by isotopic labeling, can be of great value in the interpretation of the resulting spectra, as has been pointed out in Secs. 4-5C and 5-3. From the foregoing examples, it can be seen that such modifications may lead to widely varying spectra, depending on the kind of structural change involved. For this reason, certain modifications are more useful than others and should be selected accordingly. As isotopic labeling does not affect the fragmentation process, it is most useful in marking certain groups (see Fig. 8-6), whereas removal of functional groups leads to more simplified, but possibly greatly changed, spectra (compare Fig. 8-9*a* with Fig. 8-9*c*).

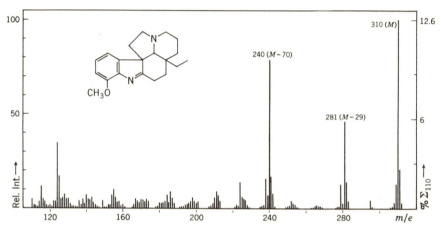

Fig. 8-12. Mass spectrum of dehydrodeacetylaspidospermine (23).

The introduction of an additional ring can entirely change the fragmentation of a molecule; this is borne out by the mass spectrum of vindolinine, for which one of the two structures (23*a*) (ring junction either at C-10 or C-11) has been proposed: [19]

(23*a*)

The new bond, particularly if connected with C-11, prevents the typical aspidospermine-like fragmentation, because the piperidine portion cannot

[19] C. Djerassi, S. E. Flores, H. Budzikiewicz, J. M. Wilson, L. J. Durham, J. Le-Men, M. M. Janot, M. Plat, M. Gorman, and N. Neuss, *Proc. Natl. Acad. Sci. U.S.,* **48,** 113 (1962).

separate from the indole moiety of the molecule as easily as if that bond were lacking.

Further examples of the influence of an additional ring in various positions will be discussed in Sec. 8-3 (see Fig. 8-16).

8-3. DETERMINATION OF ALKALOID STRUCTURE WITHOUT DIRECT CORRELATION

In the previous section it has been shown that the mass spectra of alkaloids are very characteristic of the basic carbon skeleton present in the molecule, thus permitting direct correlation of closely related alkaloids. It was also shown that the peaks can be correlated with certain areas of such complex molecules. In addition it is also possible to elucidate the structure of a new carbon skeleton on the basis of its mass spectrum.

This was accomplished [11] for another group of alkaloids which had been isolated from *Aspidosperma quebracho blanco* along with the aspidospermine derivatives discussed above. The crude mixture of bases extracted from the bark was found to contain substances yielding mass spectra which clearly indicated that they did not belong to the aspidospermine group, because they failed to exhibit an intense peak at m/e 124 and did not show the characteristic loss of 28 mass units from the molecular ion (Fig. 8-13). On the other hand, there was present in all spectra an intense peak at mass 136. The peaks at mass 130 and mass 144 in the mass spectrum of the smallest molecule of this type and also its UV spectrum indicated that all members of this group of alkaloids contain a dihydroindole nucleus. Hydrogenation of the compound, the spectrum of which is shown in Fig. 8-13a, gave a derivative with a mass spectrum which showed a molecular weight 2 mass units higher; also, the intense peak at m/e 136 had shifted to 138 (Fig. 8-15a).

While all these findings definitely excluded the presence of the carbon skeleton of aspidospermine, it seemed that the characteristic fragment of mass 136 might be formed in a way similar to the one giving rise to the species of mass 124 in the other group of alkaloids. The absence of a fragment due to the loss of ethylene indicated the absence of a bridge containing two carbon atoms in a location similar to the one in aspidospermine.

Furthermore, the molecular weight of these compounds implies that the basic carbon skeleton of this new group of alkaloids contains one carbon atom less than the skeleton of aspidospermine but that the most

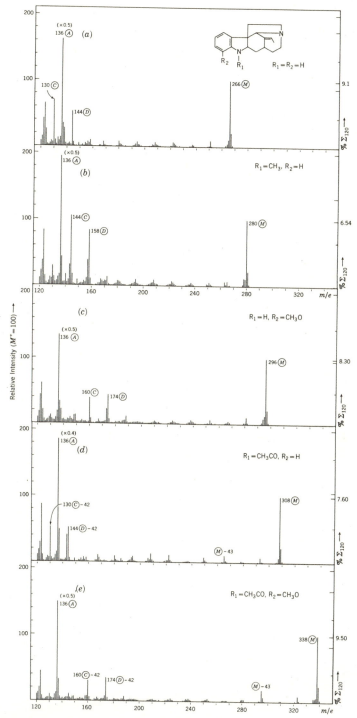

Fig. 8-13. Mass spectra of various alkaloids of the aspidospermatine type (29a to d); the encircled letters refer to the fragmentation scheme on page 330.

abundant fragment has one carbon atom more than the species giving rise to the peak at mass 124. This indicates that in the fragmentation process no neutral molecule is eliminated, and the assumption that there is present a one-carbon bridge rather than a two-carbon bridge is the most attractive one. A carbon skeleton fulfilling this requirement is (24),

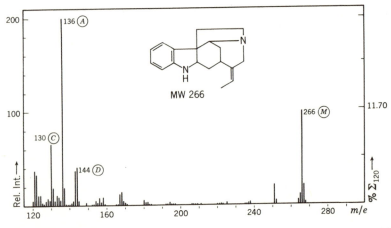

(24)   (24a)

which is present in a number of dihydroindole alkaloids related to the Wieland-Gumlich aldehyde (25) such as akuammicine (26) and various curare alkaloids:

(25)   (26)

Fragmentation of ring *C* would again lead to unraveling of the polycyclic molecule, and fragmentation (*a*) of the bond between C-8 and C-9 with the retention of the charge at C-19 should give rise to a fragment of mass 136 if R = —CH=CH$_2$ or =CH—CH$_3$. Fortunately a compound of such

Fig. 8-14. Mass spectrum of a degradation product (27) of akuammicine (26).

a structure (27) had been obtained [20] in the course of determining the structure of akuammicine, and its mass spectrum (Fig. 8-14) in fact turned out to be rather similar to the one shown in Fig. 8-13*a*, but the two spectra are definitely not identical. While this could be due to a difference in the

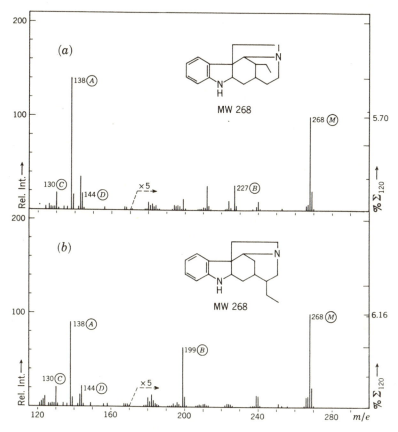

Fig. 8-15. Mass spectra of (*a*) (28) and (*b*) (27*a*).

location of the double bond, the spectrum of the hydrogenation product revealed a marked difference in the carbon skeleton (Fig. 8-15).

(27)
(27*a*: dihydro derivative)

(28)

[20] G. F. Smith and J. T. Wrobel, *J. Chem. Soc.*, **1960**, 792 and references therein.

The differences in the two mass spectra are best explained by a change in the location of the ethyl group. The intense peak in Fig. 8-15b is due to the loss of 69 mass units, i.e., a group of five carbon atoms containing one double bond; the dihydro derivative of the unknown alkaloid (Fig. 15a), however, loses only 41 mass units, i.e., two carbon atoms less. This is best explained by cleavage at b in (24a), indicating that in the new group the C_2 fragment is attached to C-6, C-11, or C-12. Since upon zinc-dust distillation a large amount of 3-ethylpyridine is formed, there must be an ethyl group β to the piperidine-nitrogen. Thus structure (28) remains as the most plausible one for the dihydro derivative of the simplest representative of this group of alkaloids. The double bond is thought to be present as an ethylidene group, on the basis of the spectrum of the compound obtained upon reduction with deuterohydrazine (see Sec. 5-3C) and of the IR spectrum, which indicates the absence of a vinyl group. The carbon skeleton of this group must therefore be the following (29):

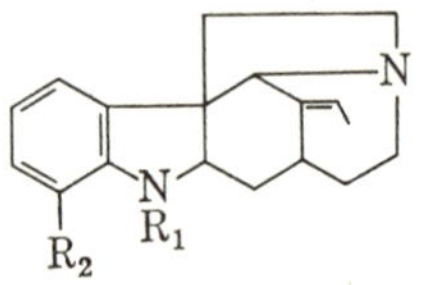

(a) $R_1 = R_2 = H$
(b) $R_1 = CH_3$, $R_2 = H$
(c) $R_1 = H$, $R_2 = CH_3O$
(d) $R_1 = CH_3CO$, $R_2 = H$
(e) $R_1 = CH_3CO$, $R_2 = CH_3O$

(29)

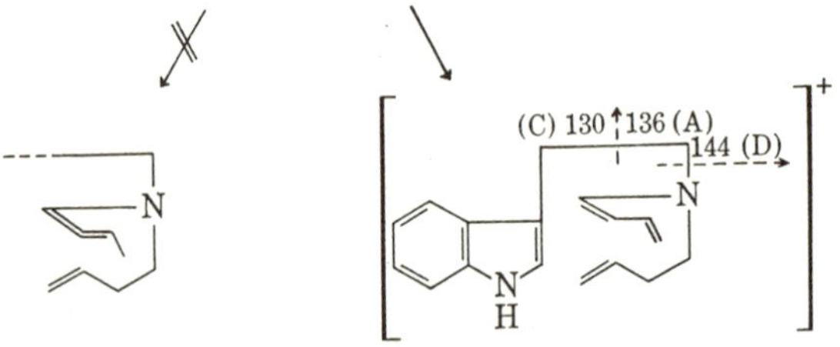

(C) 130 ↑136 (A)
144 (D)

(30)   (31)

A double bond between C-12 and C-13 might be thought of as preventing the cyclic fragmentation of ring C, because it would require cleavage of a bond at an olefinic carbon atom and formation of an allene group (30). It was pointed out in Sec. 3-2A, however, that a double bond easily migrates in the molecular ion, and if this occurs, the fragment of mass 136 formed would be a highly conjugated one (31).

The mass spectra (Fig. 8-13) show that the other alkaloids of this type are again bearing substituents in rings A and B, namely, methyl, methoxyl, and acetyl groups; they were assigned structures (29a) to (29e). The attachment of the methyl group in (29b) was indicated by its chromatographic behavior. The position of the methoxyl group at ring

A could not, of course, be deduced from the mass spectrum, but the UV spectrum of (29e) was superimposable on that of aspidospermine (17e); the identity of the chromophore in those two alkaloids and the attachment of the methoxyl group at position 4' in (29e) are therefore established.

The elucidation of the structures of these alkaloids is a good example of the power of this approach and of the usefulness of a combination of different physical methods. In the solution of structural problems of this type the complementary nature of mass spectra and UV spectra is particularly obvious. It should also be pointed out that many of the minor alkaloids of groups (17) and (29) were obtained pure only in total amounts of 1 to 10 mg. Separation and purification of these compounds by gas chromatography (Sec. 2-5D) proved to be a valuable tool in this work and permitted the detection and isolation of over fifteen alkaloids in a plant material in which only up to six alkaloids had previously been found.[21] One of these, aspidospermatine, is identical with the major component (e) of group (29), as judged from the reported physical data.

For the determination of the structure of all the alkaloids outlined above, no elemental analyses were required because the elemental composition was quite clear from the mass-spectrometric data plus other available information, such as the presence of the dihydroindole moiety.

The mass spectra (Fig. 8-15) of compounds (28) and (27a) represent other examples of changes in fragmentation brought about by a structural variation at the alicyclic moiety, in this case the point of attachment of the ethyl group. This can be studied further in the spectra (Fig. 8-16) of spermostrychnine (32a) and deacetylspermostrychnine (32b).[22] The presence of ring F does not interfere with the fragmentation implied in formula (31), and the spectra of these compounds thus correspond to that of (27a) shown in Fig. 8-15b:

(32) (a) R = CH₃CO
      (b) R = H

---

[21] For a recent review, see J. Schmutz, *Pharm. Acta. Helv.*, **36**, 103 (1961).

[22] For their structure, see F. A. L. Anet and R. Robinson, *J. Chem. Soc.*, **1955**, 2253. The methyl-substituted six-membered ring F was established by NMR spectroscopy (F. A. L. Anet, private communication).

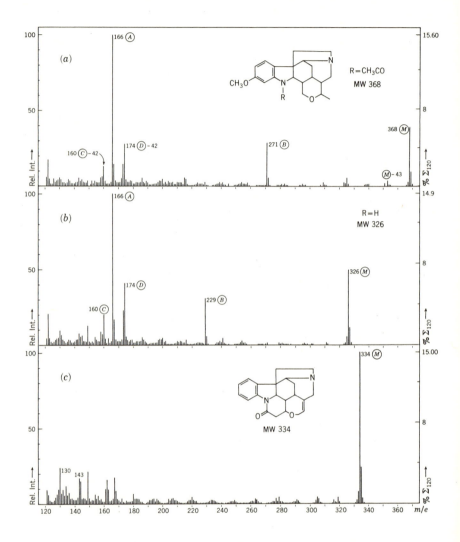

Fig. 8-16. Mass spectra of (*a*) spermostrychnine (32*a*), (*b*) deacetylspermostrychnine (32*b*), and (*c*) strychnine (33). The encircled letters refer to the fragmentation scheme on page 330.

With respect to Fig. 8-15*b*, some of the fragments are displaced 28, 30, and/or 42 mass units, if retaining ring *F*, the methoxy, and/or the acetyl group.

The addition of another ring linking rings *B* and *F* in strychnine

(33)[23] completely changes the spectrum (Fig. 8-16c), because the fragmentation discussed above is prevented. The high abundance of the molecular ion is characteristic of such a situation.

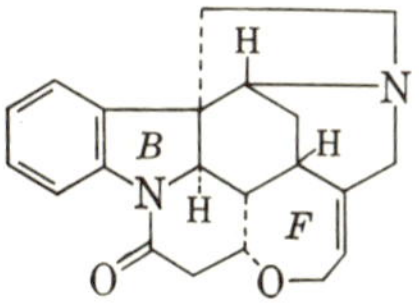

(33)

The potentialities of mass spectrometry for the determination of the structure of even minute constituents produced by a plant would seem valuable for biogenetic studies, for some of the minor alkaloids frequently turn out to be important links between major components, or between major components and simple precursors.

A further application in the investigation of the biogenesis of alkaloids will be found in the possibility of locating and estimating stable isotopes in alkaloids after the administration of labeled precursors into the plant. The incorporation of labeled tryptophan, containing N^{15} both in the indole ring and in the side chain, would be particularly attractive, as it would show whether this amino acid is incorporated as such or is first partially degraded by the plant. From the foregoing discussion of the fragmentation of these types of alkaloids, it is obvious that one would be able to distinguish both nitrogens in the spectrum of the intact molecule. The generally low level of incorporation by higher plants will, however, require rather accurate intensity measurements. Of utmost importance is the correct interpretation of the fragmentation pattern of the molecule in question to prevent serious errors.

[23] For a review on the structure of strychnine see J. B. Hendrickson, in R. H. F. Manske (ed.), "The Alkaloids," vol. 6, pp. 179–217, Academic Press, New York, 1960.

9. Steroids and Related Substances

In spite of the importance of the terpenoids, which are widely distributed in nature and frequently have remarkable biological activity, their mass spectra have not as yet been investigated thoroughly. There are a number of reasons for this situation: the complexity of these molecules and their polycyclic nature, which often requires a complex process for fragmentation; the lack of strongly cleavage-directing functional groups (the commonly encountered functionalities are either hydroxyl, carbonyl, or olefinic), which leads at times to less characteristic spectra; and finally, the mass of the fragments consisting only of alicyclic portions, which frequently gives no unambiguous clue as to the part of the molecule from which they originate, in contrast to the groups discussed in Chaps. 6 to 8.

For all these reasons the mass spectra of saturated hydrocarbons of this class are most difficult to interpret unambiguously, while unsaturated centers, hydroxyl or carbonyl groups at certain positions may induce clearly recognizable fragmentation processes. For example, the spectra of the isomeric $C_{10}H_{16}$ hydrocarbons, α- and β-pinene, camphene, α-fenchene, cyclofenchene, and tricyclene,[1,2] are very similar, with the exception of dipentene (limonene), for reasons discussed on page 103. On the other hand, α-terpineol (1) and its isomer, terpinene-4-ol (2), ex-

[1] L. Friedman and A. P. Wolf, *J. Am. Chem. Soc.*, **80**, 2424 (1958).
[2] T. Gilchrist and R. I. Reed, *Experientia*, **16**, 134 (1960).

hibit rather different spectra owing to the difference in the location of the hydroxyl group, which induces cleavage of Type *B* and yields intense peaks at m/e 59 and m/e 111, respectively.

(1)   (2)

Some of the few presently available investigations of more complex molecules will be discussed in the following sections.

9-1. PIMARIC ACIDS

The methyl esters of diterpenoid acids of the pimaric and abietic type have been the subject of mass spectrometric studies in several laboratories.[3,4,5] The full spectra of only the pimaric (3), isopimaric (4), and "cryptopimaric" (5) esters have been published,[3] and while (3) and (5) gave very similar mass spectra, the spectrum of isopimaric ester was found to differ markedly. This was interpreted in line with the then proposed structures of these acids, namely, that (3) and (5) differ in the configuration at C-13, a feature of little influence upon the fragmentation, while (3) and (4) are, in addition, epimeric at C-9. The remarkable difference in the spectra of pimaric and isopimaric ester (Fig. 9-1a and c^5) is, however, difficult to reconcile merely with such a proposal, espe-

(3) $R_1 = CH_2=CH-$
     $R_2 = CH_3$

(6) $R_1 = CH_3$
     $R_2 = CH_2=CH-$

cially as there is no cleavage-inducing functional group sufficiently close to the site of structural difference to lead to some of the effects discussed in Sec. 3-2D.

Recently it was found that the compound known as cryptopimaric acid is in fact sandaracopimaric acid (6) contaminated with pimaric

[3] H. H. Bruun, R. Rhyage, and E. Stenhagen, *Acta Chem. Scand.*, **12**, 789 (1958).

[4] C. A. Genge, *Anal. Chem.*, **31**, 1750 (1959).

[5] Unpublished spectra from the author's laboratory obtained on samples kindly provided by R. E. Ireland.

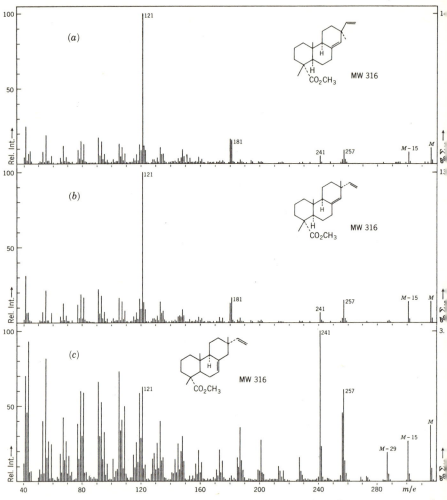

Fig. 9-1. Mass spectra of (*a*) methyl pimarate, (*b*) methyl sandaracopimarate, and (*c*) methyl isopimarate.

acid,[6] which accounts for the great similarity of the spectra of the methyl esters of (5)[3] and (6)[5] (the latter is shown in Fig. 9-1*b*). More important, however, was the finding that isopimaric ester does not have structure (4), as it is not an epimer of (3). Formula (7) was suggested as the most probable one [7a] and has now been proved correct.[7b]

[6a] J. W. Apsimon, B. Green, and W. B. Whalley, *J. Chem. Soc.*, **1961**, 752.

[6b] V. P. Arya, C. Enzell, H. Erdtman, and R. Ryhage, *Acta Chem. Scand.*, **15**, 682 (1961).

[7a] R. F. Church and R. E. Ireland, *Tetrahedron Letters*, no. 14, p. 493, 1961.

[7b] W. Antkowiak, J. W. Apsimon, and O. E. Edwards, *J. Org. Chem.*, **27**, 1933 (1962); R. E. Ireland and J. Newbould, *J. Org. Chem.*, **27**, 1934 (1962).

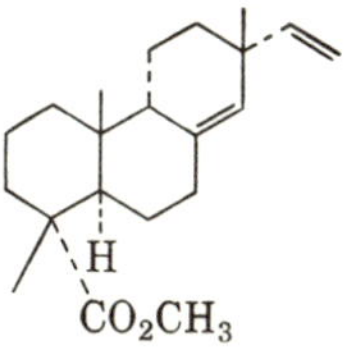

(4) 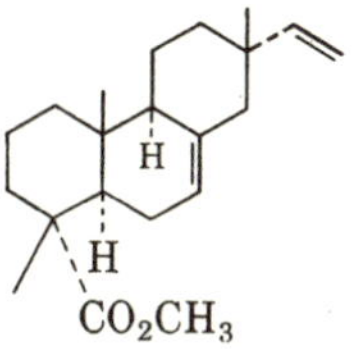   (7)

The spectra in Fig. 9-1 reveal, as the major difference, a very intense peak at m/e 121 for the epimers (3) and (6), and the most intense peak at m/e 241 for methyl isopimarate. It is important to note that the fragment of mass 121 in both Fig. 9-1a and b is much more intense in terms of Σ than is mass 241 in Fig. 9-1c, suggesting that the process leading to mass 121 is very favorable for (3) and (6) but is prevented for methyl isopimarate, and that the reverse is not so much the case for the fragmentation leading to mass 241. The former process may be viewed as follows:

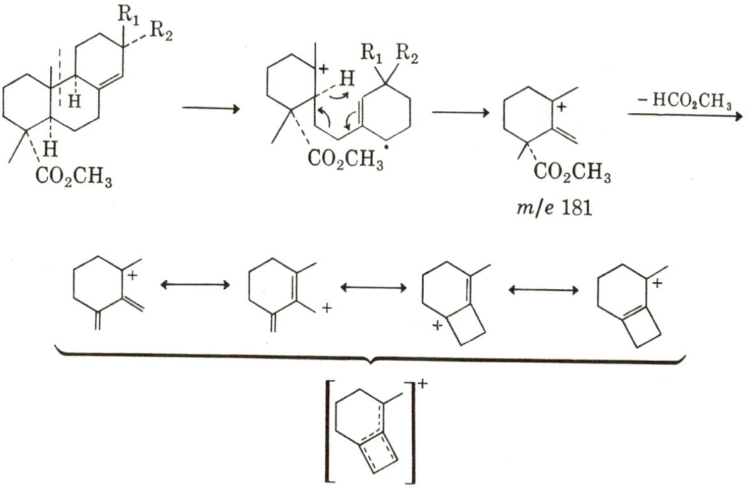

m/e 181

m/e 121

The extended resonance possibilities of the ion of mass 121 may be one of the driving forces for its formation. A process analogous to the one leading to the fragment of mass 181 seems to generally operate in compounds having a similarly substituted decalin ring system and a 8,14 double bond, such as hydrocarbons (8) and (9)[5] and manool (10), which exhibit an intense peak at m/e 137 in their spectra.

(8)   (9)   (10)

Methyl isopimarate does not seem to undergo that fragmentation which is obviously induced by the activation of the C-9, C-10 bond allylic to the C-8,C-14 double bond. The mass spectrum is thus an indication of the lack of such a moiety, a variant of which is still present in structure (7). The absence of a peak of high intensity at m/e 121 might be explained by the difference in the position of the double bond, which is now not as required for the rearrangement (Type H) leading to cleavage of the C-6, C-7 bond in the second step pictured above.

It should be noted that Type D processes do not significantly contribute to the spectra shown in Fig. 9-1, most probably because of the presence of highly substituted allylic bonds, the cleavage of which (Type A_3) is more favored, as was pointed out in Sec. 3-2A.

The earlier prediction that epimerism at C-9 alone would not drastically alter the fragmentation of molecules of the type under discussion is corroborated by the great similarity of the spectra of (8) and (9).[5]

9-2. STEROIDS

The mass spectra of steroids and related substances have received attention from various groups. As early as 1956 de Mayo and Reed [8] obtained the mass spectra of a few such compounds and showed that both the molecular weight and the size of the side chain can be determined by this technique. A somewhat more detailed paper,[9] unfortunately with only fragmentary data on the spectra, offered some explanation of the cleavage processes based on predominant rupture of highly substituted or allylic bonds. Other investigations have dealt with oxygen-substituted steroids,[10,11,12] and the most recent but also most comprehensive study of a consistent series of derivatives was concerned with saturated ketones.[13]

[8] P. de Mayo and R. I. Reed, *Chem. & Ind.* (*London*), **1956**, 1481.

[9] R. I. Reed, *J. Chem. Soc.*, **1958**, 3432.

[10] S. S. Friedland, G. H. Lane, Jr., R. T. Longman, K. E. Train, and M. J. O'Neal, Jr., *Anal. Chem.*, **31**, 169 (1959).

[11] R. Ryhage and E. Stenhagen, *J. Lipid Res.*, **1**, 361 (1960).

[12] H. J. M. Fitches, in R. M. Elliott (ed.), "Advances in Mass Spectrometry" vol. II, Pergamon Press, London, 1962.

[13] H. Budzikiewicz and C. Djerassi, *J. Am. Chem. Soc.*, **84**, 1430 (1962).

All these spectra indicate the prominence of certain fragmentation processes, such as elimination of the side chain plus 42 mass units (involving three additional carbon atoms) and elimination of H_2O from hydroxyl groups and CH_3COOH from acetates.

The first-mentioned fragmentation is of considerable value in establishing the size of the side chain and the presence of the normal tetra-

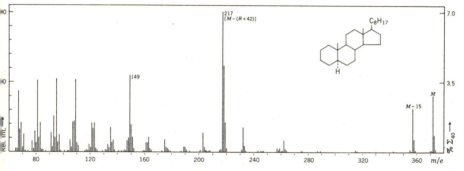

Fig. 9-2. Mass spectrum of cholestane (API No. 1,000).

cyclic steroid carbon skeleton (11). A typical example is shown in Fig. 9-2. A number of reasons have been suggested for the loss of $42 + R$, such as fragmentation along a,[9] b,[10,12] or c[11,13] without any explanation

(11a) R = H
(11b) R = C_2H_5
(11c) R = C_8H_{17}

(11)

or supporting experiments. The first two of these would involve the extremely unlikely fragmentation of three bonds without forming energetically favorable fragments, while path c could lead to an allylic carbonium ion (12) or (13):

(M^+) $[M - (R + 42)]^+$ or

(12)

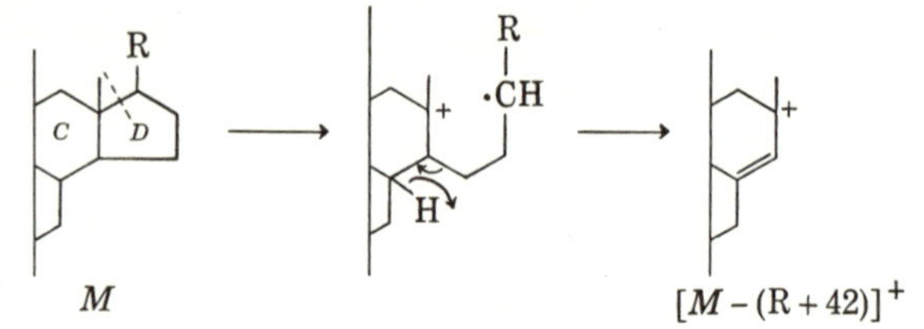

$$[M - (R + 42)]^+$$
(13)

A distinction between these two possibilities must await the preparation of suitable derivatives deuterated at C-18 and C-8, respectively.

One has to keep in mind, however, that any such process will be subject to variations in the molecule, which may either prevent the loss of $R + 42$ (if, for example, the structural requirements of process c are not met) or induce more favorable fragmentation of a bond elsewhere (for an example, see Fig. 9-4a).

Interestingly enough, a hydroxyl group at C-12 results in loss of $18 + R$ rather than $R + 42$,[11] although the commonly pictured product ion is a Δ^{11}-olefin:

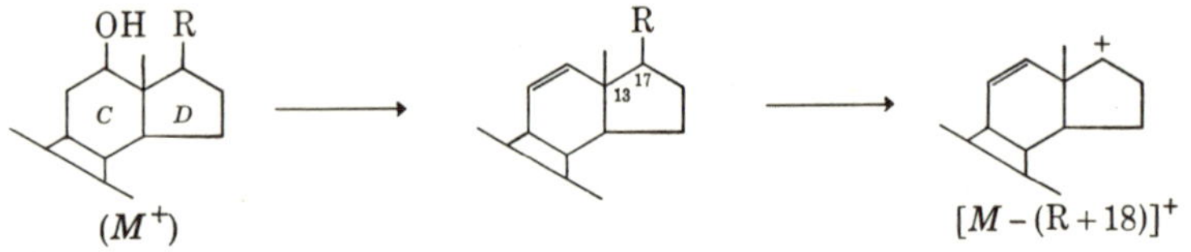

Such a double bond should facilitate rather than prevent rupture of the now allylic C-13,C-17 bond. As pointed out in Sec. 3-2B, the elimination of the elements of water from an alcohol does not generally produce olefin ions, and the cyclic product formed in the case under discussion may prevent the fragmentation normally encountered.

Loss of H_2O or CH_3COOH from sterols or their acetates is involved in most of the ions formed from such compounds on electron impact,[11,12] sometimes to such an extent that the molecular ion is hardly detectable in acetates.

As mentioned earlier, the most complete series of related steroids yet investigated[13] are mainly derivatives of androstane ($11a$), pregnane ($11b$), and cholestane ($11c$) bearing a carbonyl group in all possible positions at the tetracyclic moiety; in some instances also the C-5 epimers and a few hydroxy and acetoxy derivatives have been investigated.

These spectra indicate that, at least in the absence of other groups, a carbonyl group gives rise to specific cleavage of certain bonds, most frequently involving Type H rearrangement. In a few cases, the presence of the carbonyl group influences the fragmentation of the molecules less, and the spectrum is more characteristic of the carbon skeleton; i.e., a prominent peak due to loss of R + 42 is observed.

Some of these features are illustrated in Fig. 9-3. In 3-cholestanone the carbonyl group is pointing away from the rest of the molecule, pre-

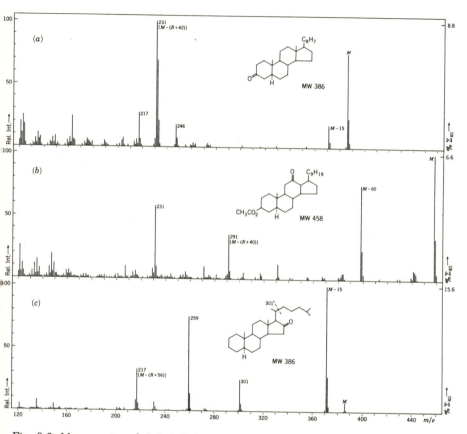

Fig. 9-3. Mass spectra of (a) 3-cholestanone, (b) 3β-acetoxyergostane-12-one, and (c) 16-cholestanone. (*From Ref.* 13.)

venting the approach of a hydrogen required for a Type H rearrangement. The spectrum obtained (Fig. 9-3a) is thus rather similar to that of cholestane (Fig. 9-2). The most important peak (m/e 231) is still due to loss of R + 42. A carbonyl group in position 12 alters the mechanism of elimination of ring D with its side chain so as to involve the gain rather than loss of a hydrogen atom during cleavage (Fig. 9-3b). This seems to be the only instance in which such a loss of R + 40 is observed and is due to the abstraction of hydrogen from C-20 by the carbonyl group:

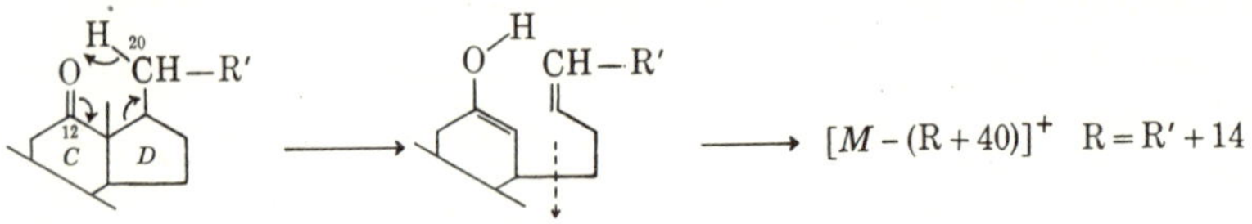

$$\longrightarrow [M - (R + 40)]^+ \quad R = R' + 14$$

As the compound shown in Fig. 9-3*b* is a 3-acetoxy derivative, the most intense fragment involves the additional loss of CH_3COOH.

Obviously, both a carbonyl group at C-12 and a γ-hydrogen atom must be present to result in such a fragmentation, and in fact, it is reported [13] that a compound unsubstituted at C-17 does not show it. As was pointed out in Sec. 3-2*B*, hydrogen attached to hydroxyl also participates with ease in such a rearrangement, and a 17-hydroxy-12-ketone would still suffer such fragmentation in spite of the lack of a 17-alkyl substituent. A 17-acetyl group, frequently encountered in steroids, again does not possess a hydrogen at C-20 and thus should not undergo this cleavage.

The presence of a substituent at C-17 is also required for the formation of the fragment of mass 259 $[M - (R + 14)]$ from 16-cholestanone (Fig. 9-3*c*) via the following process:

From this discussion it is obvious that the postulation [12,13] of more or less strict general rules about the influence of certain isolated groups upon the resulting spectrum will be successful only if considered in view of all other structural features of the molecule and only if the mechanism of the fragmentation process and its structural requirements are reasonably well understood.

Furthermore, additional groups may completely overpower the influence of a carbonyl group upon fragmentation. In 6-ketones, for example, the loss of ring A as 55 mass units is said to be characteristic [13] of, and due to, the influence of the carbonyl function, but no such process is observed in the spectrum of 3-acetoxy-19-nitrilo-cholestane-6-one.[14]

[14] Unpublished spectrum from the author's laboratory determined with a sample kindly provided by M. M. Pechet and M. Akhtar.

Cortisone (14) represents an even more important example of a polyfunctional steroid of which the mass spectrum [12] exhibits intense peaks (m/e 122 and $M - 60$) not predicted by the rules stated; [12,13] the peaks that are predicted (loss of $R - 42 - 16$ and fragmentation of ring B with retention of the positive charge at ring C, as in simple 11-ketones) are absent. Loss of the side chain, partly involving one additional hydrogen atom, leads to a peak at $M - 60$. Thus the loss is not an unambiguous indication for the presence of an acetoxy group, for it may also be due to the presence of -CO-CH$_2$-OH at C-17.

Fragmentation of ring B does indeed occur, but the dienone moiety formed in ring A dominates the consecutive step and leads to the by far most abundant ion (m/e 122).

An example of the determination of the structure of a complex steroid by mass spectrometry is some recent work on tremulone, a compound which had been isolated from *Populus tremuloides* and was known to be an unsaturated ketone.[15] It was independently found to be $\Delta^{3,5}$-sitostadiene-7-one by conventional means [15] and by mass spectrometry.[16]

The mass spectrum of the compound (Fig. 9-4a) indicates a molecular weight of 410; it is therefore a C$_{29}$ compound (assuming the presence of one oxygen atom). The rather small peaks at m/e 269 (A, $M - C_{10}H_{21}$) and m/e 227 (B, $M - C_{10}H_{21} - 42$) hint at a normal tetracyclic steroid skeleton with a saturated C$_{10}$ side chain attached at C-17, placing the two double bonds and the carbonyl function in the tetracyclic moiety. Whether all these groups are present in the most abundant fragment C (m/e 174) cannot be stated rigorously at that point but becomes more

[15] R. A. Abramovitch and R. G. Micetich, *Can. J. Chem.* (In press.)
[16] Unpublished experiments (by A. L. Burlingame) from the author's laboratory on samples kindly provided by R. A. Abramovitch.

obvious upon consideration of the spectrum of the hydrogenation product (Fig. 9-4b), which now exhibits a molecular weight of 414, indicating saturation of two double bonds. Fragments A and B are of mass 273 and 231, respectively, and C is found at m/e 178; thus the latter one must have contained both double bonds of the starting material. As the most prom-

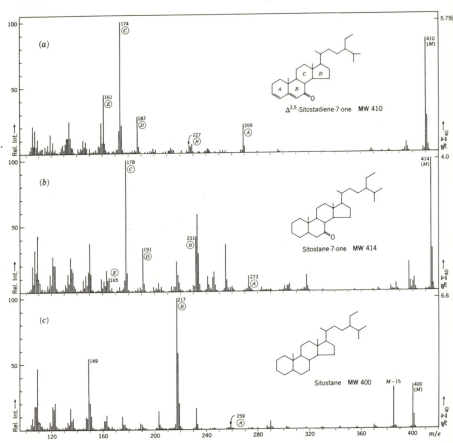

Fig. 9-4. Mass spectra of (a) $\Delta^{3,5}$-sitostadiene-7-one, (b), 7-sitostanone, and (c) sitostane.

inent peak other than the molecular ion, it is likely to contain the carbonyl group, especially in the absence of other functionalities prone to retain the positive charge. From its mass, one can deduce that this fragment must contain 12 carbon atoms, i.e., most probably rings A and B and C-11. Under the reasonable assumption that the carbonyl group initiates fragmentation leading to the ion of m/e 178, the oxygen has to be either at C-11 or C-7 and is most probably at the latter, as it would readily permit formation of a fragment of proper mass:

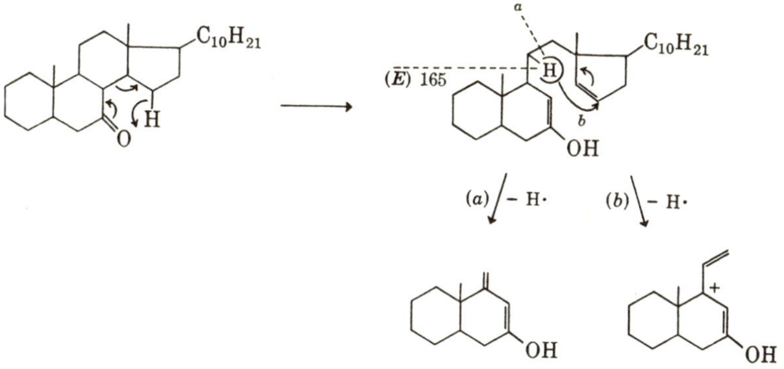

m/e 178(*C*)   *m/e* 191(*D*)

Such processes were also suggested [13] for 7-cholestanone, which exhibits a spectrum analogous to Fig. 9-4*b* except for a shift of those peaks retaining the side chain.

Fragment *E* is much more abundant in the spectrum of the $\Delta^{3,5}$-dienone (Fig. 9-4*a*) than in that of the saturated ketone (Fig. 9-4*b*) because of the extended conjugation of the allylic carbonium ion formed on cleavage of the C-9,C-11 bond.

Final confirmation of the presence of an unaltered sitostane skeleton is obtained from the spectrum (Fig. 9-4*c*) of the hydrocarbon produced upon removal of the carbonyl group. Fragment *B* (loss of R + 42) is now very pronounced, and the entire spectrum is analogous to the one of cholestane (Fig. 9-2). Fragmentation of ring *C* seems to lead to the species of *m/e* 149 in a manner resembling the process suggested earlier for the loss of R + 42:

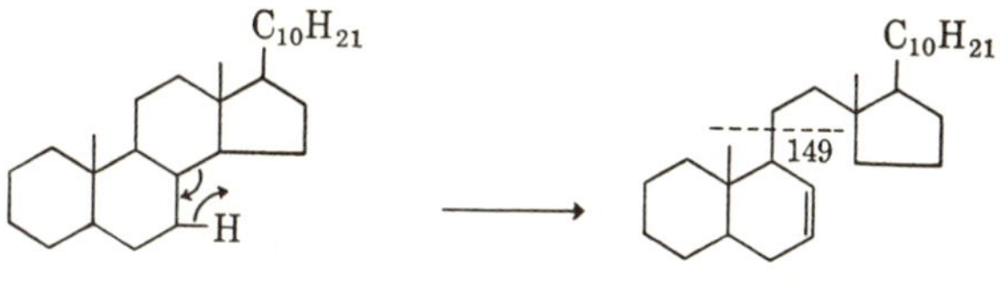

The position of the double bonds cannot be definitely established on the basis of the mass spectra, but the UV spectrum ($\lambda_{max}279$ mμ, log $\epsilon = 4.42$) indicates the presence of a heteroannular conjugated dienone chromophore, and the compound isolated from the natural source is thus represented by structure (15):

(15)

The change in the spectra upon stepwise removal of functional groups proved valuable for the conclusive interpretation of the spectrum of the compound in question, as it permitted, for example, the clear recognition of the sitostane carbon skeleton in the saturated derivatives.

The foregoing example illustrates the potentialities of mass spectrometry for the determination of the structure of steroids. More detailed investigations of the spectra of polyfunctional derivatives, whenever possible with the aid of isotope labeling, will be of great importance for a broad application of this technique.

Stereochemical differences in the structure of such polycyclic molecules make themselves felt in the mass spectra for reasons discussed in Sec. 3-2D. In steroids, such an isomerism frequently involves the mode of fusion of rings A and B (*trans* in the 5α series and *cis* in the 5β series), or the orientation of an hydroxyl group (α or β). The latter case has been studied on a number of pairs containing 3α- and 3β-hydroxy or acetoxy groups.[17] It was found also in these cases that the intensity of the molecular ion is higher in the less crowded (equatorial substituent) isomer, as discussed in Sec. 3-2D.

The difference in ring junction (A/B *cis* versus *trans*) makes itself felt in a more pronounced loss of carbon atoms 1, 2, 3, and 4 of ring A in the *cis* isomers,[10,11] which is explained by the relief of more strain in the *cis*-fused systems.

The rearrangement of Type H is rather sensitive to the position of the hydrogen atom to be transferred relative to the carbonyl oxygen (a few specific examples have been discussed in Sec. 3-2D). The spectra of keto steroids differing in the mode of the A/B ring function exhibit, therefore, pronounced variations in the intensity of those peaks originating via such a rearrangement, as outlined above. Published data [13] indicate that such a process is facilitated in the 5β series, as compared with the 5α isomer, if the intensities are considered in terms of Σ; this is a more realistic basis for such correlations, for reasons outlined in Sec.

[17] K. Biemann and J. Seibl, *J. Am. Chem. Soc.*, **81**, 3149 (1959).

2-11C. Fragments arising through initial Type-*H* cleavage of the C-9,C-10 bond, followed by further cleavages analogous to the ones discussed for 7-sitostanone, comprise in the 11-ketones (16*a*) and (16*b*) about 33 per cent Σ_{40} in the 5β isomer (16*a*) but only 16 per cent Σ_{40} in the 5α isomer (16*b*).

$\longrightarrow$ m/e 151 (5β : 7%; 5α : 2.7%)

$-$H : m/e 164 (5β : 18%; 5α : 9%)

-2H : m/e 177 (5β : 8%; 5α : 4.5%)

(16*a*) 5β $-$ H
(16*b*) 5α $-$ H

The reasons for preferred cleavage in the *A/B cis* isomer (16*a*) may be found both in the closer approach of the 1α hydrogen to the carbonyl oxygen, when compared with the distance to the 1β-hydrogen in the *trans* isomer (16*b*), and in the greater strain of the former system relieved upon rupture of the C-9,C-10 bond. Such considerations of the spectral differences would seem more reliable than the significance of the intensity (in terms of the highest peak in the spectrum) of the "satellite peaks" found at m/e 164 $\pm$ 13 mass units, an empirical rule which had been suggested.[13]

9-3. TRITERPENES

A number of pentacyclic triterpenes have been investigated by mass spectrometry, and it was found that certain features can be deduced from their spectra.[18]

The C-12,C-13 double bond present in compounds related to α- or β-amyrin (17*a* and *b*) leads to predominant fragmentation of Type *D*:

(17)
(*a*) : $R_1 = CH_3$, $R_2 = H$
(*b*) : $R_1 = H$, $R_2 = CH_3$

m/e 203

[18] C. Djerassi, H. Budzikiewicz, and J. M. Wilson, *Tetrahedron Letters.* (In press.)

It is thus possible to deduce whether or not a given compound can belong to this series and the location of additional functional groups either in rings A and B or in rings C, D, and E, depending whether they are retained on the positively charged fragment or lost with the neutral one.

However, the presence of other functional groups capable of initiating a different fragmentation process has to be kept in mind. Such an influence is borne out by the spectrum of an 11-ketone of the β-amyrin type, 18α-11-oxo-β-amyrin (18), which has the most intense peak at *m/e* 273 due to a rearrangement of Type *H:*

(18)   *m/e* 273

Taraxarenes, such as taraxarone (19), possess a C-14,C-15 double bond also suitably located for fission of Type *D:*

(19)   *m/e* 300

Only nine carbon atoms are lost in this case, as contrasted to the loss of 14 such atoms from the amyrins, thus permitting differentiation of these two groups.

10. Miscellaneous Classes

10-1. CARBOHYDRATES

The abundance of hydroxyl groups present in sugar molecules is responsible for the high polarity and low volatility of these substances, which thus present a rather difficult problem in mass spectrometry. Although derivatization along the lines outlined in Sec. 4-5 would overcome some of these difficulties, no mass spectrometric investigation of such derivatives, aside from a single compound discussed below, has—to the author's knowledge—been published.

Recently the mass spectra of methyl β-D-glucopyranoside (1) and all stereoisomers of inositol (2) were determined by vaporization of the sample into the ion source.[1]

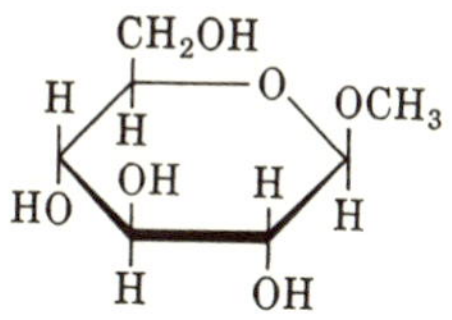

(1) 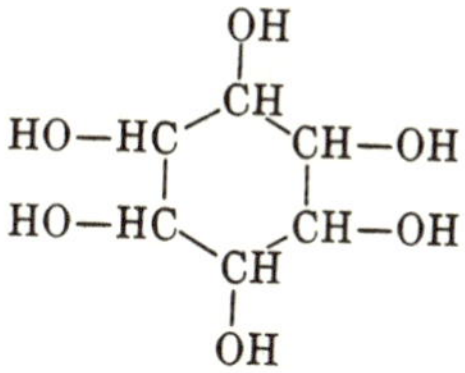   (2)

Some of the major fragments of the glucoside (1) are due to loss of methoxyl followed by loss of water:

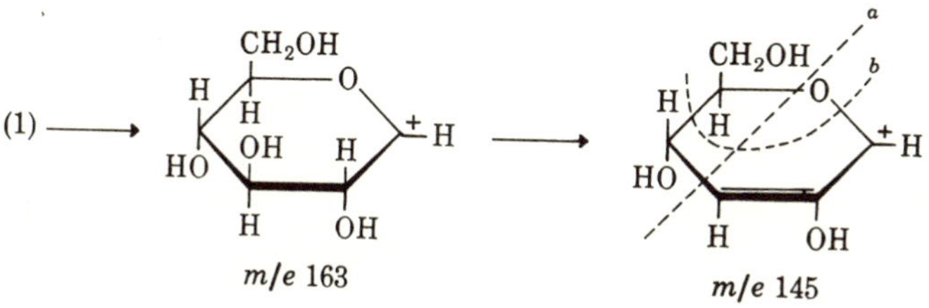

m/e 163 m/e 145

[1] R. I. Reed, W. K. Reid, and J. M. Wilson, in R. M. Elliott (ed.), "Advances in Mass Spectrometry," vol. II, Pergamon Press, London, 1962.

Further decomposition of the ion of mass 145 along dotted lines *a* and *b* is suggested for the formation of the abundant fragments of mass 74 and 71 and 85 and 60, the last one giving rise to the most intense peak in the spectrum of (1). Such processes would be plausible, as they represent fissions of Type *D* (cleavage along *a* would involve the allylic resonance from of the ion of mass 145), but the spectrum of specifically labeled (1), e.g., the trideuteromethyl glucoside, would be required to reach a definite conclusion with respect to the details of its fragmentation.

The mass spectra [1] of the stereoisomeric inositols (2) (mol. wt 180) are quite similar, as expected. Differences are observed in the intensity of the ion of mass 163. Its formation is said to be due to elimination of

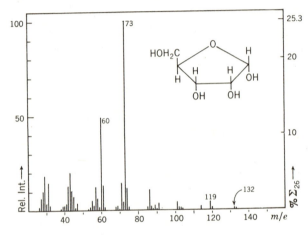

Fig. 10-1. Mass spectrum of D-ribose.

H_2O from the "$M + 1$" ion at m/e 181 (the molecular ion itself does not give a measurable peak). These intensity ratios of the peaks at m/e 181 and 163 are correlated with the number of 1:4 H,OH interactions.[1] This may, however, be fortuitous, first because 1,2 elimination was disregarded only because it did not fit the observed order and 1,3 elimination was not considered, and second because the fragment of mass 163 is more likely due to the loss of OH from the molecular ion, rather than the loss of H_2O from the "$M + 1$" species arising via collision processes.

Using the technique discussed in Sec. 2-5E, the mass spectrum of free D-ribose (3) was obtained (Fig. 10-1).[2] No peak for the molecular ion is observed at mass 150, and the fragments of higher mass (m/e 132 and 119) are due to loss of H_2O and of -CH_2OH, as expected (cleavage

[2] Unpublished experiments from the author's laboratory (by J. A. McCloskey).

of Type *B*). The most intense peak is found at m/e 73. In the absence of the necessary labeling experiments, one can only speculate as to its formation, but one of the more plausible mechanisms might be the following:

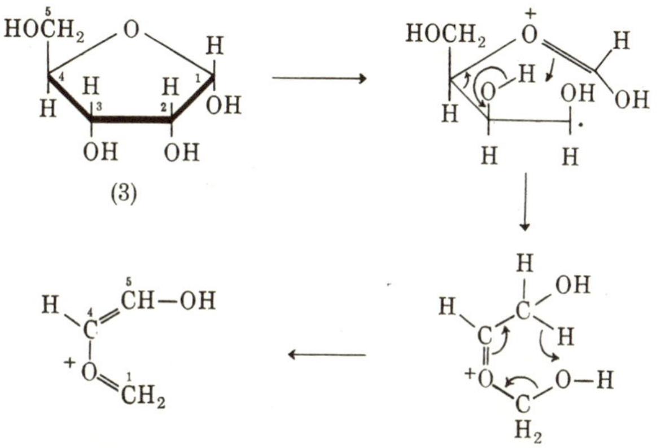

(3)

m/e 73 m/e 91

Even an oligosaccharide, laminarine, which has a molecular weight of several thousand, has been subjected to mass spectrometry in the form of its polymethyl ether.[3] Characteristic spacing of peaks by 200 to 207 mass units was observed, and its average (204) has been attributed to the successive loss of trimethylglucose units minus H_2O.

The interpretation of appearance-potential measurements on glycosides has been discussed in Sec. 4-7.

10-2. NUCLEOSIDES

The determination of the mass spectra of such polar substances as nucleosides, containing both a sugar moiety and a hydroxy- or aminopyrimidine or purine, would seem to require chemical conversion by one of the reactions discussed in Sec. 4-5, such as alkylation, acylation, or trimethylsilylation of the polar groups.

For a number of practical reasons (such as the desire to obtain spectra of only a few micrograms of substance), an attempt was made to avoid such pretreatment, which always requires more material and manipulations, and to determine the spectra of the free nucleosides. Vaporization of the sample directly into the electron beam (Sec. 2-5E) led again to useful spectra, some of which are shown in Fig. 10-2.

The results indicate that it is possible to deduce various important

[3] P. A. Finan and R. I. Reed, *Nature*, 184, 1866 (1959).

structural features of a nucleoside from its mass spectrum.[4] First the base moiety can be recognized on the basis of intense peaks at $B + 1$ and $B + 2$ (B = mol. wt of purine or pyrimidine minus 1 mass unit). Second, a peak at m/e 117 is due to a deoxypentoside, while one at m/e 133 indicates a pentoside [deoxyriboside (4) and riboside (5) in the case of natural nucleosides].

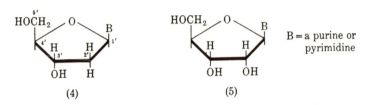

$$(4) \qquad\qquad (5)$$

The relative intensities of these $B + 1$, $B + 2$, and S (sugar) peaks also seem to be related to structure. The attachment of two hydrogens to the base fragment B is much more pronounced in the case of ribosides than it is for deoxyribosides: Uridine (Fig. 10-2a) exhibits a very intense peak at m/e 113 ($111 + 2$), while the most intense base fragment in deoxyuridine is found at m/e 112. Furthermore, the tendency for such a rearrangement of two hydrogens (formation of $B + 2$) is more pronounced for pyrimidine nucleosides if compared with the purine analogs.

Similarly, the sugar peak (S = mol. wt of sugar moiety minus 1 mass unit) is more pronounced in deoxyribosides (m/e 117) than in ribosides (m/e 133) and, in addition, more prominent in pyrimidine derivatives than in purines: The fragment of m/e 117 is thus most abundant in deoxyuridine (Fig. 10-2b), but the peak at m/e 133 is almost negligible in adenosine (Fig. 10-2c).

The molecular weight, which gives rise to an appreciable peak in the spectra of all these compounds, is a further indication of the sum of $B + S$.

Two other fragments are formed: $M - 89$ and $B + 30$. The first must involve the loss of C-3', C-4', and C-5', possibly in the following manner:

$$(5)$$

---

[4] K. Biemann and J. A. McCloskey, *J. Am. Chem. Soc.*, **84**, 2005 (1962).

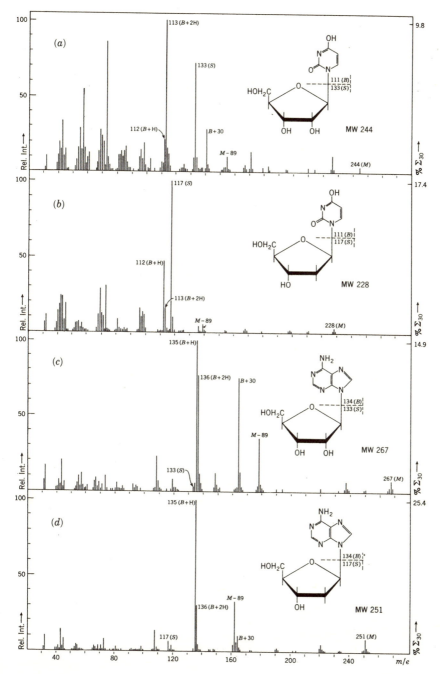

Fig. 10-2. Mass spectra of (a) uridine, (b) deoxyuridine, (c) adenosine, and (d) deoxyadenosine.

Retention of 30 mass units with the base moiety involves migration of a hydrogen from a hydroxyl group (in the 5' position?), as was shown on the basis of the spectra of O,N-perdeutero nucleosides, resulting in the formation of

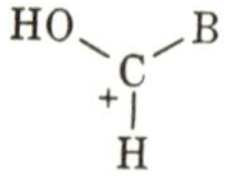

$$\underset{\overset{+|}{H}}{\overset{HO\diagdown\,\diagup B}{C}}$$

m/e (B + 30)

These spectra of the deuterated species also indicate that the formation of the $B + 1$ fragment involves a hydroxyl hydrogen exclusively while the second hydrogen, required for the $B + 2$ species, comes to a smaller extent also from a C-H group. The abundance of the $B + 2$ fragment seems to be related to the presence of a hydroxyl group at C-2'.

Such deuteration experiments involving deuterium on O, N, or S are particularly easy to perform if the sample (after dissolution in D_2O and evaporation to dryness in sample cup b in Fig. 2-8) is introduced directly into the ion source. In this way the molecules are vaporized into the electron beam without a chance of equilibration with water absorbed on the inner surfaces of the instrument, making the determination of such spectra difficult or impossible (see Sec. 5-2B) if a conventional inlet system is used.

10-3. BITTER PRINCIPLES OF HOP

Humulones and lupulones are not related to carbohydrates, with respect to chemistry or taste. Nevertheless, they will be discussed here since their mass spectra, including a new group, the hulupones, have been determined recently.[5]

The spectrum of lupulone (Fig. 10-3a) clearly indicates the molecular weight (414) of the compound, and fragmentation seems to consist mainly in the loss of one or two side chains. In agreement with the earlier discussion of multistep fragmentation (Sec. 3-2C), one of the two side chains must be lost in a rearrangement process (which in the case of a dimethylallyl group may require either rearrangement of the double bond or an eight-membered, cyclic transition state), and the resulting

[5] S. Brohult, R. Ryhage, L.-O. Spetsig, and E. Stenhagen, *European Brewery Conv. Proc.*, 1960, p. 121.

peaks are thus found 1 mass unit higher than expected for simple loss of both constituents.

The spectrum of humulone (Fig. 10-3b) generally corresponds to that of lupulone except that the fragments of high mass are much less abundant, probably because of the presence of a tertiary hydroxyl group.

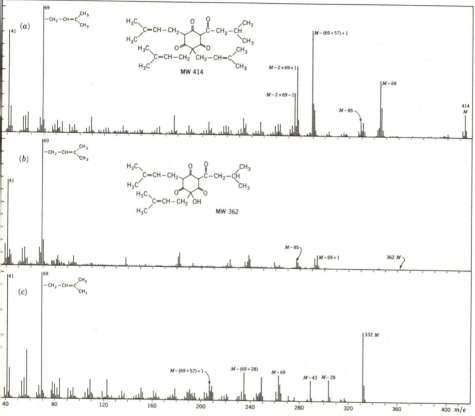

Fig. 10-3. Mass spectra of (a) lupulone, (b) humulone, and (c) hulupone. (*From Ref.* 5.)

For a new group of hop substances, the hulupones, a cyclopentatrienone structure was suggested on the basis of the mass spectra of hulupone and its di- and hexahydro derivatives, of the UV spectrum, and of the acidity of the parent compound. The mass spectrum of hulupone (Fig. 10-3c) indicated a molecular weight of 332 and the presence of dimethylallyl and (iso?) butyryl groups $[M - (69 + 57) + 1]$. The presence of a peak of $M - (2 \times 69) + 1$ in the spectrum of the dihydroderivative is interpreted as an indication of two dimethylallyl groups, thus leaving C_5HO_3 for the nucleus of hulupone. Its structure is best represented by (6), which has also been recently proven by synthesis.[6]

(6)

[6] Personal communication by E. Stenhagen.

11. Applications to Synthetic Problems

Throughout the previous chapters the main emphasis was on the structural information obtainable from the mass spectrum. At first glance such problems seem to be of little interest to the chemist primarily concerned with the synthesis of organic compounds. Very often, however, his problem is to find out whether or not the product of a reaction is in fact the desired substance. There may be many situations in which the use of an instrumental method, even if it is as expensive as a mass spectrometer, is warranted if it permits more economical designing of an experimental procedure for the synthesis of a particular compound or to elucidate the path of an abnormal reaction. If the products can be identified in the crude reaction mixture and their yield determined with as little separation or purification as possible, optimum reaction conditions can be found within a short time.

Ultraviolet and infrared spectroscopy have in the past been used mainly for this purpose. In many cases where the reaction does not involve a change in the chromophore or in a functional group associated with intense bands in the IR spectrum, or if the by-products or solvents absorb too strongly in the spectral region of interest, other techniques have to be employed.

The mass spectrum of the reaction mixture is particularly useful in cases where the reaction involves the addition or elimination of certain groups in the molecule, thus changing the molecular weight or the weight of certain fragments produced upon electron impact. The mass spectrum of the crude product permits the detection of both starting material and product, and at least a semiquantitative estimate of their yield. Two examples will illustrate the technique.

In the study of the dimethylation of amino acids and peptides for purposes discussed in Sec. 4-5C it was necessary to prepare all dimethyl derivatives of the common amino acids. Reductive alkylation was the method of choice, but for other reasons the use of catalysts had to be avoided. Sodium borohydride was found to be a useful reducing agent, and almost quantitative methylation of most amino acids was achieved: [1]

$$R-\underset{\underset{NH_3^+}{|}}{CH}-COO^- \xrightarrow[\text{NaBH}_4]{\text{CH}_2\text{O}} R-\underset{\underset{N(CH_3)_2}{|}}{CH}-COOH$$

Only certain amino acids, namely, those containing a polar group on the β carbon atom, particularly serine (1), were difficult to methylate.

$$\underset{(1)}{\overset{60}{\underset{\underset{OH}{|}}{CH_2}-\underset{\underset{NH_2}{|}}{CH}\!+\!COOR}} \qquad \underset{(2)}{\overset{74}{\underset{\underset{OH}{|}}{CH_2}-\underset{\underset{NHCH_3}{|}}{CH}\!+\!COOR}} \qquad \underset{(3)}{\overset{88}{\underset{\underset{OH}{|}}{CH_2}-\underset{\underset{N(CH_3)_2}{|}}{CH}\!+\!COOR}}$$

The formation of a cyclic condensation product of the hydroxy amino acid with formaldehyde seems to be the reason for this difficulty, and the reaction proved to be very sensitive to the pH at which it was performed. Maximum methylation was finally achieved by variations of both the pH and the rate of addition of borohydride, after many experiments. The extent of methylation was easily followed by esterification of the reaction product and determination of the mass spectrum of the crude ester mixture, as outlined in Chap. 7. The intensities at m/e 60, 74, and 88 indicated the extent of methylation under the conditions of the particular experiment. In Fig. 11-1 are shown graphic representations of these peak intensities as obtained in various experiments. The absolute height of the peaks is no indication of the actual yield unless the molar intensities of these fragments have been determined previously. This could be done by completely working up one experiment giving both mono- and dimethylserine, (2) and (3) respectively, in order to prepare a mixture of known composition as a standard. In most cases one merely wants to find the conditions under which the highest yield is obtained, and the relative peak heights suffice for this purpose.

As can be seen from the data presented in Fig. 11-1, only little dimethylserine is formed upon addition of sodium hydroxide to the reaction mixture, while at lower and lower pH the extent of methylation increases. In a solution buffered with carbon dioxide virtually all serine is converted mainly to the dimethyl derivative. If the reducing agent is

[1] W. Vetter, H. Vetter, and K. Biemann. (To be published.)

added too slowly, it is consumed by the carbonic acid, and the yield of methylated product drops.

A more complex molecule is involved in another example.[2] For the correlation of the alkaloid quebrachamine [formula (1), Chap. 8] with

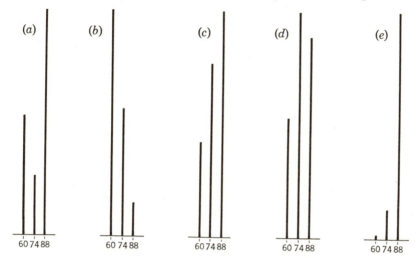

Fig. 11-1. Relative intensities of m/e 60, 74, and 88 in the spectra of various crude methylation products of serine (determined as ethyl ester). An aqueous solution of the sodium salt of serine was treated with formaldehyde and addition of (a) an aqueous solution of NaBH₄, (b) 0.1N NaOH and NaBH₄, (c) NaHCO₃ and NaBH₄, (d) NaHCO₃-CO₂ buffer and NaBH₄ dropwise, (e) same as (d) but addition of NaBH₄ repeated.

aspidospermine it was necessary to oxidize deacetylaspidospermine (4) to dehydrodeacetylaspidospermine (5). It was then to be reduced further to methoxyquebrachamine [formula (16), Chap. 8]. This oxidation proved to be quite difficult because of the instability of the product (5):

(4)   (5)

Reaction conditions that were too mild did not attack the starting material, while more drastic treatment destroyed the product.

Since during oxidation two hydrogen atoms are removed from the starting material, the molecular weight of the product is 2 mass units

[2] K. Biemann and G. Spiteller, *Tetrahedron Letters*, no. 9, p. 299, 1961.

lower. The mass spectrum of the crude reaction product, obtained by dilution of the mixture with water and extraction with ether, permitted the detection of the product and its approximate ratio to the starting material by monitoring the peaks at mass 312 and 310. By varying the reaction time, temperature, and sequence of addition of the reagents, it was possible to determine the conditions of optimum reaction, leading to a mixture of starting material and product in a ratio that made it worthwhile to proceed immediately with the further reduction. This was necessary since the dehydro product (5) could not be isolated as such because of its instability. Although the chromophore present in the starting material is extended in the product, UV spectroscopy cannot be used to follow this reaction, because indolenines of this type have the tendency to add hydroxyl-containing solvents; in addition the presence of starting material, iodine, and polymeric material in the crude mixture made it impossible to detect the desired product in the UV spectrum.

These two examples may suffice to point out the use which can be made of mass spectrometry in the design and perfection of synthetic organic reactions.

There is, however, another aspect of mass spectrometry that may aid in the development of synthetic processes. The close resemblance of some electron-impact-induced reactions taking place in the ion source of a mass spectrometer to certain pyrolytic, photolytic, and radiolytic reactions has been noted several times [3] and is borne out clearly by some of the processes discussed in Sec. 3-2A, especially Types *D*, *E*, and *H*.

It is conceivable that a detailed interpretation of a mass spectrum may permit predicting the products formed on pyrolysis, photolysis, or radiolysis. One may obtain information from appearance-potential measurements about the conditions (temperature, wavelength, energy) which would be required to perform the reaction in the laboratory.

[3] See, for example, D. P. Stevenson and J. A. Hipple, *J. Am. Chem. Soc.*, **64**, 1588 (1942), and F. W. McLafferty, *Anal. Chem.*, **31**, 82 (1959).

Name Index

Subject Index

Numbers in **boldface** type indicate figures showing the full spectrum of a compound

ERRATA

P. 40, last line: ...ionizing... instead of ...ionization...

P. 47, Fig. 3-1: (C_5H_5N) instead of (C_6H_5N)

P. 62, Fig. 3-5, x-axis: ‰ instead of %

P. 70, line 3: ...possible... instead of ...posssible...

P. 97, line 29: ...tetrahydrofuran or tetrahydropyran... instead of ...tetrahydrofurane or tetrahydropyrane...

P. 100, Fig. 3-16: insert MW 146 under structure

P. 101, line 3: ...148... instead of ...178...
    line 4: ...(146 to 148)... instead of ...(176 to 178)...

P. 108, 2nd equation: add a over CH_2 - X bond, interchange (3-36) and (3-37)

P. 108, line 23: ...propionitrile... instead of ...proionitrile...

P. 117, line 5: ...129. instead of ...128.

P. 136, structure (62): ...CH... instead of ...CH_2...

P. 156, Fig. 3-32, x-axis: ...297... instead of ...287...

P. 170, line 18: ...page 119... instead of ...page 118...

P. 187, line 28: ...acids... instead of ...acid...

P. 196, Fig. 4-11: ...doublet and adjacent lines... instead of ...lines indicated...

P. 206, Table 5-1: CHD_3 instead of CHD

P. 225, line 16; 17: ...of... instead of ...and...; ...is... instead of ...are...

P. 229, second equation: ...89.7... instead of ...98.7...

P. 235, line 7: ...bound... instead of ...bond...

P. 241, line 16: ...saturated... instead of ...unsaturated...

P. 243, line 8: ...atoms... instead of ...atom...

P. 252, Fig. 6-2: ...$CH_3(CH_2)_{10}$-... instead of ...$CH_3(CH_2)$-...

P. 272, Fig. 7-12: ...N-formylisoleucine... instead of ...N-formylleucine...

P. 275, line 1: ...duramycin... instead of ...duramycine...

P. 294, ref. 18: ...3192... instead of ...2005...

P. 308, Fig. 8-4(c): ...CH_3 instead of ...C_2H_5; delete (181) M, add (180)M to preceeding peak

P. 321, line 19: ...monoxide... instead of ...dioxide...

P. 324, structures (22) and (22a): replace $CO-OCH_3$ by H

P. 330, structure (31): delete broken arrow and B

P. 332, Fig. 8-16a: delete M-43

P. 340, line 2: ...C-18... instead of ...C-19...

P. 350, line 10: ...(2)... instead of ...(1)...

P. 355, Fig.10-3: ...lupulone... instead of ...lupolone...

P. 359, structure (5): delete H from indole-nitrogen

P. 369 (Index): ...Space charge... instead of ...Space change...

Table of Atomic Weights: I^{127} instead of J^{127}